Der

By

Publish

Copyright © Ian S Varty 2015

Acknowledgements

Thanks to Richard J. Galloway for his help and encouragement into the world of publishing. Also, to the many colleagues I have worked with over my years in the military, for their support in this venture. I would also like to thank Jim and Margaret Gardiner, for translating my spoken word into some legible form of English. In memory of my father, Thomas William Varty 13th June 1943 – 27th April 2010.

Contents

Prologue 6

Chapter 1 Departure 10

Chapter 2 Basic Training Junior Leaders Regiment RAC 20

Chapter 3 A new dawn 33

Chapter 4 Physical Training 44

Chapter 5 - Drill 54

Chapter 6 - Locker layouts and bulling 63

Chapter 7 - Drill Part 2 70

Chapter 8 – A Typical Evening in Training 77

Chapter 9 – Battle PT 84

Chapter 10 – A trip away to Renney Lentney Camp 89

Chapter 12 – Escalation 102

Chapter 13 – Escape and Evasion 107

Chapter 14 – Leave and final term 111

Chapter 15 – The Regiment 118

Chapter 16 – Commanding Officers Interviews 122

Chapter 17 – The Tank Park 125

Chapter 18 – Practical Jokes 131

Chapter 19 – Guard Duty 136

Chapter 20 – Wine, Women and Song 144

Chapter 21 – Soltau Training Area 151

Chapter 22 – Hide Drill and Advance to Contact 160

Chapter 23 – Squadron and Battlegroup Training 167

Chapter 24 – Vehicle Maintenance and Squadronn Smoker 175

Chapter 25 – Battlegroup Final Exercise 183

Chapter 26 – Berlin Bound 194

Chapter 27 – Berlin the Party City.........................201

Chapter 28 – Parades and Crash Outs 212

Chapter 29 – Sports and Competitions 226

Chapter 30 – Nautius Maximus, and all things must come to an
end 239

Chapter 31 – North Rhine Westphalia and Hohne Ranges 251

Chapter 32 – Courses and change of job 269

Chapter 33 – Command Troop 287

Chapter 34 – Northern Ireland Training 299

Chapter 35 – Tin City..312

Chapter 36 First tour of Northern Ireland and The Troubles....325

Prologue

It had been a long, hard day, and Richard Hunter gave a great sigh of relief as he turned the key to his home in the North East of England.

'I'm home,' he called out, to no one in particular.

'Tea will be ready in half an hour,' came the reply from the back of the house. Richard continued along the corridor and into the kitchen. Here, his wife Birgit stood with her back to him, stirring a pan of stew on the ceramic hob. He moved forward, encircled her waist with his arms, and kissed her neck.

'Smells good, I'm starving,' he said.

She smiled and rubbed her cheek against his. He smelt of work, but she knew better than to remind him of that. 'You've still time for a shower if you want?'

They had been together for twenty nine years, and her slight German accent still gave him a thrill. 'I think I will, it's been a crap day.'

'Why, what has happened today' she asked apprehensively.

'We got a call for a monitor that had failed, and when I got there it was turned off at the wall! He bellowed.

Birgit sensed the frustration in his voice. The other night they'd been out with friends and Richard had started to tell a tale about his former life in the Army. It was one he'd told before, about serving in Northern Ireland in the 1980s. It had been his first tour, and although he was somewhat nervous he was also excited. On his first mobile patrol, he had been travelling in the second of two Land Rovers. They had been passing a school as it was finishing for the day. The sight of the first Land Rover immediately caught the attention of the schoolkids. They searched around for anything they could use as missiles. By then, the first Land Rover had passed, so their attention was drawn to the one in which Richard was travelling. Richard was totally unaware of this, until the shout came up from the vehicle commander.

'Incoming!'

The missiles began to rain down. Richard, looking out the rear of the vehicle, turned to his left. As he did so, an object struck him above the eye. He saw stars and everything started to go black. He touched his left breast pocket, to feel the talisman his future father in law had given him prior to deployment. However, on doing so he found it was gone. As he slowly slipped into unconsciousness, he thought to himself, 'just my luck'. The next thing he remembered was looking up and seeing the face of one of his patrol smiling at him.

'Your first war wound, mate.' he said, laughing.

The stone had split his eyebrow and had caused blood to run into his eye.

'How long was I out?' he asked, groggily.

'Only a couple of minutes' his friend replied.

Although he had recounted the story a number of times, on that night there had been a bitter edge to it, he'd ended the story on a melancholy note, not his usual funny tone.

He turned, left the kitchen and made his way upstairs. Entering the bedroom, Richard opened the door to the ensuite bathroom and started the shower running. He quickly undressed, laying his work clothes on the laundry basket, as he did every day. As he stepped into the shower, the feeling of the warm water against his skin gave him a feeling of release. Picking up the shower gel, he vigorously massaged his scalp to wash away the smell of the hospital where he was employed. Covering his body in lather, he hastily cleansed himself and with each hand movement felt better for it. Stepping from the shower, he picked up the towel he had placed on the toilet opposite and began to dry himself. Completing his cleaning routine, he re-entered the bedroom and picked a pair of jogging bottoms and a sweat shirt from the wardrobe and dressed. He made his way downstairs, to be greeted by the welcoming smell of the stew, which had been placed in a bowl in the dining room. His wife and son Ryan were already seated, smiling as he took his place. The table seemed empty. Some weeks earlier their daughter Sonia had left to begin three years of study at University. It seemed alien not to have all the family sitting down at meal times but he was slowly becoming used to it. Looking across at his son, he felt a swell of pride. Ryan was growing up to be quite the handsome young man. Richard was reminded of himself at that age and started to feel regret that the years were marching on. Long gone were the chiselled good looks and sculptured physique that he had had at fifteen.

'How was your day at school?' he posed, without looking up or making eye contact.

'Not bad.' Ryan retorted.

Richard contemplated the fact that his son had reached that difficult age, where he found it hard to communicate with adults. He always seemed to use the least amount of words to convey his answers, usually delivering them in grunts. Looking across at his wife, Richard asked how her day had been. He was then given a blow by blow account of her last eight hours in the call centre where she worked. Now that the usual pleasantries had been exchanged, he moved his attention to the bowl of food in front of him.

'Looks like range stew.' he joked, out loud.

It seemed that more and more recently he was making references to his former life in the military. The twenty three years he served Queen and Country were memories always lurking in the background. Without further comment, he began to tuck into his evening meal, soaking it up with chunks of bread roll. The evening meal finished, they began the ritual of clearing away. Ryan carried out this function, as that was one of the few chores set out for him. As soon as the dining room was back to its former state, Ryan disappeared to his room, probably not be seen for the rest of the evening. Both Richard and Birgit completed the task of cleaning the kitchen together, before retiring to the living room. He rested himself in his favourite spot on the settee, and let out a deep sigh. Birgit assumed her position in her armchair to his left, as she did every night.

'I've bought you some Spätburgunder.' she informed him.

He smiled and his eyes were drawn to the wall unit where two bottles of the German red wine stood proudly, as if on parade.

'That's kind of you,' he replied and she gave him a knowing nod, and smiled in return.

The sound of the news presenter on television was just a background noise, as Richard stood up and made his way to the unit where he picked up one of the bottles. Opening the centre portion of the glass unit, he removed a glass and placed two coasters on the coffee table, one for the wine bottle, the other for the glass. It seemed that this was becoming a regular thing, and he pondered the reason behind it. He didn't have to think for long, he already knew the answer. His life seemed to have hit a point where he felt that he was just treading water and the challenges that he had faced most of his life in the Army were missing. He reached forward, raising the glass of wine to his lips and closed his eyes as the velvety liquid trickled down his throat. After a few glasses, he started to feel a little better. Soon, he made his way to the left hand unit on the wall and opened the door.

'What you looking for?' Birgit asked.

'A photo album,' he answered curtly. 'The one of me before I joined the army,' he murmured to himself.

'The older ones are on the bottom shelf,' she said. After selecting a couple at random and flicking through the pages, he finally found the one he was looking for. Richard returned to his seat and began at the first page. He leafed through the pages, smiling to himself. After a couple of minutes, he arrived at the page he was looking for, where he removed one of the pictures from its mounting. As he stared at the somewhat blurred, slightly out of focus picture, his mind drifted back to the summer of 1979.

Chapter 1 Departure

The warm glow of the Lower Saxony sun bathed the garden, as four friends engaged in nervous conversation. They had been to school together in this part of Germany for the last four years, but they were now drawing to a close. The long summer holidays had come to an end and it was time for two of them, to start their own journeys in life. Although it was only eleven o'clock in the morning, the temperature had already reached 30° C. Richard wished that he was wearing shorts and t-shirt, rather than the brown cord trousers shirt and sports jacket which adorned him. Richard eyed his best friend with his newly cropped hair, flared jeans, shirt and tank top and wondered if he was having the same feelings of anticipation and excitement as himself. The two of them had grown up together, as their fathers were members of the same Regiment. Wherever they were posted, the families followed, as was the Army way. This nomadic existence helped form a bond, not only for the soldiers, but also the children and wives. The families often lived in close proximity to the barracks where the soldiers were stationed. They were accommodated on estates with other military families, and largely cut off from the local population. It was under these circumstances that friendships were forged that regularly would last a lifetime.

Pete had always been a good looking child. As he grew into a young man, with his blond hair and piercing, blue eyes, he had girls swooning over him. At times Richard came second best to him, although he also had his share of female admirers. They had shared some good times together, and scrambled out of the same scrapes too. Pete seemed oblivious to his stare and continued in conversation with the other two. A deep, hearty cackle rang out, which broke Richard's train of thought.

Ivan, as usual, was playing the joker and making light of the situation as he made fun of Steve, the other member of their close-knit group. Ivan had met the other three when his father was posted into the town where their parents' Regiments were stationed. Although his father was an Infantryman and the other three boys' fathers were from Tank or Armoured Regiments they immediately got on like a house on fire. This was not always the case for the soldiers from different Regiments who, on occasion, did not see eye to eye, to put it mildly. Ivan was a happy-go-lucky type of lad, and a very keen sportsman. This was to prove key to the growth of their friendship over the years. Steve was trying hopelessly to defend himself against Ivan's jibes, but was fighting a losing battle. He was the most quiet and reserved member of the group. This was something of a paradox for a long haired, heavy metal fan. His slight, lanky frame and gangly appearance, confirmed the fact that he was not a keen sportsman like the other three. Regardless of these facts, Steve had qualities that endeared him to the friends. Richard did not have a favourite, but the length of time he had spent with Pete over the years had created a special bond between them. Would he ever feel this same bond with others as he did now with these three? Time would tell, but he was sure that the career that he and Pete had both chosen, as had their fathers before them, would provide the same feelings of camaraderie and a sense of belonging.

'Are you two ready then?' came the voice from behind.

As he turned, he saw his father standing there, smiling. He was a small man in stature, but powerfully built. His name was renowned throughout the Regiment and he was well respected. Richard just hoped that he could live up to his father and emulate what he had achieved during his military career.

'I think so,' he replied, looking at Pete, who nodded his assent.

His mother appeared at her husband's shoulder. Richard could see that she had been crying. She had chosen not to accompany them to the airport. Pete had already said his goodbyes to his family, now it was Richard's turn. He moved forward apprehensively and gave his mother a hug and kiss. This was not a natural thing for him, as he had been brought up not to show affection. Although his parents loved him dearly, they found it hard to show signs of outward emotion.

'Goodbye, mum, see you when I get my first leave,' he stammered.

She stared at him through misty eyes.

'You take care now and look after yourself,' she answered.

He turned away quickly, to prevent her or his father seeing the emotion welling up. As Richard turned, he saw that Pete was already shaking hands with Ivan and Steve. Fighting back his feelings, he moved towards them and extended his right hand.

'Bollocks to that!' exclaimed Ivan,' come here, you big pussy,' and grabbed him in an embrace.

Richard could feel Ivan's heart beating strongly as they hugged each other longer than the usual couple of seconds that a man-hug allowed.

'What are you like you big gayer,' Richard said, trying to regain his masculine reserve. 'You will want to take long, windy walks along the beach before long.'

They both fell about in fits of laughter. He then turned his attention to Steve, who was staring at this exchange. Offering his hand, Steve took it with a firm grip, surprising Richard with the power in such a slightly built, young man.

'You keep your head down, mate,' Steve offered.

'I will,' he answered in return. 'We will see you both when we come home on leave and we'll put a few beers down.'

The farewells over, Pete and Richard picked up their cases, which had been placed against the garden fence and made their way to Richard's father's car. His father had the boot open ready for them, and they placed their cases and bags inside, filling it to capacity. The sound of the boot being slammed shut confirmed to him that this was final, and he was leaving to start his new career. He took a deep breath and the two of them climbed into the car for the journey to the airport. As the car reached the end of the road, his father gave a blast on the horn, before turning right, off the estate. Richard looked back to see their two friends and his mother waving them away.

'Well this is it,' he thought to himself, 'no turning back now.' The journey along the autobahn was completed in almost total silence. Pete was staring out the window, lost in his own thoughts. Richard's father tried to interject with the odd snippet of advice for the two. He knew that his father meant well, as he had been through the same experience when he had joined up, some seventeen years earlier. They had talked through the many scenarios that the two of them may encounter and the best way to deal with them. They couldn't cover every topic: Richard was resigned to the fact that each situation would be different and determined to deal with it as it occurred. Although the training methods employed by the British Army had changed very little over the last couple of hundred years, he was sure they would experience new, innovative methods of breaking down civilians, to turn them into soldiers. He recalled stories from his father, who would reminisce on his own experiences in the different theatres of operations he had served in during his own time in the services. These were almost invariably carried out after he had consumed large amounts of brandy and coke. They became known as *'Tommy's tours'* throughout the family, and became the highlight of many a Friday night. Richard called to mind his father's story of serving in Aden in the 1960s and the hardships and adventures that went along with it.

The Aden Emergency was an insurgency against British Crown forces in what is now the Yemen. It lasted from 10 December 1963, when a 'State of Emergency' was declared until 30 November 1967, when British forces left. The emergency began when members of the National Liberation Front (NLF) carried out a grenade attack against the British High Commission. This attack killed one person, injured fifty, and caused the British Government to declare a State of Emergency. In January 1964, the British moved into the Radfan hills in the border region, to confront Egyptian-backed guerrillas, later reinforced by the NLF. This operation was code-named 'Nutcracker.' In April, a second operation called 'Cap Badge' had the overall political objective of reasserting Federal Authority and making the Dhala Road safe for traffic. By October the insurgents had largely been suppressed, and the NLF switched to grenade attacks against off-duty military personnel and police officers elsewhere in the Aden Colony. Amongst the forces sent there were Squadrons from the Yorkshire Dragoon Guards, including a certain Trooper Tommy Hunter. Although he came from a pit village in the mining area of the North East of England, he had chosen to join this Regiment, rather than a local one. The Squadrons quickly established bases in the Radfan, and proceeded to take the fight to the guerrillas. Living conditions were basic, to say the least, with most of the Troops living in makeshift tents. It was not all bombs and bullets, but often included long periods of inactivity. Richard would later find this to be the case in many hostile Theatres of Operations. To pass the time the Troops would do anything from carrying out scorpion fights to donkey racing. Tommy had even taken up learning the guitar to pass the time. It was on a day such as this, his father sat on a wall of sandbags and strummed his guitar. He had been playing for about five minutes when he heard a popping sound. Looking around, he thought it may have been someone trying to provide some percussion to his playing. There was no one in sight but he heard it again, this time like a muffled pop.

'Incoming !' came the cry, away to his left.

Tommy immediately flung himself to the ground behind the sandbag wall. He hastily donned his webbing pouches and grabbed his submachine gun (SMG), which was to hand at all times. Looking over the parapet, he observed a puff of smoke halfway up a mountain to the North East of their position. He quickly deduced that it was a mortar firing point and the crump of the explosions had begun to fall within the compound. Over to his immediate right from one of the makeshift tents, sprinted the hunched form of a man. Tommy immediately recognised him as Ray Blenkinsopp, Corporal of one of the Troops. He cut a path across the compound floor, varying his direction as he went. His goal, Tommy could see, was one of the Squadron's 'Saladin' armoured cars, parked 100 metres in front of him. The mortar rounds continued to rain down and Tommy was transfixed at the sight of Ray, who had made it to the Saladin and had climbed inside the turret. This was his first real engagement and he had little idea of what he could do to assist. Within seconds, the 76mm gun of the Saladin was belching flame and rounds were being put down in the direction of the mortar firing point. It was not until afterwards, it came to light that Ray had been alone and had both loaded and fired the gun. This action was later recognised and Ray was awarded the Military Medal (MM) for his actions on that day. *'When you join the Regiment, pick a person you consider to be the perfect soldier and try to be that man'* were the words his father told him after he had finished relating the story. With these words ringing in his ears, he heard the screech of the brakes as the car ground to a halt.

'We're here,' his father called out to him, breaking his thoughts.

Both Richard and Pete climbed out of the car and made their way round to the boot. They removed their cases and bags and prepared to head for the departure terminal.

'Get used to carrying heavy things,' his father joked and put forward his hand. Richard took it and felt the warmth that pulsed from it. Glancing towards Pete, his father continued, 'You watch each other's backs.'

Pete held his gaze and replied, 'we'll try, Tommy.'

With that parting comment, they turned and made their way inside the terminal. Richard didn't look back. He had chosen his path and nothing could change that now. As they waited in the departure lounge, they chatted over what might lie ahead of them. Pete seemed excited about the prospect of starting their training that week. He had his own vision of how he saw it enfolding. Richard fed off his enthusiasm, but knew things were not going to be as straightforward as Pete perceived. Within the hour, they had boarded the VC10 military flight from Hanover to Luton. After a short flight time of only one hour fifteen minutes, they touched down in the UK. They mingled with the families and soldiers returning home for leave, who had congregated around the baggage carousel. After collecting their luggage, they made their way to the exit for the onward journey by train to Waterloo Station in London. The brief journey to Waterloo lasted only 30 minutes and before long they were staring at the departures board. Searching for the Weymouth train, the friends noticed a number of young lads sporting very close cropped haircuts. This group was surrounded by suitcases and bags and were anxiously scanning the board. Richard, being the more forward of the two, called over to them.

'You boys going to Bovington?' he enquired. One of the young men turned round to face him. He looked like he had been the victim of a hard upbringing. His rugged face was a network of scar tissue not unlike the map of the underground that was on a placard opposite them.

'Aye, pal, we are,' was his abrupt and gruff Glaswegian reply. Richard made a note to himself that this was one to keep on the good side of, if their paths were to cross in the near future.

'It's leaving from platform six in half an hour, if you fancy a pint.'

A broad grin spread across the chiselled features of the dour Scotsman.

'Now you're talking pal! I'm Stephen Angus, by the way, just call me Steve.'

With the ice broken, they all made their way to the nearest bar for a swift drink prior to departure. As they drank their beers, they chatted amongst themselves. They took turns introducing themselves, with a brief explanation of where they came from. Richard listened intently and soon realised that both he and Pete had led quite privileged lives, compared to some of their newly acquired acquaintances. Noticing that the clock had almost reached five minutes before the train's departure, he suggested they leave at once. A couple of the lads groaned, unwilling to leave the security of the bar. After a little persuasion, they moved on mass to the platform, quickly boarding the train, which was to leave very shortly.

The banter carried on among them all as they were joined by others who, on investigation, were found to be travelling to the same destination. Not all had the military style haircuts the majority had felt necessary to acquire. The mixture of accents was a veritable smorgasbord of the diversity of Britain. One of the newcomers arrived in the coach and announced that the train had a buffet car. This was, of course, met with a loud, raucous cheer and a stampede in the direction indicated by his thumb. The carriage was soon full of young men laden with different drinks. The party began to flow: little did they know this would be their last chance to drink for the next three months. As the drink flowed, the group chatted about how they imagined the training they were about to endure. Some were nonchalant about it, others had a genuine dread of what they feared may be about to happen. Richard took in the scene and from the conversations he had, formed the opinion that both he and Pete were the only two from military families. He was unsure if this would be a help or a hindrance. If the instructors were to find out that they were 'pads brats' (this was the word given to children of serving soldiers), would they be treated more harshly than their counterparts? This would be answered sooner than he expected.

'D'ye fancy a wee dram?' came the offer from Steve, who sat opposite.

He winced, knowing this was his Achilles heel. Whisky was one of the few drinks which could change him from a coherent, affable, young man into the most obnoxious person on the planet! Not wanting to lose face in front of the heavy set Scotsman, 'Love to' he replied. His new friend poured him a huge measure into the plastic cup he had brought from the buffet car. As he raised the cup to his lips, Richard thought, 'this is the point of no return.'

'Slainte!' his host proclaimed.

The liquid burned his throat as it scorched its way down and began to make its way into his bloodstream. He recalled the television series about The Incredible Hulk, where a meek scientist, once enraged would become a monster. Richard wondered how long it would be before the same started to happen to him. After the third whisky, and all inhibitions abandoned, he began asking personal questions about Steve's life and why he chose to join up. The answers Richard received were a litany of misery and loneliness. This confirmed the opinion Richard had formed on their first meeting under the train times in Waterloo. He thought to himself that this guy would breeze through the training. He could not imagine that the Army could throw anything at this person that he had not already experienced in some shape or form. Richard had started to form a slight bond with Steve and hoped that they would be put into the same Troop for their training. Along with these thoughts, he suddenly realised he had not spoken to Pete since they had boarded the train. Peering over at him, he saw Pete was in deep conversation with a Cockney lad, who seemed very slight and fragile. How many of these young men in the carriage would be there at the end of training, he mused. The stations flew by and it wasn't long before the announcement rang out:

'Next station Wool!'

Richard glanced across at Pete and grinned,

'This is it mate, the pain starts here.'

Pete returned his grin and stood up to make his way to locate his luggage. The rest of the carriage began to do the same. Some were less stable than others, due to the varying effects of the alcohol. As the train slowed, preparing to stop in Wool station, the young men were looking anxiously out the windows at their new environment for the next fifteen months. The train squealed to halt causing a couple to lose their footing, which was met with a great cheer. However, this frivolity was to be short lived. Their transport spewed its passengers on to the platform and prepared to move on to its final destination. The whistle blew and the train departed the platform, leaving its contents looking around bewildered.

'You lot pick up your kit and get yourselves over here!' sounded the voice from behind them.

Turning 180 degrees, Richard observed six stern looking individuals in uniform. The one who had issued the order was pacing the small car park, obviously not in a very good mood. He could tell from the man's rank slide that he was a Sergeant and he noted the other five were Corporals.

'Am I talking to myself?' the NCO reiterated, 'Move yourselves.'

The gaggle of new recruits realised that this person was not one to be messed with and quickly assembled in the car park. The group of soldiers formed them up in three ranks and read out a roll call. They instructed them that once their names were read, they were to place their belongings on the 4-Tonne trucks parked in the corner. The roll call and loading of the trucks complete, the group was ordered to assemble in three ranks again. The Sergeant paced along the front rank eyeing each individual closely. He stopped and faced one of the crowd who had been in Richard's carriage. This young man was somewhat unsteady on his feet and swayed like a sapling in a storm.

'Have you been drinking?' the now irate soldier bellowed, as his face turned crimson.

Without hesitation the young lad answered,

'Just a couple,' he smirked.

Richard winced as the words came from his mouth. 'This will not end well,' he thought to himself. The Sergeant stepped back and addressed the whole assembled throng.

'I am Sgt. Portwood, you will address me as Sarn't or Sergeant.'

He then introduced the five Corporals who were behind him glaring at them.

'It looks like we have not got off to a good start. As some of you are obviously a little worse for wear, due to the consumption of alcohol, I believe you require freshening up. To that end, if you turn 45 degrees, you will notice a white bus.'

They all complied and noticed the vehicle at the entrance to the car park, with its engine running.

'Well, gents, that's what you would have been travelling in. Instead, because of the foolish actions of some of you, we will march to Stanley Barracks. Shouldn't be a problem for you, as it is only two miles!'

Richard's heart sank, it had only been twenty minutes and they had already made an enemy. They were all turned round and the command rang out:

'By the right, quick march!' and the column of disillusioned adolescents trudged off, heads hung low.

Chapter 2 Basic Training Junior Leaders Regiment RAC

The aim of the Junior Leaders' Regiment was to train the boys to become future Non-Commissioned Officers and Warrant Officers of their chosen Regiments/Corps in their adult service.

Life in the Regiment was demanding and varied. Apart from general military training such as drill, field craft and weapon training, expert instruction was given in gunnery and radio operating. This training was designed to prepare the young soldier for his future role as a tank or armoured car crewman. Specialist training was also provided for boys joining other Corps.

To support these military and technical subjects, part of the training was given over to military studies in which subjects such as trade science, communication skills and military affairs were taught. As in all work of the Regiment, emphasis was placed upon the development of leadership qualities.

For outdoor training the Regiment had an Adventure Training Centre at Renney Lentney near Dartmoor where the young soldiers spent two weeks of each fourteen week term taking part in outdoor activities such as potholing, sailing, rock climbing, orienteering and cliff rescue.

Of course, it was not all hard work. Clubs and hobbies were held twice a week and offered a wide range of activities from sub-aqua diving to water skiing, and archery to go-karting. Sport was part of the weekly training programme and there was also ample opportunity for competitive sport against outside clubs and other Junior Regiments. http://www.jlrrac.co.uk/

The sweat had started to flow down Richard's brow like a river as they rounded the corner, and 100 metres in front of them he could see the sign for Stanley Barracks, home of the Junior Leaders Regiment (JLR). The journey had taken them a mere thirty minutes, but already he could tell that some of the group were suffering. He knew that this was just a stroll in the park compared to what they would have to endure in the next few weeks. As they entered the gates to the camp, he noticed three soldiers wearing arm bands with the letters R.P. on them. He knew at once that they were members of the Regimental Police, who were the custodians of any offenders housed in their cells. They sneered at the group as they trudged passed the guardroom. They reminded him of Orcs from '*The Lord of the Rings*'. He could only imagine the sadistic thoughts they were having over the arrival of this 'new meat'. They were assembled on the drill square and a roll call was taken again. As each name was called, they were informed which Squadron (Sqn) they had been assigned to. Richard's name came out early and he was listed as being C Sqn. Making his way to the allotted part of the square, he waited anxiously for Pete's name to be called. It was obvious they were not doing this in alphabetical order, as his name came after Pete's in the alphabet. Then, after what seemed like an age,

'Burgess, C Sqn!'

'Thank God for that,' Richard said aloud, happy that both he and his friend would go through their training together. There were only a few people left of the original group, one of them being Steve. He was looking like the last person to be picked in a game of football. Then his name was announced.

'Angus', the pause seemed to go on forever, then finally, '... C Sqn.'

Steve made his way across to them and seemed genuinely happy to be in their company. The last few were allocated their Squadrons and during this time, two rather imposing figures marched on to the square. Their backs were as straight as ramrods and their feet marched in unison. The one on the left was approximately six feet three inches, wearing a Khaki suit, with what Richard recognised as a Sam Browne belt. He knew that these were normally reserved for officers, but Richard saw no 'pips' on his shoulder. His hat had a slashed peak, resting on the bridge of his nose. The other uniformed man was of the same height and also dressed in Khaki, but his hat was a different shade, with a white band around it. He wore a red sash across his ample barrel chest. When the one wearing the Sam Browne belt spoke, his voice reverberated across the whole square.

'Intake of September 1979, I am Warrant Officer Class 1 Burrows and I am the Regimental Sergeant Major (RSM) of the Junior Leaders Regiment here in Bovington. I am responsible for the discipline and smooth running of this establishment. You address me as "sir" if I have occasion to speak to you. The person to my left is Drill Sergeant Rudd of the Coldstream Guards; you will become more intimate with him during your time here.' The Drill Sergeant gave a sardonic grin and surveyed every one of them with a steely stare. 'You will shortly be taken away by your Squadron Instructors and be given a time to collect your equipment from the Quartermaster's (QM's) Stores,' continued the RSM.

His speech concluded, both the RSM and Drill Sergeant smartly performed an about turn and marched from the parade square. After five minutes, the group was collected by five Corporals. Richard's heart sank when he saw that their Sergeant was to be Portwood, the very man who had just marched them from the station.

'Fall in three ranks!' Portwood screamed. The newly formed Troop hastily organised themselves into lines of three and awaited further instructions. They looked around at each other, each with a look of uncertainty.

'Listen to my words of command. By the right, quick march!' shouted their new Troop Sergeant. Although they did not know what the command meant fully, they instinctively stepped off with their left feet. They were shepherded by the Corporals in the direction they were to take. As they had not yet been instructed on the use of drill movements, they were forgiven for not swinging their arms to the regulation height and 'getting on the heel.' This would all come later, during the many hours of practice on the drill square, Richard thought to himself.

Within a short space of time, they arrived outside a long building where people were coming and going through a single door, carrying suitcases and kit bags. Richard could tell by their gait, that the items they were carrying were not light. He had once looked in his father's wardrobe at home, and had seen the amount of equipment that is issued to a soldier for his personal use.

'When I call your name, you will break ranks and make your way inside that door there,' Portwood indicated the door Richard had observed moments earlier. 'You will be issued with all the equipment you require for your stay here. Once you have signed for it, you will fall back in here.'

The names were called one by one and each disappeared inside. Within five minutes, they were returning, laden with their new acquisitions. Then Richard's name was called and he made his way inside. As he entered, he was confronted by a rather sour faced individual, who obviously loved his job. From behind the counter, he looked like a not too friendly assistant in a department store.

'Neck size?' he grumbled, without looking up.

'Not sure,' Richard replied.

The happy chap looked up from his paperwork with a wry smile and eyed Richard up and down. Richard felt as though he was being measured for his coffin by an undertaker.

'14 ½, ' the 'undertaker' sneered.

Turning to his assistant, who also seemed full of the joys of spring, he called out,

'Shirts No2 dress for three, Shirts combat for three, PT vests two red one white,.......'

The list went on till the counter was awash with a sea of clothing and equipment. The final two items were a suitcase and kit bag. Richard thought to himself unless these items had TARDIS like qualities, akin to the police phone box in Doctor Who, there was no way on earth this equipment would fit in.

'What are you waiting for?' screamed the storeman, 'get your kit packed and get out of my fucking sight!'

Richard hastily stuffed the equipment into the two receptacles provided, making best of a bad situation. The perspiration was running in rivulets down his brow and he could feel his shirt wet under his sports jacket. Only after placing his whole weight on the suitcase was he able to close it. He pulled the kit bag onto his shoulder and took hold of the handle of the suitcase, lifting it from the counter. As his body took the weight, he felt himself shrink under the load. It was like transporting a small meteorite, and he shuffled from the store to assume his place in the squad outside. The process of issuing the equipment to the whole Troop took over an hour. At last, the final recruit had been called and had returned, laden with his new possessions. The Troop was marched from the stores to what would be home for the next fifteen months.

They were divided into three ten man rooms and told to pick a bed space and place their cases and kit bags on it. A couple of the guys thought they would take a rest and sat down on the bed springs of their chosen spots.

'What do you think you're doing, you lazy twats? Get up and get fell in outside!' screeched Portwood, as he entered the room.

Richard could see that this was going to be a long day and he was going to be proven right. Once everyone had vacated the Barrack Block and assembled in their three ranks once again, they were marched to another store building. Repeating the procedure as before, they were called individually by name and entered a single door to their front.

As Richard entered the room, he was reminded of a smell from his father's military clothing. He had asked him once what it was and was given the answer, 'moth balls'. This smell gave him a sense of familiarity and a feeling that this was where he belonged. The room was slightly smaller than the one they had previously been in to be issued with their clothing. It did, however, contain the same shelving system as the previous one, with items arranged very neatly, as though they were soldiers, waiting for inspection. Richard approached the counter and his eyes were met by a slightly overweight, jovial looking person. Richard noticed by the rank slide on his combat dress that he was a Staff Sergeant, as was his father.

Turning to the soldier who was standing by the shelves, the Staff Sergeant called out,

'One counterpane, four blankets, two sheets….' the list went on.

The last item to be placed on the counter was a mattress and Richard was invited to inspect it.

'Make sure you check it for piss stains and sweat marks. The condition you take it from these stores is the condition that you will return it when you leave.'

Richard was advised that to return it in any other condition than pristine would mean that he would be charged for a new one. Smiling to himself, he turned on his heel and made his way to the rest of the men, who had also been issued their bedding. The training staff formed them up in ranks as best they could, under the weight of their baggage. The Troop made its cumbersome way back to the Barrack Block. They resembled a Bedouin travelling caravan making its way across a desert of tarmac. Arriving back at the Block, they were quickly ushered inside and told to place their bedding in their allocated spaces. Richard looked around his room and caught the eye of Steve, who was chuckling to himself.

'What's tickled you?' Richard enquired.

'Was just wondering if this is what it's going to be like for the rest of our time here,' replied the Scotsman, jokingly.

'I think they are taking it easy on us, seeing as it's our first day,' Richard quipped back.

Richard knew that this was not the case and began to wonder how Pete was feeling, as they had been separated and he was in an adjoining room. Although Richard would have preferred it if they had been placed together, he knew that it was probably inevitable at some point that they would have been moved apart.

The sound of ammunition boots striking the floor outside the room heralded the arrival of Sgt. Portwood and a squat powerful looking Corporal into the room. Richard had noticed the NCO earlier in the day, but did not pay him too much attention. The Corporal surveyed the men in the room, taking note of each individual. Richard likened him to the owner of a gladiator school looking to purchase likely candidates for the arena. He was immaculately turned out. The creases in his shirt and lightweight trousers were as keen as a knife edge. His boots resembled a mirror, not one speck of dirt or blemish on them. Richard wondered how this could be, as the Corporal had accompanied them on the march from the station.

'This is Corporal Creggan, he will be your room instructor for your time here. Listen to what he has to tell you, as he has a wealth of experience.' Portwood explained and promptly left the room.

'The first thing I will go through is how to make your bed, military style.' Creggan grunted.

He approached the bed nearest to him and placed the contents on the floor. Picking up the mattress cover, he turned to face the room.

'Firstly, you need to cover your mattress with this, to prevent any sweat staining. Then, take one of your two sheets and place it on the bottom, tucking away the excess at the foot. Take hold of the bottom sheet and pull it up forming a triangle. Fold this back at an angle of 45 degrees and tuck in under the mattress. This is what is known as a hospital corner.' he continued his demonstration with the blankets and the counterpane. The demonstration complete, he took out a coin from his pocket and dropped it onto the bed where it bounced, much to his delight.

'This is how you will make up your bed after inspection each morning.' He then proceeded to tear his work apart.

'You will now make up your beds just how I have just shown you,' he commanded.

The room was an instant hive of activity as young men began making up their bunks. It was obvious that either some of them had never done this in their lives or they were just not paying attention to the demonstration. A few were just holding the sheets trying to figure out which way they were to go on the bed. They looked around, bewildered, looking for guidance from other members of the room. This was not forthcoming, as most of them were in the same situation. Richard, having been shown this before by his father, had his bed completed in no time. Noticing one particularly frustrated case, he decided to give a helping hand. With Richard's tuition, his roommate completed the allotted task and stood back to admire his work. Taking a lead from Richard, some of the rest, who had finished, started to help others who were having difficulty. In the space of ten minutes the men in the room were standing proudly at the end of their beds, feeling chuffed with themselves.

'Not bad, ladies, for a first attempt,' Creggan sneered. 'It was good to see some of you helping others. That will help you in your time here. It's all about teamwork, you need to think as a single unit in everything you do,' he continued. He then proceeded to explain how to make up a bed block.

'A bed block is how your bed will look during the day. You take the two sheets and fold them to a width of 21inches. You then repeat this with your three blankets and stack them, beginning with a blanket on the bottom then a sheet, blanket, sheet ending with a blanket on top. The final blanket you fold length ways to the width of the others, and then wrap around the others squaring off the sides. To complete it, you place your pillows on top ensuring that you tuck the excess of the pillow case underneath each pillow,' he finished off.

This demonstration complete, as before, the room was tasked to copy his example. This took slightly longer than the making of a bed and Creggan prowled round the room offering advice to those who seemed more lost than the rest. Richard found this job not as easy as the previous one, but had finished long before most of his companions. After 25 minutes, the room had managed to succeed in producing their own bed packs in some shape or form. Creggan inspected each one with a critical eye, pointing out the individual failings.

'You obviously will need to practice this one I think,' he commented, sarcastically. 'I am sure over the next few weeks and months you will master it,' he grinned at the dejected young recruits.

Creggan then left the room for a short while. He returned with an ironing board under his arm and carrying an iron. He proceeded to set up the board, plugging the iron into a nearby socket. Creggan left the room once again and returned with a number of items of clothing, which he placed on a bedside table to his right. Picking up the first item from the pile, he beckoned to the recruits.

'Gather round, gentlemen. I will now give you a brief demonstration of how to iron your clothing, military style. This is one of the most important skills you will learn while you are here and will be used throughout your careers, however long they may be.'

This sounded like a slight jibe to Richard, but they all gathered round for the demonstration. The onlookers seemed genuinely interested in what was about to be shown to them. Richard thought to himself that this was probably the first time that most of his new comrades had been introduced to this experience. He had been fortunate to have been shown from an early age how to use an iron.

The room Corporal folded the first item on the board and with swift strokes quickly finished pressing the garment, folded it, placed it down and retrieved the next one. He continued the process until the pile was finished. The whole demonstration took less than twenty minutes. The roommates seemed in awe of this new skill which they would have to master during their training. Some of them looked at each other, doubting they would ever be able to achieve the same result.

Creggan packed away the board and iron and returned them, along with the clothing items from where he had brought them. On his return, he surveyed the young men milling about the room, chatting. He had seen a number of individuals pass through his care in the two years he had been at the Junior Leaders Training Centre. He knew that they were mostly feeling apprehensive and unsure of what to expect during their initial few days there. Although he was not a sadistic character, he felt a warm glow, knowing how uncomfortable they were. It was good to take a person out of their normal environment and plunge him or her into something unfamiliar. This enabled the staff to mould them into the type of soldier that the Regiments required. It also gave the training staff an opportunity to see who worked well as team players and who did not.

'The next demonstration that you will be taken through will be on hygiene matters,' Creggan interrupted the voices of the room. 'We are not saying that you do not know how to wash yourselves. Only, there is a requirement for us to show you, so you can do it to the standard required by a member of Her Majesty's Armed Forces. If you would like to follow me, I will take you to the washrooms and enlighten you.'

With this, the Corporal smartly turned about, made his way from the room, down the corridor and entered a door on his right. The ten young recruits followed him like lemmings and entered the washroom facility. Here, they were confronted by six sinks, in two banks of three, each with its own mirror. On the left of the room were situated three showers, complete with curtains. Richard noticed how the enamel shone and reflected from the fluorescent lights. He thought to himself, how long it had taken to get them to this immaculate condition, as the building itself was not a new one. This would soon come to light, as they progressed through their training.

The room Corporal began to unbutton his shirt and undo the belt on his lightweight trousers. Leaning forward, he began to unlace his boots, removed them and placed his socks inside. This complete, he removed his shirt and trousers and placed them in a neat pile on top of a nearby bench. Standing only in his boxer shorts, the young men marvelled at his sculptured, well defined physique, wondering if they would look like that when they left the gates in fifteen months' time to join their Regiments. Richard could tell that some of them seemed somewhat intimated by Creggan and a little inadequate. With a grin on his face, Creggan continued.

'I will now explain how we shower ourselves to the correct standard.' After this statement, he pulled down his boxer shorts and stepped into the nearest cubicle to his right. 'We start from the head and move down the body ending with the feet. This is so you wash all the shite you have accumulated away from yourself and do not transfer it from one part to another,' He began to apply shower gel to his hair and to scrub vigorously, moving from head to shoulders in a rapid motion. Once he had cleansed these areas, he stopped and addressed the assembled recruits.

'You must ensure that the areas that are prone to sweating, this includes your armpits, crutch and arsehole, are given particular attention.' This brought a titter from his audience, who could not believe that they were being instructed on how to shower. This caused Creggan to explode in a tirade of abuse. 'This is not a laughing matter, you set of pricks, a clean soldier is a good soldier. Cleanliness of yourself, weapon and equipment are valuable lessons that will serve you through your careers!'

He finished off his demonstration, stepped out of the cubicle and began to dry himself. Satisfied that he was dry enough, he started to dress himself, finishing by lacing up his boots. Before completing this action and without looking up, he ordered that they all pair off, undress and choose a cubicle. They were then to perform the same drills he had just shown to them. Richard found that later this would be known as an 'Explanation, Demonstration and Confirmation' lesson.

They quickly chose partners and began to disrobe, the floor of the washroom becoming a sea of littered clothing. One by one, they entered the cubicles, while their partners waited their turn.

'I want each partner to ensure that his opposite number carries out the drills exactly as I have just shown you'' bellowed Creggan, as he strolled around the washroom, inspecting each cubicle in turn. The recruits were hastily applying shower gel and carrying out their ablutions as quickly and efficiently as possible. As Creggan came to their cubicle to see how they were doing, their tempo and effort was raised immediately.

After the first person finished, his partner then stepped into the vacant cubicle and the process was repeated. It had been only ten minutes since they had begun and Creggan was prowling around in the steam created by the very hot water. Richard, who had finished, could tell that Creggan was becoming slightly agitated and prepared for the inevitable outpouring of abuse that was to follow. As if on cue, Creggan roared at the top of his voice.

'Come on, get a move on, you set of fannies. It should only take you a maximum of five minutes to perform this exercise. I want to see the last pair dressed afterwards.'

This caused an increased amount of activity, as bodies started to emerge from the cubicles, reaching for their towels and hastily rubbing their bodies to remove the water. The washroom floor was a mass of arms and legs, as they searched for their discarded clothes. People were falling over each other and cursing, as they scrambled into their clothing. In their earnest rush not to be last, Richard could see that some were not fully dried, as wet stains quickly developed on their clothes.

'Well, that was a parcel of shite, you lot. We will go through the same procedure tomorrow morning, prior to your first Physical Training (PT) session. Now, get yourselves back to the room and make a start on ironing your kit……..Move!'

With these parting words, the half sodden group vacated the washroom quickly. On entering the room, they started to search for the ironing boards, but unfortunately, only one was available. A mass scrum ensued, while people argued over who would be first to use it. Richard thought to himself that surely there would be more than one to use, so proceeded to search in all the cupboards outside the room. Inside the third door that he opened, he found a quantity of cleaning materials and five ironing boards and irons, stacked neatly in a corner. Picking up one of each, he returned to the room to inform his roommates. On hearing his news, the recruits immediately rushed out of the room to acquire the precious items.

After five minutes, the room was a hive of activity, as the friends began the task of ironing their clothing. Some of those who had never performed this function, watched with interest, as the more proficient of them made short, sharp work of the pile of clothing with which they had been issued.

Richard put the earlier training from his father to good use: he felt happy that he had listened, all these years ago. In under an hour he completed his pile and proceeded to fold and put the clothes away. He remembered that his father had always said to him that an effective team was only as good as its weakest link. He looked around to see if he could find anyone who may be having any difficulty.

In the far corner was a heavy set guy he had not yet spoken with, trying to figure out how to put a crease in a set of lightweight trousers. Richard slowly made his way over to him, to see if he could lend a hand.

'Hi, mate, I'm Richard, do you want any help? I've finished mine.'

The bemused recruit looked up and said, 'Yes please, buddy. It's my first time doing this shit, I haven't got a clue. I'm Mike Sheperton, by the way.'

'No problem, mate, let's have a look. Richard accepted the iron offered to him and began to lay out the trousers, ready to apply the regulation crease, as Creggan had shown them. After a five minute refresher, he handed the iron back to Mike, who took it and proceeded to work on the next pair of trousers. With Richard's instruction and guidance, he flew rapidly through his pile of kit. As he completed the last item, he looked up at Richard and smiled.

'That's much appreciated, mate, I was never very quick at picking things up but I seem to have got the hang of it now.'

Richard felt satisfaction, as he answered with a grin, 'No problem, mate. I am sure there are things that you can teach me as we go through the next fifteen months.'

With this comment, he made his way back to his bed space and as he neared it, Corporal Creggan entered the room. The Corporal surveyed the hive of activity and allowed himself a smile of satisfaction at his industrious new charges. Most of them had completed the task he had set them, others were struggling slightly, but that was the norm. He had seen this process on numerous occasions and knew with confidence that he could do something with this bunch. There would be a number that would not make the grade, whether from homesickness or the lack of physical or mental attributes. Not everyone was cut out for a life in the military, but that was the same for any job in life. He had nurtured countless individuals in his time at the training centre, so felt positive at the start this new cohort had made. These were early days, so he would not let them know this.

'Right, guys, not a bad effort for your first day. Now, get yourselves ready for bed, lights out in 30 minutes. You have an early start in the morning, Reveille will be at 06:00. Breakfast is at 06:30. You will ensure you are washed and shaved and standing by your beds by 07:00, dressed in PT kit for your morning inspection.'

Richard looked out the window of the Barrack Room and could not believe that it was starting to get dark. The first day had flown by and he wondered if the tempo would be the same over the coming days. He looked across at the Scotsman Steve, who was busying himself for bed. He ambled across to him to ascertain how he felt the first day had gone.

'Well, mate, what did you think of that then?'

The Scot looked up and grinned, 'Pure magic, man. I think they are going to keep us busy, eh?'

'I think you're maybe right,' replied Richard, returning the smile. He turned away to go back to his bed space and ready himself for bed. He looked at his bed pack and thought it looked too nice to destroy, but he knew he would have to. He started to dismantle it and make up his bed. This being complete, he climbed in and shivered as the cold sheets touched his skin. The blankets were like wire wool as they scratched his neck and chin. As he stared around the room, he noticed some of the lads had made the decision to remove only the outer blanket from their bed packs. This would save them time in the morning, albeit at the of a warm night's sleep. The chatter among the roommates was starting to subside, when it was interrupted by the sound of a bugle outside their Barrack Block. This was a sound they would soon become used to every evening and morning.

'Lights out!' came the sound, echoed by the NCOs, as they walked around the accommodation. As Richard closed his eyes to try to go to sleep, he wondered what delights were in store for them when the sun rose. As he drifted into sleep, he realised that not once had he thought of home.

Chapter 3 A new dawn

Richard's eyes opened suddenly and he instinctively lifted his arm to look at his watch. The dial indicated it was 05:45, fifteen minutes before he was due to get up. This was normal for him, as he had always wakened before the time he was supposed to rise. He wondered if this was a subconscious thing, drummed into him by his father.

Richard looked around the room. No one seemed to be stirring. He decided he would make his way to the washrooms, shower and shave so that he had a head start on the day. He removed his wash kit, towel and some PT shorts from the steel locker and made his way quietly from the room. Entering the ablutions area, as he suspected, he was the only one there. Stepping into the first shower cubicle, he started the water running, while he undressed. His clothes placed neatly on a bench, he climbed into the shower. The water against his skin felt good. He started the routine from head to toe, just as he had been shown the previous day. He chuckled to himself recalling this, wondering how many others would be doing the same in the next half hour.

His body cleansed, he exited the shower and began to towel himself down, then put on his boxers and PT shorts. They were blue and almost reached his knees. They reminded him of footballers like Stanley Matthews in the 1950s. He moved toward the nearest wash basin and turned on the water. As the bowl filled, he removed his shaving implements, toothpaste and brush from his wash bag. Applying shaving foam to his face, he started to remove the 36 hours' worth of stubble which had accumulated. Just has he was about to rinse off the excess foam, he was startled as the sound of a bugle blew, just outside the Barrack Block. This was obviously the Reveille that Creggan had mentioned the evening before. Richard put toothpaste onto his brush and began the process of cleaning his teeth. The sound of heavy footsteps and raised voices filled the corridors, as doors were flung open.

'Get out of bed, you lazy shits! Move!'

Richard could hear beds being overturned as he made his way back along the corridor, towards his room. From a room to his left, Pete emerged, with a large grin spreading across his face. He carried his wash bag and towel under his arm, and was obviously heading towards the ablutions. It was only now that Richard realised that he had not seen or spoken to Pete since they had entered the Barrack Block the previous day.

Throughout their lives, Pete had always seen the humorous side of things. That would, no doubt, be tested over their time in training.

'Looks like it going to be another interesting day,' he quipped.

'Think you could be right, mate,' Richard replied 'I will catch up with you at breakfast.'

With this, the two friends carried on their separate journeys. As Richard entered the room, he could see bedding and bodies strewn all over the place. It resembled a gypsy caravan site. Creggan was in the middle of it, spewing a tirade of abuse at his young charges. The guys who had tried to be clever and save some time by not using the blankets in their bed blocks looked dejected. Creggan had approached those beds in turn and ripped the packs apart.

'Good try, you stupid feckers, but you will soon learn not to take short cuts. You will use all your bedding every night to make up your beds. Then, in the morning, you will take them apart and build your bed blocks, as I showed you yesterday.'

The faces of the young soldiers were pictures of desperation. Richard could see that Mike Sheperton, whom he had helped iron his clothes the previous day, was almost in tears. Although such a well built, some would say overweight, young man, Mike seemed very sensitive. Richard wondered if Mike would make it over the first three gruelling months of training. These twelve weeks were supposed to be the most arduous of all. His father had told Richard that he would be physically and emotionally drained by the end of it. The trick was, he said, not to stand out too much in the first few weeks. Try to blend in and become the "grey man."

With this thought, he walked to his bed space trying to avoid eye contact with Creggan, who was looking round the room for his next victim. Just as he had almost reached his bed space, Creggan noticed him. His heart sank as he knew that he was about to be singled out in front of the rest of his new mates.

'You've been a busy little bastard, Hunter,' was Creggan's opening gambit.

Richard stopped in his tracks and turned to face the Corporal. He was not sure if he was supposed to answer or not. Examining the look on Creggan's face did not help him come to a decision. The heavy set NCO was very adept at showing no emotion. There was an awkward silence between the two, which seemed to go on forever. This was broken at last by Creggan with the words:

'That is what is called being organised. Up, shat, showered and shaved prior to Reveille, gentlemen,' he said, as he addressed the whole room. 'Good drills, Hunter, let's hope you can instil the same principles in your peers. Now, get your idle arses into that washroom, make up your beds and get to breakfast. Like I said last night, I want you outside the block at 07:00 in PT kit. Prior to that, there will be a quick room inspection.'

Richard felt himself blush and knew he had failed in the first task his father had given him. He had been identified as someone with potential the bad side to this being; that he would be under Creggan's watchful gaze. Any slip up would be noticed and punished accordingly. As Richard continued to his locker to put away his washing kit, Creggan marched out of the room. Putting away his things neatly in his locker, he felt a tap on the shoulder.

'You fuckin', creeping shite,' came the gruff, Glaswegian accent from over his shoulder and as he turned round, Steve was standing there laughing. Richard could tell by his tone that he was only joking, but still felt a pang of embarrassment.

'I feel a right tool now, proper little teacher's pet,' he replied, sheepishly.

'Someone has to be,' Steve returned, 'I'm off for a shower. See you at breakfast, if you're not here when I get back.' With this comment, he vacated the room and headed off down the corridor.

Richard removed a white PT vest, a pair of green socks and the black plimsolls issued to him from the locker and started to dress. As he laced up the plimsolls, he wondered if they gave any form of cushioning. They seemed very thin, being made out of canvas and not the least bit fashionable. Now ready, he took his green mug and knife, fork and spoon (KFS) and made his way to the room next door, where Pete was also dressing. He gave a wink of greeting to his friend, which was returned to him.

'You about ready for scoff?' asked Richard.

'Give me two minutes,' was Pete's reply, as he finished dressing. He then reached for his mug and KFS. The two friends, now suitably equipped, departed the room and exited the Barrack Block on their way to the 'cookhouse', as it was later to be known to them. As they walked the two hundred metres or so towards their destination, they chatted over the previous day's events. Pete seemed genuinely keen to experience more of the same hectic lifestyle and new skills that awaited them.

They opened the door to the cookhouse and began to search for the hot plate, where the meals would be served. On the far side of the expansive room was a series of stainless steel counters. Above them were situated lights shining down on the food, not only to highlight the offerings, but also as a means of keeping them warm. The cookhouse itself was quiet, with only a handful of people either seated, already tucking into the first meal of the day, or moving along the hot plate, loading up their plates. Both Pete and Richard joined the end of the line, picking up a plate each, as they did so. They were surprised at the range of food being offered. This ran from a full English cooked breakfast, with fried, scrambled and poached eggs and everything that went with them. There was also cereal or porridge and fruit, which seemed a little odd first thing in the morning. Richard decided to have a full English and proceeded to load his plate with a little bit of everything on offer. Suddenly, as he neared the end of the line, a figure in full chef's uniform, tall, white hat, apron and checked blue trousers made a bee line for him from the back of the serving area.

'One choice of scrambled, poached or fried egg, you greedy twat,' he barked at Richard, pointing to the plate that had both scrambled and fried egg on it.

Richard hesitated, before deciding that the stern faced chef obviously was expecting him to return one of the items to the receptacle from which he had taken it.

'Sorry, I didn't know. There isn't a sign,' he replied, innocently.

'Sorry *"Chef"* you fecking, cocky shit. Well, you know now, so put one of them back!'

Richard did as he was commanded and returned the scrambled egg to its former home. After finishing loading up their plates, the two friends looked around for a table. There were enough to choose from, as the dining area looked as though it could cater for around a thousand people. They found a convenient one next to a couple of stainless steel urns. These obviously housed tea and coffee and Richard was dying for a cuppa.

'You want a brew, Pet?' he asked his friend.

'Would love one, mate,' Pete answered.

Richard picked up his and Pete's mugs and walked to the table the urns were sitting on. He knew that, like himself, Pete drank coffee with two sugars, so he filled both mugs and spooned in the required amount of sugar, then returned to the table.

There was a silence for the next couple of minutes, as the friends began to consume their breakfasts.

The amount of calories that the average soldier needs whilst in training is vast. The meals provided by the catering staff in establishments like this (and later as he was to find in regular units) were of a high calorific content.

As they continued devouring their breakfasts, they stopped occasionally, to make small talk. Richard spotted that Steve had just entered the dining hall, so he raised his arm, to let him know where they were located. Steve acknowledged the sign and, after making his selection from the hot plate, joined them at the table.

'Looks alright, eh?' he pointed to his plate, which was piled so high, they could not see any white space.

'Tastes ok too,' Pete answered. 'Think we might need this to get us through whatever they have planned for the day.'

They all nodded in agreement and continued to wade their way through their breakfasts. Richard noticed a group of four older looking soldiers, two tables away from them. On the epaulettes of their shirts sat yellow slides with a white stripes down the middle. A couple of them seemed to be looking over and laughing. This made Richard feel a little uneasy and he made the other two aware of his observations. Steve peered over his shoulder and gave the four of them a scowl. He was obviously not one to be intimidated, this was probably borne out of his rough Glaswegian upbringing. They were later to discover that these soldiers were in 'pass off'. This meant that they were in their final term of training and would be joining their Regiments and Corps in the next few months. Richard knew that it would be a long haul before his group reached that point.

Finishing off their breakfasts and swilling down their brews, they decided it was time to return to the Barrack Block. They cleared their plates into the swill bins provided and sat them on the trolleys placed there for that purpose. They saw a couple of other members of their new Troop enter the cookhouse. 'They're cutting it a bit fine,' Richard thought to himself, checking his watch. It was 06:35, which meant there were only 25 minutes until they were to be by their beds for the room inspection, prior to their first introduction to Physical Training (PT).

'I would get a shift on, guys, room inspection in 25 minutes!' Pete called over to them.

Pete, obviously, had been thinking the same thing. However, some of the newcomers did not seem too bothered by the remark, while others, realising the urgency, moved quickly to the hot plate to fetch their breakfasts. Shrugging with resignation, Pete turned away and the threesome started the short journey back to the Block. Reaching their destination, both Steve and Richard fired a parting remark to Pete, as they went into their separate rooms. Richard noticed that Steve had already made up his bed block and decided he must do the same. He carefully placed the counterpane on the bed and stretched it tightly, just as he had been shown. He ensured that the hospital corners were 45 degrees, also as instructed the previous day. After folding his blanket and sheets and constructing the bed block, he laid it at the head of the bed, with the two pillows adorning the top.

The room was a melee, with some making up their beds, while others were busying themselves with brushes, sweeping around their bed spaces. However, Richard noticed two of them standing chatting and he felt a surge of frustration well up inside. It reached a point where he knew he would have to say something.

'Guys, it's 06:45, room inspection is in fifteen minutes. Do you mind giving a hand getting the place sorted?'

One of the two was Mike Sheperton, who blushed on hearing Richard's remark. He seemed to have taken a shine to Richard after being aided by him the previous day. Not wanting to let him down, he called over.

'No problem, mate. What do you want us to do?'

'Just grab a couple of brushes and start around your bed spaces, we can all help doing the rest,' Richard replied.

With this, Mike scurried out of the room and returned with a brush and dustpan, which he handed over to the recruit with whom he had been chatting. This lad took it grudgingly but Richard could tell, by the look on his face that he did not wish to help. He had probably been brought up in a household where his mother had done everything for him. So that there were no hard feelings, Richard thought he had better introduce himself. If they were to work effectively as a team, they needed to gel, with no feelings of animosity.

'Hi there, buddy, I'm Richard,' as he held out his hand to introduce himself.

The man looked at Richard as if he were something he had stepped in. His features were angular with not a blemish or spot in sight. His voice was well spoken, probably from the Home Counties, probably maybe Hertfordshire or Buckinghamshire, Richard hazarded a guess. It was blatantly clear that he was not used to being asked or told what to do. This could prove difficult over the coming weeks and Richard doubted if he would make it through. At least not without being detrimental to the effectiveness of the Troop.

'Justin Taylor-Forbes,' the ferret faced individual retorted. Without taking the offered hand, he continued sarcastically, 'I never realised Creggan had put you in charge.'

Richard was rapidly taking an intense dislike to this bloke, and had to bite his lip and think before replying.

'We're all in the same boat, mate, the only way we are going to get through this is by working together.'

Before the two could continue their conversation, they were interrupted by the sound of boots marching down the corridor. Creggan burst into the room and announced that the room inspection would begin in five minutes. Everyone was to be stood by his bed. As quickly as he appeared, he was gone, and the room burst into panic, making last minute checks on their bedding and immediate area around their beds. Each room had between eight and ten, making the total of the Troop around forty. However, in Richard's room, as the men began to stand by their beds, it was noticeable that two of the bed spaces were empty. He guessed that these two must have been in the party they saw entering the cookhouse, twenty minutes earlier. He had a bad feeling about this, if they were not back in the next few minutes, someone was going to pay. As if on cue, the sound of Sgt. Portwood' voice bellowed.

'Right, stand by your beds!'

Everyone took a last look round their beds for anything they may have missed, although it was probably too late now. Creggan entered the room and glanced around, to see that everyone was accounted for, before Sgt. Portwood began his inspection. He picked up on the fact that there were two empty beds and his colour visibly changed. The veins on his temple began to pulsate, as he wound himself up for the onslaught. Richard and Steve exchanged glances and cringed, awaiting the inevitable outburst.

'Where the feck are the owners of those bed spaces?' Creggan spewed forth, showering the immediate area in saliva.

Some men looked at each other, others at the floor. No one wanted to make eye contact with Creggan. Then, from the corner, a gruff Scots accent piped up.

'Think they might still be at breakfast, Corporal. It was Steve who volunteered the information.

Creggan's face was a picture of disbelief and loathing, but before he could vent his rage on anyone, the two hapless missing persons ambled into the room. Sauntering straight past, totally unaware of the situation that was unfolding in front of them. To a man, everyone turned in their direction, wide eyed with disbelief. Chatting between themselves, they nonchalantly strolled to their lockers and began to put away their mugs and KFS. It wasn't until they turned round and saw everyone standing to attention, glaring in their direction, did they realise something was wrong.

'Have a nice breakfast, did you?' Creggan sneered. 'Feeling nice and full, are we?'

There was an uneasy silence, as the two culprits looked at each other, wondering which one would come up with the better excuse. However, they knew, no matter what they said, it would not be the answer Creggan was after. Eventually, one of them gathered enough courage to attempt to justify their actions.

'It was very nice, Corporal, we never realised the time was so late,' was the only excuse he could give. Richard and others in the room closed their eyes, cringing at this poor reason for their absence.

'I am so glad you enjoyed it,' was the calm, quiet reply from Creggan. 'Now that you are fully fuelled...' his voice level was rising as each word passed his lips. Get down and give me twenty press ups, assume the position!' The word "position" was screamed and barely discernible.

As the two offenders began their punishment, Creggan addressed the room as to how the inspection would go. He explained that when Sgt. Portwood entered the room, he would bring them to attention and would move around the room to each bed space, in a clockwise direction, starting with the first bed on the left. As he finished giving his instructions, he turned his attention back to the two guilty parties, still attempting to complete their twenty press ups. From the room next door, came a tirade of abuse and the sound of furniture being thrown around. Richard looked in Creggan's direction and saw him looking to his left, in the direction of Pete's room. Creggan noticeably stiffened.

'Room, room shun!' he instructed. On doing so, he brought up his left leg and drove it down, as if he was going to smash through the floor. Standing ramrod straight, he turned to face Sgt. Portwood, who was now in the doorway. A knowing, almost humorous, look was exchanged between them. They had been through this process too many times to count, but it still gave them a sense of excitement the first time, with a new set of recruits.

'Room 2 C1 ready and awaiting your inspection, Sgt.,' he officially greeted his superior.

'Thank you, Corporal Creggan. Let's hope they are a better shower than the last bag of bollocks,' he answered, with a glint in his eye. 'By the way, what are those two retards doing on their bellies?' he indicated, with a nod of his head to the far end of the room.

'Both of them late for inspection, thought they would have a leisurely breakfast, rather than grace us with their presence,' Creggan replied, with a chuckle.

'Well, they can carry on with their punishments while I inspect the room, then.' With that, Portwood began his tour of inspection.

On arriving at the first bed space, he simply took the mattress and heaved it over onto the floor, complete with bed block. He offered no words to the bewildered soldier as to the reason why. Creggan moved swiftly on to the next one, where he proceeded to do the same.

As Portwood continued on his journey of destruction, the roommates looked at each other, not knowing what was happening. To them, the room had looked spotless and they were actually expecting praise, rather than this. As the Troop Sgt. reached the final bed space and tipped all its contents on onto the floor, he turned to Creggan.

'Well, Cpl Creggan that was a parcel of shite. Let's see if it is any better tomorrow, shall we?' he barked. This was a question that demanded an answer and Creggan was eager to respond.

'I am sure it will be, Sgt.,' came his reply. Turning to the dejected young Junior Troopers, Creggan issued his next order. 'Right, get your lazy arses outside and fall in in three ranks …..Move!'

The shocked recruits headed rapidly for the door, tripping over bedding and each other as they did. Entering the corridor, they collided with other members of the Troop, who were also scurrying toward the exit from the Barrack Block. Once outside, they attempted to line up as they had done the day before, in lines of three. After some confusion, they mastered it and awaited the return of the training NCO's. Richard looked around and everyone, to a man, had a confused 'what just happened?' look on their faces. They were soon to find out this would be a normal everyday occurrence.

From out of the door of the Barrack Block, emerged the four room NCOs and Sgt. Portwood, chatting to each other, generally looking pleased with their morning's work so far. However, the look of mirth was soon replaced by severity, as they approached the waiting young Troopers.

'Right, gents. I must admit, that was a fecking bad start to my day. I expect a 100 percent improvement tomorrow morning. Troop Corporals, take over, please.'

His announcement complete, he turned about smartly and marched back into the Barrack Block, no doubt to put his feet up in his office and have a well-deserved cup of tea.

'Listen in to me,' came the command from one of the other room Corporals, 'move to the right in threes, right turn!'

The Troop changed direction to the right, or rather, about ninety five percent of them did.

'That's Army right, you set of twats!' barked out the room Corporal 'By the right, double march.'

On this command, the group started off at a jog, being led by the room NCOs in the direction of the gymnasium, where their first PT lesson would be given.

Chapter 4 Physical Training

The rhythmic sound of plimsolls on the hard tarmac road reverberated in Richard's ears, as the Troop made its way towards the gymnasium. The distance was just under half a mile but he could feel his breathing starting to labour. He had always had a dislike for running but knew it was part of the job. He had represented his school in various sports during his time at secondary school. He was also the Captain of the rugby team, so was physically robust but always found it difficult over endurance events. He looked around the squad and found that some of them were finding it hard going too. It gave him extra strength, to know that he was not the only one struggling.

Pete had always been better at endurance events and was happily chatting away to the runner next to him. Pete had been a member of the school cross country and athletics team: although he had asthma, it never seemed to bother him. The room NCOs were assessing the members of the Troop for any signs of weakness. This would be a continuing process throughout the rest of their stay at the training centre.

The group continued for another 100 metres, then made a sharp right turn. In front of them was a large building. The building was covered in large glass panels and they could see inside what would become a familiar sight. As they neared the entrance, they were given the command to halt by the room NCOs, the senior of whom taking over once again, instructing them to fall out and make their way into the gym.

Some of the group started to amble towards the doorway and were immediately harangued by the Corporals.

'Who said you could walk?' came the vicious question from Creggan, 'At the double, you shit heads!'

With this ringing in their ears, the recruits set off at a sprint but quickly realised that only one, maybe two people at a time, could fit through the doorway. This caused a massive bottleneck, as they struggled to gain entry. As they finally all filtered through, they stood in a disorganised rabble in the massive hall. The floors were wooden, adorned with various different coloured lines. This was so that various sports from volleyball and basketball to five a side football could be played. They were soon to find out that this would not be the norm, as most lessons would consist of a 'beasting'.

At the far end of the hall stood a slender dark skinned man in uniform. He was dressed in long, deep blue trousers with sewn-in creases and a navy blue top with a cross swords badge on the upper right arm. His waist looked almost feminine, but from there his torso and shoulders spread out. He was almost 'V' shaped and his arms seemed disproportionate to his bottom half. He eyed the recruits like a predator sizing up its next meal. To the young soldiers, he seemed like a colossus guarding his Empire. Richard was immediately in awe of this giant and wondered how many hours of training it had taken to create such a physique?

'Right, you lot, line up in three ranks with the front rank on that white line. Go!'

The Troop sprang forward as one and began to assemble into the required three ranks, with the first rank lining up on the white line, as instructed. This took them only a matter of 30-40 seconds, as they were becoming better accustomed to the manoeuvre. Before long, they straightened up their lines and positioned themselves, one behind the other. The imposing individual was quickly losing patience.

'Come on C1, get yourselves sorted out!' he ranted. 'I am Corporal Steve Francis. I will be your Physical Training Instructor for this lesson and most of your stay here at the Junior Leaders Regiment. Prior to each lesson, you will be inspected to see that you are correctly turned out for my lessons. To that end, face front, while I give you a quick once over!'

With this, he started with the front rank, left hand man and began his tour through the assembled ranks. He picked out almost every individual for some misdemeanour or another. Richard recognised a recurring theme, it seemed that nothing they did was ever quite right. This was the Army's way of putting pressure on people, to see how they would react. It was what was known as 'character building'.

'Right, gents, as this is your first lesson, a gypsy's warning for you. You will attend these lessons, dressed and turned out as follows. You will all wear the same colour PT vest, either white or red: you will ensure that you have creases on the arms and also on the legs of your shorts, front and back: you will also ensure that you have applied black boot polish to your plimsolls and that they are free of dirt on the sole: your socks will be turned down, so they are a hands width showing.'

Some of the young recruits looked around at each other, wondering if they had heard correctly. Whoever applies polish to their plimsolls? Corporal Francis did not miss this and inwardly smiled, knowing full well the thought behind the perplexed looks coming from the young men before him.

'Has anyone got a problem with something I have just said?' he asked, not really expecting a reply.

There was an uncomfortable silence throughout the hall but no sound was forthcoming. Richard knew that it was not wise to upset Physical Training Instructors (PTIs) as they could make their stay very harsh indeed. The PTI, satisfied that no one was going to question his instructions, decided to continue with the lesson.

'Before we commence each lesson proper, we need to warm our bodies up. This is to raise the heart rate and warm up the muscles, preventing you from injuring yourselves unnecessarily. So, on my command, start jogging round the hall, keeping to the white line, one behind the other, in a clockwise direction. Go!'

The recruits turned about and led off round the hall in a clockwise direction. Moving into single file, one behind the other, they eventually formed a mobile square. Once into a rhythm and satisfied that their heart rates had been elevated, Francis started to make things interesting.

'Right, still jogging round the room, listen in to me. When I say the command "one", you will touch the floor with your left hands. When I say "two", you will touch the floor with your right hands. On "three", you will change direction!'

They continued to jog round the room, listening intently for the first word of command. Francis watched them keenly, waiting for the most convenient opportunity, when he believed they would not paying attention.

'Two!' he barked loudly, overcoming the sound of the pounding feet.

Most of the group leaned down and touched the floor with their right hands, a small minority touching with the left. This was immediately rebuffed by the PTI.

'Two was right hands, you retards. Listen in carefully and pay attention!'

A small titter spread throughout the hall, as they all grinned at each other. Those who had been wrong blushed visibly. They carried on around the hall, eagerly waiting to make amends on the next command.

'Three!' came the command from Francis, as he surveyed the recruits, looking for any mistakes. This was not hard, as some were attempting to touch the floor with their left hands, while others were changing direction. This, of course, caused some of them to collide and bodies were strewn all over the gym floor.

'Sort it out, you lot!' screamed the now irate PTI.

Picking themselves up and deciding which direction they should now be heading, Richard and his companions returned to running round the gym. At irregular intervals, Francis would call out a number and the runners would react accordingly. As they progressed, they were slowly getting the hang of it. Looking up at the clock on the wall, Richard noticed that fifteen minutes had gone by. He felt great, although a little out of breath and beads of sweat ran down his brow.

'C1, C1 halt!' Cpl Francis called out.

The Troop came to a grinding halt, some of them leaning over, with hands on hips, trying to draw breath. Others seemed still fresh and Richard looked over at Pete and Steve, who fell into this latter category. He knew that Pete would not find this difficult but was not sure about Steve, who was heavy set and did not look the least like the athletic type. Richard was to learn never to judge a book by its cover.

'Right, Troops, now you are nicely warmed up. Stand up straight and suck the air in. You will not inflate your lungs doing teapot impersonations,' the Corporal quipped, sarcastically. 'The first exercise I am going to demonstrate is to build upper body strength and it is done on the ropes. Follow me.'

The PTI made his way diagonally from his position to the opposite side of the gym, toward five ropes, all about four inches in diameter. They followed him obediently, waiting for him to perform his demonstration.

'Step 1, hold the rope at arm level, in front of your chest. Place one hand below the other, knuckles facing away from you and elbows bent, so both arms are parallel to your chest.' He began grasping the rope in the prescribed manner. 'Step 2, place one hand at about chin-nose height. Keep your arm parallel to your chest.' He continued, ensuring that they were all paying attention. 'Step 3, pull your arm down, so that your hand is around nipple height. Once your higher hand is at step 3, repeat steps 2-3 with your other arm, 'walking' up the rope.'

As he finished explaining the demonstration, he began to ascend the rope in well-practised movements, smoothly climbing the rope until, after 30 seconds he had reached the top. The group was amazed at how easy Francis had made it look and guessed that their efforts would be nowhere near the same.

As there were 40 in the class, and only five ropes, Francis instructed them to dress off in front of the ropes, into groups of eight. They jostled each other, trying not to be first but as near to the back of the line as possible. This would allow them to watch the techniques of the others but, more importantly, allow them maximum rest, or so they thought.

'Right, number ones, assume the position in step one, as I showed you in the demonstration.'

The first in each line moved forward to take up the initial position.

'On my command, you will make your way to the top, using just your arms, in your best time. However, the rest of you will jog on the spot until the man in front of you has finished and has tagged you.'

The whole room groaned as one, their cunning plan had been foiled. As the first recruits began to climb, the sound of stamping feet reverberated throughout the hall.

The first five recruits began their ascent, with varying levels of success. Richard watched Pete, as he attempted to climb the rope. He seemed to be struggling with the technique and was on the end of a scathing torrent of derision from the PTI. He finally made the top, then began his gentle descent to tag his team mate. The rest of the first wave had already finished and the second wave had reached the halfway point. Richard readied himself, as he would be next. He had watched with interest the different techniques employed by the various Troop members. Before he realised, his turn had come and he had been tagged. He dressed forward and took the rope in his hands. Moving hand over hand, he started upwards; in no time at all and to his surprise, he had gained the top and touched the metal pin from which the rope was hanging. As he began to lower himself, he glanced across and saw that Steve had also reached his goal and was already on the way down. The rest of the wave had barely reached midpoint on the way up. Richard felt his feet touch the ground and he immediately turned to tag the next person in his team.

The process went on until all Troop members had completed the exercise. The remainder were still jogging on the spot, until Francis called out, above the din.

'C1, C1......halt!'

The sound of heavy breathing and near exhaustion for some filled the gym hall. Perspiration was running down their faces. Little did they know that this was just a warm up. The PTI gave the command for them all to form one continuous line, in front of him. He then began to explain the next set of exercises.

'The next exercise we are going to carry out is the "sit up". I will first demonstrate and then you will copy my example. Lie with your back on the floor. Get on a completely flat surface, either on an exercise mat or on the grass if the lesson is outdoors. As we are inside on this occasion, we will just use the floor. We will use the mats next time. The next stage is to bend your knees at a 90° angle. Your feet should be flat on the ground, no more than twelve inches apart. During test conditions, you will have a partner who will hold your feet, so they are anchored to the floor.'

As he explained the exercise he lay down and explained each section.

'Lace your fingers behind your head. They need to stay laced throughout your set of sit ups; if you remove any man undoes them from this position at any time, that man will be disqualified.' He continued demonstrating the next part of the exercise.

'Raise your torso to a vertical position. Use your abdominal muscles to lift your body, until the base of your neck is above the base of your spine. Stop when the bend in your hips is at a 90° angle.' Raising his own body to that angle, he carried on.

'Lower your back until your shoulder blades touch the ground. Use a steady motion; do not let yourself bounce back up and do not rest when you return to the starting position. That is the exercise complete, so down on your backs, go!'

The recruits all began to lower themselves down to the horizontal position. They tried hard to get in a comfortable position on the gym floor. Slowly, the noise of chatter died down, as they adopted the first position, ready to begin the exercise.

'On my command, I want to see ten good press ups in the same manner as I have just shown you. Do not arch your back, it should remain straight. Do not raise your buttocks off the ground to lift your body. Get ready ....begin!'

With a motion like a Mexican wave, the recruits began their exercises. Richard had always found sit ups easy, and in no time at all had completed his ten. He lay down, waiting for the others to finish. Again, some of them had obviously never done this type of thing before and groans could be heard emanating from some. As the last one finished, Cpl Francis issued his next instruction.

'On your feet, up!'"

They all struggled to regain their feet, some swaying as they did so. The last wearied recruit finally stood to attention and Francis, satisfied they were paying attention, continued without further pause.

'The next exercise I will demonstrate is the "burpee". Watch carefully, as I will once again explain as I go through it and demonstrate each step. Step one, begin in a standing position. Your feet should be shoulder-width apart. Now, lower your body into a squatting position, placing your hands on the floor in front of you.' As he explained the first movement, he once again demonstrated it to the Troop.

Second step, kick your feet back, so that you are in push-up position. Keep your hands firmly on the ground to support your body. The third step, lower your chest to do a push-up. Bring your chest back up. Finally, to complete, kick your feet back to their original position. Stand up and then jump into the air, while clapping your hands overhead. Are there any questions?'

There was an awkward silence as the young soldiers looked at each other, wondering if anyone would come forward. At last, the silence was broken by Mike Sheperton.

'Could you go through that again, please, Corporal?' he asked, nervously.

'Of course I can, lad. Right, everyone, look in while I go through a complete demonstration of the exercise.'

The PTI gave an effortless explanation and demonstration of the exercise, once again. Confusion reigned over the faces of some of the assembled Troops, as they tried to remember each phase. Richard had a head start as his father had shown him all the exercises employed by the British Army. He did not profess to be an expert in them but at least he was familiar with them and could carry out most to a reasonable standard.

The demonstration over, Francis directed them to assume the first position, which they all did. This time, there was no idle chat, as everyone seemed to concentrate on what the steps were again. Some looked around at others for guidance, as the PTI requested that they begin the exercise and, once again , complete it ten times. They were ordered to stand to attention when finished.

As the Troops entered this phase of the lesson, it was easy to tell which of them were totally uncoordinated. It was akin to a clown show in a circus, Richard thought to himself. All they required were a couple of red noses and big, floppy shoes. Eventually, everyone had finished their 'ten' to the PTI's satisfaction. Looking at the clock on the far side of the hall, Richard could see that it was 08:45, and he guessed that there were only around fifteen minutes remaining of the lesson. He had learned, once again from his father that indoor PT lessons lasted no longer than an hour. He would soon turn out to be right, but, meantime, Francis had a little surprise in store for them.

'Ok, gents, can some of you collect eight benches from around the gym and bring them over to me.'

They all realised that this was not a request, but an instruction, and they darted off to fulfil his wishes. As the benches arrived one by one, in the centre of the hall, Francis directed them to form a square, with two benches on each side. Once complete, he asked the Troops to take a seat facing inwards, where he now stood.

Richard had an uneasy feeling about this. There was something about the growing smirk and look of enjoyment on the PTI's face that did not bode well for the young would be squaddies. This was confirmed by the arrival of the room NCOs and Sgt. Portwood, who, to a man, were grinning as they approached. It seemed to him that this was to be a highlight of the training staffs' day. Portwood surveyed his new Troop and appeared to be looking for someone to select. For what purpose, Richard had no idea. He was soon to find that he was close to the mark, as Portwood produced two pairs of boxing gloves from behind his back. Cpl Francis addressed the bewildered looking youths.

'Right C1, we have a little treat for you, to round off your first lesson here at the Junior Leaders Royal Armoured Corps Training Centre.' He spoke the words with relish, registering the look of apprehension on the faces of the young men, gathered around on the benches.

'What we are going to do next is a little test of aggression and character. The exercise is what we call "milling" In a moment, I will pair two of you up. You will don the gloves provided by Sgt. Portwood here.' He accepted the gloves offered by Portwood, who had at this point, stepped into the ring.

'Next, we want to see each pair of recruits go hell for leather against each other for one minute. If we see any hesitation or someone not showing any effort, that person, or indeed both of them, will fight again.'

Portwood stepped out of the ring, as Francis selected his first pairing. Richard was hoping that he would not be paired with Pete. Although he did not have a problem with fighting *per se*, he might find it difficult with a friend. The minutes flew by, as each pair tried their best to knock the living daylights out of his opponent. Before he knew it and just as he thought the lesson would come to an end, Richard's name was called, but thankfully he was paired with someone he had not yet met in the

Troop. As the two moved forward to put on the gloves, he quickly whispered an introduction to Richard.

'I'm Fred, by the way mate, let's give them a good show then, eh?' he smiled at Richard.

The PTI gave the command for the beginning of the minute and the two recruits stepped forward and proceeded to give an aggressive and what looked like professional bout to the onlookers. The minute flew by and once the two protagonists had been told to stop, they patted each other on the back. A great cheer went up and applause, not only from the Troop, but from the Instructors also. Richard was not to know it, but these two were to become good friends. Although a twist of fate would change their lives forever.

As the pair of them began to unlace the gloves, the PTI barked out orders to the rest of C1 to put away the benches where they had found them. He asked that someone go and get a mop and bucket from the toilets and clean up the sweat and blood accumulated in the small area where the "milling" had taken place. The kit put away and the floor cleaned, Cpl Francis continued:

'Well, C1, that was not a bad first lesson. At the beginning of each lesson I explained we warm up. So, at the end of the lesson, we warm down. We do this by gentle stretches, so everyone, copy me.'

The PTI began to demonstrate the various stretching exercises that they were to carry out. One by one, they stretched and warmed down their muscles for the next five to ten minutes. Francis satisfied, he handed them over to the room NCO's and Sgt Portwood.

'Ok, C1, get fell in outside in three ranks, move!'

The exhausted Troops filed out of the gym and fell in outside, ready for the steady jog back to the accommodation block. Richard glanced at the clock on the way out. It was only 09:00, the day had just begun. This was not going to be easy, he thought to himself. This was reaffirmed to him by the less rhythmic sound of the feet, as they made their way towards what was now their home.

Chapter 5 - Drill

One of the objects of drill is to teach Troops by exercise to obey orders- and to do so in the correct way. For this slovenly drill is harmful; all movements on parade will be performed smartly. Noisy stamping of the feet in such movements as turning, coming to attention or standing at ease is forbidden. (Manual of Elementary Drill (All Arms) (1935)

On reaching the Barrack Block, the recruits were curtly dismissed and instructed to go inside. They were to shower quickly, then don barrack dress order and be outside at 10:00 hours, in three ranks.

The Troop quickly dispersed and made its way through the entrance. Each room quickly opened their lockers, withdrew their washing kit and headed for the washrooms. It was every man for himself. As the cubicles rapidly filled up, there was a queue of half-naked young men waiting their turn and chatting excitedly about the morning events so far. Others seemed to be quiet and withdrawn. It would come to light by the end of that first day, hectic, military life was not everyone's cup of tea.

In the space of 30 minutes, the shower rooms were empty and the tired men had returned to their rooms, searching out the barrack dress trousers, khaki shirts, ties and boots (DMS) that were required for all drill lessons. As it was still classed as summer, shirt sleeve order was the dress of the day. This meant that the sleeves were rolled up a hand's width above the elbow. The trainees did up their ties with the regulation small Windsor knot they had been shown the previous day. To complete the ensemble, they laced up their boots and inserted green plastic belts through the loops on their dark green, barrack dress trousers. This belt would be replaced with their Regimental stable belts, once they had entered into their final term at the Junior Leaders Regiment. Their head dress was a black beret, all with the same cap badge: a mailed fist which represented the Junior Leaders Regiment. These would, in turn, be replaced in the final term, when each member would be issued either with their Corps or Regimental badges. Some of the young men would be joining Corps such as the Army Air Corps or the Corps of Royal Military Police. The majority though, would be 'badged' Cavalry or Royal Tank Regiment.

After checking themselves, and each other, in the mirror, which hung at the end of each room, slight adjustments were made. Satisfied with the results and confirming that it was time that they should be making their way outside. Each room, in turn, began to emerge from the building.

A couple of minutes prior to 10:00, five minutes to be exact, the NCOs started their vocal encouragement in a manner only they could:

'Get a move on, you lazy twats! Get fell in on the road in three ranks!'

Richard and the rest of his comrades soon found out that when they were given a time to parade, this meant they should be there five minutes beforehand.

Once assembled in the correct formation, they were ordered to move to the right, with a command, which they would soon find so familiar:

'By the right, quick march! They stepped off with their left feet and made their way towards the drill square, which would become like a second home over the coming months.

Marching on to the square, they could see the form of the same giant of a man, with the red sash across his chest, who had greeted them with the RSM the day before. Richard could see that he was eyeing their every movement critically. The Troop Instructors turned the squad so that were directly in front of the imposing figure of the Drill Sergeant. Here, they were halted and advanced to face him.

Creggan turned around smartly, bringing up his knee parallel to the ground, drove his foot down and, stepping off with his left foot, advanced towards the Drill Sergeant. When he was approximately three paces from the DS, he came to an immediate halt, once again driving his right foot in to join his left.

'Sarn't, C1 on parade and awaiting your instruction,' he formally introduced the recruits.

'Thank you, Corporal, you and the other instructors may fall out, I will take over from here.'

With this, all four room NCOs turned, as one, to their right and marched briskly from the drill square, back towards the accommodation.

The Drill Sergeant cast his gaze across the formation standing before him. His slashed peaked forage cap and the white band which surrounded it gave him a sinister appearance. In the centre of the cap shone a golden coloured star, known as "The Star of the Order of the Garter". This was the cap star and cap of the Coldstream Guards, a Regiment of Her Majesty's foot guards. After making his way through the ranks of the assembled Troops, he slowly came forward to face them.

'For those of you with very short memories, I am Sergeant Rudd of the 1st Battalion, Coldstream Guards and I will be your Drill Instructor during your time here at this training establishment. I expect the same standards of both turnout and effort as do your Squadron Instructors!' he trumpeted at the young, innocent faces. 'This morning's lesson will be an introduction to basic foot drill, employed by the '"*All Arms Training Manual*".'

Looking about at the nervous sea of faces and happy with the look of fear on some of them, he continued:

'The first thing we will tackle is how to come to attention,' he snarled.

'On the command, "Squad – Attention!" you will spring up to the following position: heels together and in line, feet' turned out at an angle of about 30 degrees and knees straight. Body erect and carried evenly over the thighs, with the shoulders level and square to the front down and moderately back. This should bring the chest to its natural forward position, without any straining or stiffening,' he explained as he demonstrated the routine.

'Arms hanging from the shoulders, as straight as the natural bend of the arm will allow. Wrists straight. Hands closed but not clenched. Backs of the fingers touching the thigh lightly, thumb to the front and close to the forefinger and immediately behind the seam of the trousers. Neck erect. Head balanced evenly on the neck and not poked forward, eyes looking their own height and straight to the front. The weight of the body should be balanced on both feet and evenly distributed between the fore part of the feet and the heels. Breathing must not in any way be restricted and no part of the body should be either drawn in or pushed out. The position is one of readiness, in expectation of the word of command and is adopted when addressing, or being addressed by, a superior officer.'

As Rudd continued to explain the drill, he demonstrated each movement. Once he had confirmed that his new charges were paying attention, he addressed them:

'We will now practice each movement, which I will break down into numbers. On the word "Squad", you will brace up thus.'

He forced his arms down behind his back and seemed to grow in height by a few inches.

'After a momentary pause, you will then receive the word "Attention!" At this time, you will raise your right legs with the thigh parallel to the ground, at an angle of 90°.' He demonstrated the action before once again continuing, 'you then drive down your right foot, so that the heels are together and forming an angle of 30° between the feet. As you drive the foot down, you will call out the number, "One!" Now, listen to my word of command,' he paused, waiting for the full attention of the squad.

'Squad!' the Troops immediately attempted to copy his example, some being more successful than others. Some of them were trying a little too hard, which went against his instruction that it should look natural and not appear forced.

'Relax, you fecking mongs, we will try that again,' he scolded them.

'Heed my word of command once more. Squad!'

The recruits grew again, a little more controlled this time.

'Attention!' continued Rudd after the regulation pause, satisfied this time that the squad had made a reasonable attempt at the first movement.

The recruits raised their legs to the required height but it became apparent very quickly that some had their left leg raised, while others raised the right. Their timing was also all over the place, which was confirmed as they drove their feet into the parade square, shouting out the number, "One" as they did so, in a vain attempt to cover up their mistakes. This, however, was not missed by the eagle eyed Drill Instructor, who visibly changed colour, as he drew in breath to vent his anger upon the luckless Troops.

'What the feck was that?' he bawled at the now embarrassed recruits. 'We obviously are not listening to my lesson. I think you need to be woken up a little. I want you all to turn to your right.'

The squad moved in the direction in which Rudd was indicating with his pace stick. Once in position, the Drill Sergeant continued:

'When you hear the letter 'B', your left heel will strike the floor. When you hear the letter 'R', your right heel will strike the ground. Now, listen, carefully. By the right, quick march. 'BRBRBRBRBRBRBR!' He screamed out, between pursed lips.

The formation set off at lightning pace across the parade square, till they reached the far side, where Rudd halted them, turned them around and continued at the same pace, back across the square. This continued for the next five minutes, by which time the late summer sun had begun to reach its height and the recruits were starting to perspire heavily.

Satisfied that his charges were now fully awake and therefore prone to learning quicker, Rudd assembled them once more in front of him and once again went through his demonstration of how to come to attention in the prescribed manner. It was not till after a further fifteen minutes, that he decided to move on to the next part of the lesson.

'Once you have been standing in that position for a length of time, there will be an interval where you are given the opportunity to relax slightly. This will be given by use of the words "Stand at Ease". This will be given with a precautionary word of "Stand at", which will be followed by a short pause. You will then be given the second part of the command, which is "Ease". You will carry out the following action: look this way.'

Rudd waited till they were all focused on him once more. 'Carry the left foot about twelve inches to the left, so that the weight of the body rests equally on both feet. At the same time, carry the hands behind your back and place the back of the right hand in the palm of the left, grasping it lightly with the finger and thumb and allowing the arms to hang at their full extent.'

He demonstrated the full movement. Then, turning to the squad, he explained that he would give the precautionary word of command, followed by the executive word. At this time, he commanded them to carry out the movement, calling out the number "one" again, as they did so.

'Squad stand at..............Ease!' he screeched.

This time, the whole Troop carried out the drill movement without hesitation, and although the timing was not perfect, it was enough not to warrant a tirade of abuse from Rudd.

'Just to ensure that was not a fluke, and I was not dreaming, we will do it again.' So it carried on for the next ten minutes, the recruits being brought up to attention and then stood at ease, until Rudd had confirmed that his lessons had finally been effective.

'The final word of command after being stood at ease is "Stand Easy". It is carried out thus:

the limbs, head and body may be moved but you will not move your feet.' He performed the action at the same time as giving the word of command. Then, he proceeded to test his charges on this final movement, until he was happy with the result.

'Right, gents, that was not a bad first effort, this morning. The next lesson will be this afternoon, when we will go through left and right turns at the halt. Then, once we have that cracked, we will proceed with what carries every soldier into battle; the march. I know you are mostly Cavalry types and are too lazy to march into battle. However, before you leave these "hallowed gates",' he pointed with his pace stick in the direction of the guardroom, which they had passed as they entered the training centre. 'You will be fully proficient in "All Arms Drill". With this, he called out to the Troop Instructors, who had silently made their way on to the parade square and had assembled behind the training recruits.

'Okay, guys, you can take them away. Can you ensure that you show them how to bull their boots, and press their uniforms to the correct standard to grace my drill square?'

This was acknowledged by the NCOs, who gathered their recruits together and marched them from the parade square, for the next event of the day. This would entail showing once again how to iron their uniforms but this time how to fold them to fit into their lockers. They would also be shown how to polish their boots to a very high standard, known as 'bulling'. Richard smiled to himself, as this was another little trick his father had taught him. He had spent many happy days bulling his father's boots, in return for his pocket money. He was actually looking forward to this part of the training, he thought, as the young soldiers marched back once again to their rooms.

Whilst looking at the photograph, Richards mind slipped back to Germany and the celebration of his engagement to Birgit, in the summer of 1985.

This event in his life had been tied into the tercentenary (300 year anniversary) celebrations of his Regiment. This meant that the Regiment received a new Standard, to be presented by HRH the Duchess of Kent. As his father had left the Army a year or so earlier, both his parents had come over for the celebrations. This was also a good time for them to meet their son's future German mother and father in law.

The car was full of nervous anticipation, as Richard and his parents made the trip from where his Regiment was based, half an hour up the road, to Birgit's place of birth. On arrival, they climbed out of the car and made their way to the front door of the three storey German house. His parents could not believe that such a house could belong to one family. As Richard rang the bell, he saw Birgit's face appear at the glass panel in the wooden door. She smiled at him and opened the door to welcome them in. Both Tommy, his father, and Christine, his mother, gave Birgit a hug of greeting.

'Where are your parents, then?' Tommy asked, in his constantly loud Geordie accent.

'They are upstairs, waiting for you.'

Both Richard's mother and father were easy going people, and not used to the formality that came with the German culture. As they made their way up the staircase to the first level, Richard and Birgit looked back at his parents, smiling reassuringly.

'What do you call your parents, again?' whispered Tommy to Birgit.

'Reinhard and Karin,' replied Birgit.

'Sounds like a fecking SS Tank Commander and his missus,' muttered Richard's father, under his breath.

Richard cringed, as he knew how straight talking his father could be and was dreading what could happen at their first meeting. It was too late now; they had rounded the last flight of stairs and Richard could see his prospective parents in law waiting outside the door to their flat, on the first floor. Birgit spoke to them in German and introduced Richard's mother and father. Reinhard immediately clicked his heels together and bowed his head, offering forward his right hand.

'Reinhard Lindenberg' he announced, formally.

'Aye, Tommy Hunter. This is my wife, Christine. Where's the beer, then?' his father replied.

Reinhard looked confused, as he could speak very little English, so Birgit and Richard translated between them. A big smile broke over Reinhard's face and he motioned them inside, followed by Karin. The beers were poured, the ice was broken and after this they retired down stairs, to the back garden.

After many more drinks and the arrival of more and more guests, Richard's father decided to hold an impromptu parade. He lined all the young people up, and with a stick he had found by a nearby tree, placed it under his arm. He had left the Army as a Squadron Sergeant Major (SSM), and immediately slipped back into that persona. Once he was satisfied that his new 'Troops' were in the correct position, he addressed them with his gruff SSM voice:

'Right, listen in, we will parade the length of the garden. Stepping off to my timing. By the front, quick march!'

The assembled young people, both English and German, set off down the path, which ran the length of the 120 metre garden. They were guided by words of encouragement from Tommy; not that all of them understood a word he was saying, but they caught the gist of his intended meaning.

The spectacle was one of great amusement, for both young and old. This, regardless of nationality and with the aid of alcohol, helped bond the families and friends together, for the first time. These happy memories were interrupted as Richard drifted back to his days in training.

'C1, C1.......halt!'

They had arrived back at the Barrack Block and were quickly ushered inside.

Chapter 6 - Locker layouts and bulling

After receiving the order to fall out, the recruits 'bomb burst' for the entrance to the accommodation. They realised quickly that being last usually resulted in receiving a punishment, in the form of physical exercise. It was mayhem, as they all tried to squeeze through the gap, designed for one person. When they had all managed to navigate their way in and assembled once again in their respective rooms, they awaited their room NCOs. The conversation flowed around the morning's activities. Some of them were laughing and finding the whole thing rather amusing. However, there were a couple in the room who were keeping to themselves, not joining in with the 'banter'. Richard thought to himself, was it just that they were happy about how things were going? Or, maybe, it was the fact that they could be struggling already. One of these was Justin Taylor-Forbes, the self-important individual he had crossed swords with earlier. He made a mental note that he would approach them, when the opportunity arose. Before he could give it any more thought, he was interrupted by the sound of boots coming along the corridor. Out the corner of his eye, he saw Creggan enter the room.

'Room, room shun' Creggan belched. The recruits straightened up and came to the position of Attention.

'That was not the correct drill movement, as you have just been shown!' Creggan bawled at them. 'Let's try it again, shall we? Room, room shun!' The command, this time, was delivered a number of decibels higher.

This obviously instilled some form of urgency, as the recruits executed the movement flawlessly.

'That's better, I want to see it like that every time. Now, gather round and I will show you how to fold your clothing to the required dimensions to fit in your lockers.'

The Troop immediately made its way to the end of the room, where a table had been set up, with a wooden board in the centre. The board had divisions marked on it, both along vertical and horizontal edges. Once the young soldiers had gathered around the table in a semicircle, Creggan instructed one of them to go to his locker and bring a certain number of items back with him. Dutifully, the chosen one jogged off to his locker and returned with an armful of various types of clothing. He handed them over to Creggan with a beaming grin, obviously expecting praise for his prompt actions.

'What the feck are you smiling at you, feckin arse wipe?' was the response he received from Creggan.

The grin quickly disappeared from the recruit's face, as he realised that he would need to find an answer rapidly. He looked around for support; all he could see were the smiling faces of his comrades. They were obviously happy that they were not in his position. They would all get their turn in time, thought Richard to himself.

'Seeing as you can't give an answer, drop and give me twenty push ups,' Creggan commanded forcefully, indicating the direction of the floor with his forefinger.

He now turned to face the rest of the room and began the lesson on how to fold clothing to the correct size to fit a locker.

'You will observe this board, which is marked in inches,' as he spoke, he ran his finger along both the horizontal and vertical edges.

'They measure exactly nine inches in both directions, thus forming a square,' he continued. 'You take your freshly ironed piece of uniform and lay it flat on the board like so.' As he spoke, he deftly placed the shirt he had picked up and placed it, front side down, on the board. 'Take one arm and fold it in, so that you take the edge of the garment to the edge of the board.' He completed the first half of the shirt, before repeating with the other side. 'Once the edges of the garment are flush on both sides, take the bottom and fold it up to the top, so that it forms a perfect square on the board.' Creggan looked up to see if his audience had taken in his instructions. Then, taking another piece of clothing, he repeated the process, this time more quickly. On completion, he eyed the recruits, starting on his left and working along the line. The grinning recruit had, by this time, finished his punishment and stood up.

'You. Come out and fold this jumper the way I have just shown.' He pointed in Steve' direction. Steve stepped forward without hesitation. He walked around the table and accepted the jumper offered to him by Creggan. Facing the crowd, he began to lay the pullover face down on the board. Following the NCOs example, he expertly folded the jumper into the required shape on the board. Finishing, he looked up at Creggan, to see if he had completed the task satisfactorily.

'Not bad at all,' the instructor grudgingly admitted. 'Now, all of you return to your bed spaces, repeat the same and place the garments in your lockers. They are to be laid out exactly as in the diagram pinned to the inside of your lockers. I will be back in one hour, to see how you have done.' With that, he turned on his heel and marched out of the room.

There was a buzz of excitement, as the recruits returned to their beds and began to remove all of their uniforms from the lockers. Each man placing the nine inch board on his bed, they began to fold the uniforms into nine inch squares and placed them, carefully, in the lockers as shown on the photo layout. Richard found the task strangely therapeutic and hummed to himself as he went back and forth from his bed to his locker. In no time at all, Richard had finished most of his clothing. He was left with four pairs of socks and thought to himself,' how on earth do I fold these?' He inspected the locker layout picture intently. It appeared that the socks had been folded in on themselves, forming a roughly six inch package. The opening to the socks faced the front of the locker, almost a mouth type effect. There were two sets of pairs, stacked on top of each other. Richard made his best attempt at copying the picture layout. Standing back to admire his work, he glanced around, to see how everyone else was doing. Mike Sheperton seemed, like yesterday, to be having a little difficulty. Richard checked his watch and confirmed they still had fifteen minutes until the allotted one hour expire. He made his way over to Mike's bed. As he neared it, he noticed that Justin Taylor-Forbes was cursing his clothing. He, too, was obviously having problems, but since their altercation the previous day, Richard was not willing to give him a helping hand. He did think it expedient to ask if he had a problem.

'Look like you're struggling there, mate,' he said, trying to sound empathetic.

'This is just total bullshit. I cannot see the reason why clothes need to be stored in a certain way. This fucking place is really starting to irritate me!' Justin spat out the words, without making eye contact with Richard.

Richard ignored the remark and continued over towards Mike. If this stuck up twat was complaining at something as trivial as this, it was going to be a long fifteen months for him. No one else moved or offered any encouragement to the spoilt brat. So, Richard was not the only one in the room who had formed a negative opinion of the young man.

'Can I help you, Shep?' he called out to Mike, as he approached.

'It would be appreciated, bud,' Shep replied, looking up, sheepishly.

Richard stepped forward and took the shirt that Shep was trying to fold.

'Lay it face down on the board like this.' Richard looked up to make sure Shep was following his actions. 'Then fold in one side, so that it is level with the board, like so. Take the other side and do the same. Once you have it square on the horizontal, you fold it from the bottom so that the vertical sides align. You happy with that?'

Shep nodded his assent, took the next item and copied Richard's example. Richard would find out later in his career that this would be known as an 'Explanation, Demonstration and Confirmation.' (EDC) lesson. It was to hold him in good stead on the various courses he would attend throughout his time in the Army. Shep was almost finished, when they were startled by the words.

'Room, room....shun!' As Creggan marched into the room.

Richard had lost track of time and was now caught at the other end of the room, far away from his own bed space. He stood still, not wanting to draw attention to himself by making a bolt across the room. Nothing, however, went undetected by Creggan, who scanned the room like some type of android robotic being. His eyes were drawn towards the empty bed space and, when he located its missing occupant on the far side of the room, he drew in his breath, sharply.

'Hunter, what the fuck are you doing in Sheperton's bed space? Are you forming a romantic connection?' He screamed, sarcastically. It was a rhetorical question that did not require an answer, or at least one that would satisfy him. 'Get your carcass back where you belong, you shit!'

Richard sprinted across the room and came smartly to attention, next to his open locker, at the foot of his bed. Once Richard was in position, Creggan paused for a moment. He noticed that about 90 percent of the recruits had managed to complete the task he had set. What standard they had achieved, he was about to find out. Once again, starting from the first bed on the left, Creggan toured the room in a clockwise direction. As he came to each recruit, he asked them to turn around, so he could highlight any mistakes they had made. Everyone received scathing remarks, some more than others. When he finally reached Richard, he addressed him, before inspecting the contents of his locker.

'Seeing as you had time for your gay liaison, your locker should be immaculate, eh?' He smirked, as he posed the question.

'Not sure, Corporal,' was all Richard could reply.

Creggan ignored the answer and moved Richard to one side, as he started his inspection of the locker, starting at the top and working down. Although it took only a minute or so, it seemed like an eternity to Richard. Once Creggan had finished, he turned round and looked at Richard.

'That's really quite good Hunter, have you done something like this before?' he asked, this time seeming genuinely interested in his reply.

My dad is in the army, Corporal. I used to have to keep my wardrobe tidy at home.' He cringed as he said it but it was now too late. He had made a promise to himself that he would not mention his military connection, until they were some way into the training. Now that the cat was out of the bag, he expected to be singled out. As he thought, Creggan stepped back, sizing him up from top to bottom.

'So, a "pad's brat" eh? (this, was the term used in the military, for the children of serving soldiers) We will have to keep an eye on you,' he whispered into Richard's ear.

'Right, room that was abysmal! We will have a full blown room and locker inspection before first parade at 07:00, tomorrow. I expect a marked improvement.

Creggan continued, 'Gather round once again, I will now show you how polish your boots to the standard required for parades. The term used for this throughout the army is "bulling". I will take you through it, a step at a time.' He paused, waiting for them to gather round the table once again. He produced, as if by magic, a brand new pair of Directly Moulded Sole boots (DMS) from under the table. Next to these, he placed a yellow coloured rag, two tins of polish and a cup of water. He explained that getting brand new boots out of the stores and then spending hours bulling them would ruin them. They should be worn in for a few weeks, if possible. If there wasn't time to wear them in, they were to put them on and submerge them in hot water for twenty minutes or so. Then, they were to walk around; helping to speed up the process. The boots would take time to dry, so Creggan had already prepared the ones sitting on the table, facing the recruits.

'Once you have prepared the boots, you can then move onto the next step. Build up normal polish on the boot by brush polishing the boot for a few days, building up layers. Again wear them whilst doing this but try not to scruff the toe or chip the boot; this will affect the end outcome, so don't take them on the assault course. That is the reason you have been supplied with two pairs. One is for normal work, the other for parades. Once a few layers of polish is applied, buy yourself a good quality duster. Selvyt cloths are a good choice. Wash it a few times, and brush it with a nail brush and washing up liquid will make it softer and less likely to scratch your boot. Be aware that this can be done whilst doing the first steps.' he explained. Happy that he still had the young soldier's attention he carried on with the next part of the demonstration.

'Buy a new tin of Black Kiwi boot polish, or use one that you have not used for brush polishing. For a deeper shine, also buy a tin of dark brown to top the look off with.' he indicated the two tins on the table You'll need a small bowl of water, your black and brown polish, Silver cloth, and the boots' he said pausing for breath. 'Wrap one or two fingers with your cloth. Make sure it is flat on your fingers; twisting the access can help to tighten on fingers. Apply a layer of black polish to your whole boot. Wipe it until it's covered, using a circular motion of an inch diameter. Rub in until you think the polish is drying. 'The next step is to remove any excess polish. Do this by dipping your cloth on water and repeating the last step.

The whole room were engrossed in Creggans actions. They watched his every movement, soaking up the tips like sponges. He looked up once more confirming he still had their interest. Satisfied that he was obviously getting his message over, he moved to the next section of the demonstration.

'Repeat the layering, polishing, and removing process three times. Each time, use less and less new black polish. Finish up with a very thin brown layer. Do as you have done for the black layers; again stop when you think it's drying and removing any leftover polish with water. Brown polish seems to be softer than black, so it fills the tiny holes you want to get rid of to make the best shine.' He validated his previous statement, giving them an insight into the process that was used by all soldiers in the British Army. 'Stop at this point and maybe wear them in again for a day. You don't want your hard work to crack and fall off. Continue the polishing process after a few hours of wear, or the next night after work. Repeat daily until you get the results you want. This normally takes a week of around an hour a night, to see good long lasting results. So in a week's time you should have made some progress, but I will be checking daily how you are doing.' he said glaring at each person in turn. 'Right that's the demo complete' and looking at his watched he confirmed that it was time for lunch, so he dismissed them until 13:30. They were to be stood outside in barrack dress order, ready for their second drill lesson. With that parting comment he turned sharply to his left and left them to their own devices.

Chapter 7 - Drill Part 2

The dining room was absolutely jam packed, by the time the recruits made it there. The queue for the hotplate extended almost to the door. They would soon realize, that meal times were always busy occasions. The amount of fuel necessary to carry out training on a daily basis meant that all young soldiers needed to attend all meals. The only problem was that they were only given a limited amount of time to take in the calories they needed, before the next lesson began. So, once they had loaded their plates up, they hurriedly found seats and began to consume their lunches. On completion, they placed their plates on the racks provided, after scraping any excess into the swill bins. There was never really any waste, as the recruits were always hungry, due to the physical exertions they went through. They returned to the accommodation and sat on their beds, relaxing for fifteen minutes, before having to parade on the road once more.

Richard had noticed that, as they walked down the corridor, the door to the instructor's office was slightly ajar. Peering inside, he observed Justin Taylor-Forbes standing to attention in front of Sgt Portwood and Cpl Creggan. His absence at lunch was not missed. In brief conversations that Richard had had with other members of the room, it was apparent that he had not endeared himself to the Troop. Not wanting to linger, and not hearing what was being said anyway, Richard carried on to the room.

The fifteen minutes they had remaining of the dinner hour flew by and in no time at all the recruits were arranging themselves in three ranks on the road outside the block. As before, Sgt. Portwood and the room NCOs briefly inspected the Troop, prior to them being turned in the direction of the parade square. With the command, 'Turn to the right in threes,' they were stepped off for their second helping of 'square bashing'.

The rhythmic beat of the DMS boots striking the concrete echoed across the parade square. As the recruits were brought in line with Sgt. Rudd, who awaited them eagerly, they instinctively began to step short, pre-empting the order for them to halt. Because the command was given as the right foot was passing the left, they took a check pace with left foot and brought the feet together as had been shown, that morning. The sound was like a machine gun, not one sound as it should have been: Rudd immediately exploded.

'What was that, you shower of shit?' again, a rhetorical question. 'Turn around and face your left, stepping off to my timing. By the right, quick march. Left, right, left, right......' the words were barely audible due to the speed they were being delivered. For the next five minutes, they were bounced up and down the square, until once again, the sweating individuals were brought to a stop, in front of the Drill Instructor.

'Now that you are suitably warmed up, I will take you a stage further in your drill. We will now proceed to teach you how to change direction at the halt. We will first go through turning to the right. This will be done by numbers, so pay attention to my demonstration;' placing his pace stick on the floor, he stood to attention, perfectly still. 'On the command "Right turn," you will keep both knees straight and the body erect, turn to the right on the right heel and left toe, raising the left heel and right toe while doing so. On the completion of this preliminary movement, the right foot must be flat on the ground and the left heel raised, both knees straight, and the weight of the body, which must be erect, on the right foot. On completion of this first movement, you will shout out "One!"' He instructed whilst performing the action, 'you will now perform that first movement, calling out the timing. Listen to my words of command,' pausing, he drew in breath, 'the squad will move to the right in threes.....right...turn!'

The formation forced their bodies to the right, holding themselves erect and locking the thighs as they did so, calling out... 'One!' at the top of their voices.

'Hold it' Rudd commanded, as he prowled through the ranks, correcting anyone not in the correct position. Once he had been round everyone, he once again took his position at the front of the squad. He adopted the first position he had just shown them, before continuing;

'As you were, watch for the second part. I left you in this position,' he checked that they were watching him, 'bring the left foot smartly up to the right, whilst shouting out the number "Two!"' He executed this second and final part of the turn. The sound of his hob nailed ammunition boots, striking the floor, echoed across the square. The squad copied his example, shouting out the number, "Two" as they did so. The Drill Sergeant practised the squad until he was sure that they had grasped it. He then went on to explain the movement in reverse, for the left turn.

'Okay, this time we will turn to the left from the halt. Keeping both knees straight and the body erect, turn to the left on the left heel and left toe, raising the right heel and right toe in doing so. On the completion of this preliminary movement, the left foot must be flat on the ground and the right heel raised, both knees straight and the weight of the body, which must be erect, on the left foot. Again, on completion of the first movement, you will shout out the number "One!" Carry that out now.' The Troop did as it was instructed and stood perfectly still, waiting to be adjusted by Rudd. Once again, after he was happy, Rudd continued.

'Bring the right foot smartly up to the left, calling out the number, "Two" as you do so. Do that now!' he roared. Obeying the command, the squad carried out the second part of the movement. For the next ten minutes, Rudd practised them at both left and right turns at the halt. Richard looked around and felt that they were actually getting there. A marked improvement on the morning's efforts. Some of them even appeared to be enjoying it. Before they could get too complacent, Rudd broke his train of thought.

'Right, there will be occasions where a body of men require to advance, or retire in the opposite direction. This will also be done in two phases and by numbers. Once again, look in and I will go through each movement. On the command, "About turn," keeping both knees straight and the body erect, turn to the right-about on the right heel and left toe, raising the right toe and left heel in doing so, but keeping the right heel firmly on the ground. On completion of this preliminary movement, the right foot must be flat on the ground with the left heel raised, both knees straight and the weight of the body, which must be erect, on the right foot. Again, once in this position, call out the number "One!" Listen in to my word of command. The squad will retire, about turn!' the command was delivered at a higher pitch than normal. After the recruits performed the first movement, they were braced in position. The Drill Instructor made his way round to what was now the front rank. 'Once in that position, bring the left foot smartly up to the right, and shout out, "Two!" He paused then screamed, "squad, two!" The recruits obeyed as commanded, bending their left legs and driving them down onto the parade square. On doing this, as one, they shouted "Two!" As before, Rudd drilled them in the complete movement for the next five to ten minutes. Acknowledging their progress, he stood them at ease.

'Right, we will have a five minute break at this point. All those of you who smoke, and wish to do so, make your way to the drill shed.' He indicated a covered building, at the far end of the square, with his pace stick.

After falling out in the correct manner, the Troop made a hasty retreat to the drill shed. Excited conversation broke out, as cigarettes where offered and taken. It was the first time that Richard had an opportunity to converse with others, outside of his room. He noticed a giant of a man, dark hair and dark brown eyes, puffing away on a cigarette. It was not his stature that first struck him, but the loudness of his broad Geordie accent. It reverberated throughout the shed, as the big man laughed out loud, at something that had obviously tickled him. He was engaged in conversation with a smaller, stockier person. He also had a North Eastern accent and Richard wondered if they came from the same town. As Richard's father had come from County Durham, he thought he would make their acquaintance. He ambled across to where they stood and introduced himself.

'I'm Richard, guys,' he said offering his hand.

'What sort of accent's that like?' the large mountain of a man said, jokingly.

Richard had not realised that his and Pete's accent must sound strange to all of their new comrades. Having been brought up in a military environment, moving from garrison to garrison, mostly overseas, Army 'brats', as they were affectionately known, developed their own unique accent. It was akin to someone from the Home Counties, but a little more refined. They were often assumed to be upper class by their peers.

'It's a military one mate, although I was born in the North East, where my dad is from; we moved around a lot.'

'You some sort of a posh gypo, then?' was the big Geordies retort. This seemed to break the ice, and the three of them were in fits of laughter. 'I'm Mark Newbottle,' the big fella grinned, extending his right hand, which Richard took, warmly.

'I'm Dave Franklin,' the other lad piped up, 'just call me Frank, this is Tiny pleased to meet you, marra,' again, Richard took the offered hand and introduced himself.

'The reason we moved around so much was that my dad is in the Army, so we moved wherever his Regiment was sent to,' he said, but before he could expand more on the subject, they were being hailed to return once more, to the drill square. With great haste, those that were smoking extinguished their cigarettes. In an organised gaggle, they made their way to the centre of the parade square. When they were dressed once more in their three ranks and were stood stiffly to attention, the lesson carried on.

'Right, you creatures, now that you have almost mastered changing direction at the halt, I will now proceed to instruct you how a single man, or body of men, moves from point A to point B. This, in the military, is known as marching,' he sneered, sarcastically. 'by the end of this lesson, you will be able to carry yourself in a professional, smart and soldier-like manner. 'So, once again, pay attention to my demonstration,' he announced, placing his pace stick on the ground. 'In marching, the soldier will maintain the position of the head and body, as directed in the lesson of "Attention". He must be well balanced. In slow time, his arms and hands must be kept steady by his sides. In quick time the arms, which I am now showing you, should be as straight as their natural bend will allow. They should swing naturally from the shoulder, hands reaching as high as the waist belt in front and rear. Hands should be kept closed but not clenched, thumbs always to the front,' he explained and demonstrated at the same time. 'The legs should be swung forward, freely and naturally from the hip joints, each leg, as it swings forward, being bent sufficiently at the knee to enable the foot to clear the ground. The foot should be carried straight to the front, without being drawn back, placed upon the ground with the knee straight but so as not to jerk the body. 'Now, I want each of you to find a space and practise this, trying your best not to injure yourself or others.'

With this, the squad dispersed and attempted to find a clear space, where they could put into practice what they had just been shown. It must have looked comical to an outsider looking in, seeing these young men attempting to march for the first time. There were, obviously, the inevitable collisions. This was mostly due to the recruits trying too hard to get it right. They ended up not looking where they were going. It was then that Richard called to mind Rudd's words, 'keep the body and head erect, as in the position of "Attention"'. It was not just to look smart, but also so you could see where you were going. The Drill Sergeant was cutting about the square, giving colourful words of encouragement to his charges, as he did so.

'What the fuck are you doing, you fecking cretin?' Rudd was standing directly in front of 'Tiny', his face as crimson as his sash. Everyone turned as one in his direction. It was then that they noticed, the big Geordie was marching with his left leg forward with his left arm at the same time. It looked like something out of Monty Python's '*Ministry of Silly Walks*.' It did not look natural at all, and Richard, like the others he was sure, was thinking it was almost impossible to do.

'There is always one in every intake, who fecking 'tick tocks' on my square!' the instructor screamed at the recruit. 'I can see you are going to be one of my special children. I will have to spend a little time with you, bonny lad,' he said in homage to the young Junior Troopers birthplace. Taking Tiny to one side, Rudd gave a full demonstration of the drill movement. He continued to practice with him for the next ten minutes, until Rudd was sure that he had got it right. Now that he had corrected Tinys mistakes, he decided to fall the squad back in.

'Now that we have practised on our own, we need to put it together as a formation.' He grinned openly, knowing full well that this would be a disaster. 'Listen to my command. Move to the right in threes.......Right,' a slight pause 'turn!' The Troop forced their bodies round in the direction given, allowing the pause before driving their left feet down onto the tarmac. 'By the right......Quick March. Left, Right, Left!' The squad stepped off with their left feet, throwing forward their right arms and at the same time, forcing their left arms to the rear. The sound of their boots striking the concrete reverberated across the square. Once they had reached the far side of the parade square, Rudd halted them and turned them about. He drilled them back and forth for the next twenty minutes. The recruits' arms were starting to become heavy and tired. Perspiration marks were clearly visible around the armpits and on the backs of their khaki Number 2 dress shirts. Just as they thought it was never going to end, the Drill Instructor halted them directly in front of him. He advanced them so they were facing him. 'You have worked well, boys. As none of your Squadron NCOs are here, one of you can march the squad back to the block,' he said, looking around for anyone who may look like they wanted to volunteer. As he suspected, not one of them dared to make eye contact. In a twisted attempt at humour, what he did next shocked the whole Troop. 'Junior Trooper Newbottle, fall out. You can have the privilege of taking the squad back to the accommodation.' No one was more shocked than Tiny himself. Hel clumsily turned to his right, stamped in his left foot and took his position in front of the squad.

'The command that you will give, Junior Trooper Newbottle is, "Move to the left in threes, quick march." Then, call out the timing, to ensure they keep in step.' Tiny did as he was commanded, his voice sounding like a bull elephant seal, as it rang out over the square. Unfortunately, as the whole squad turned to their left, he turned to his left. This was the opposite direction to the Troop. He had not taken into account that he was facing them. So, their left was the opposite of his.

'What the fuck are you doing, you fecking retard? Turn yourself about and get off my parade square!'

The big Geordie bashfully turned around, gave the order to step off and hastily marched the Troop from the parade ground. As they trudged towards the Barrack Block, Richard mused to himself that things were slowly starting to fall into place.

Chapter 8 – A Typical Evening in Training

On reaching the accommodation, they were received, as normal, by the room NCOs who ushered them inside, quickly. There were two hours before the evening meal, the recruits did not know what was on the agenda. At that moment, they had not been given a timetable to work from. This was to change; as they entered their respective rooms, their attention was drawn to an A4 piece of paper, pinned to their room doors. Everyone huddled round the door, excitedly, if not apprehensively, to see what was in store for the next week. The timetable, in fact, listed all their activities for the whole month. It seemed to be dominated by drill, PT and clothing and room inspections. They would find out that this would be a big part of their military experience, over the initial three months. Some of the assembled recruits groaned at the amount of PT and drill lessons planned. They were interrupted by Creggan, as he strode into the room.

'Getting yourself acquainted with the timetable; that's good. You must ensure that, when it states a particular time, it means that you are to parade five minutes beforehand!' He looked around at each recruit in turn as he said it. 'Also, while you have been enjoying yourselves on the drill square, we have drawn up a rota for the cleaning of communal areas, washrooms, toilets, corridors and outside areas. These will be done on a daily basis, prior to room inspection, every morning. If you follow me, I will show you, so that there is no ambiguity as to what is required.' With that, he turned smartly about and beckoned the Troops to follow him.

Pinned to the wall in the corridor was another A4 piece of paper. It was titled 'C1 Block Job List', and contained the areas already mentioned by Creggan. For each job, one or two recruits were named for each day, covering a weekly period. Creggan gave them time to digest the list, before asking.

'Are there any questions about the list?' He looked around, to see if anyone seemed perplexed or confused. With no questions forthcoming, he continued. 'Right, follow me and I will go through each job and what is expected of you.'

Like sheep, they all followed behind Creggan into the washrooms. He made his way to the first sink and waited for them to gather round. Happy that they were all there and paying attention, he proceeded to explain how he expected the washrooms to be cleaned. It was not just a case of wiping over the sinks with a cloth. He wanted them to be free from water marks and shining. No mildew or splash marks on the taps. Floors were to be mopped and streak free. He pointed in the direction of the shower cubicles and repeated the same specifications. This time, he advised them to pay particular attention to the removal of pubic hair and other foreign matter from the plug holes. This brought a titter amongst the assembled young adolescents.

Like a volcano erupting from his mouth, Creggan screamed, 'This is not a laughing matter, you set of fuckwits. If these washrooms are not to my exacting standards tomorrow morning, I will skull fuck whoever is assigned to them for that day!'

Richard looked across at one of his roommates, who visibly gulped. He was on the rota for the following morning and he knew that his card was going to be marked. The NCO then proceeded to walk them round the other morning tasks and explain each, in turn. On their return down the corridor to the room, he stopped and opened a door on the right. Inside were shelves, containing all types of cleaning products. They ranged from wire wool, Vim, polish and dusters to mops and buckets. 'Here, you will find everything you need to keep the accommodation spotless. Let's go back to the room and I will show you how to polish the floors.' He picked up a large, cylindrical, silver tin, a piece of old blanket and an implement, the like of which none of them had seen before. It was a broom handle with a metal end. Through this was a bolt, attached to a rectangular piece of cast iron. This pivoted and Richard could tell, by the tensing of Creggans muscle, that it was not light. Creggan moved from the cupboard into the room.

'The way we apply polish to the floor is like so;' he removed the lid from the cylindrical container, and inside was a bright orange mixture. He tore a piece from the old blanket and dipped it into the tin, taking a copious amount of the substance on to the cloth. Getting down on his knees, he started to apply the day-glow polish, in circular motions, to the floor. 'We continue this procedure, starting at one end of the room and working to the other. This ensures that you do not have to walk over it. Once the floor is covered, you take a clean piece of the blanket, and place it under the hand buffer, so.' Demonstrating, he lifted up the heavy weight and placed a piece of folded blanket under it. 'You can tie it around the handle if you wish. This will prevent it from slipping, as you move the bumper from side to side like this.' Creggan began to swing the bumper effortlessly, from side to side. The young Troopers were amazed at how quickly he produced results. 'You're a big lad, you have a go,' he said, as he handed the buffer over to Steve.

'I'll give it a shot,' Steve replied, taking hold of the buffer handle. He began to swing it from side to side. The recruits could tell that it was not as easy as Creggan had made it look. Although Steve was powerfully built, for a young man of his age, he was finding it difficult to get into a rhythm. They would soon get enough time to practise, as this would become part of a daily routine.

'Okay, that's enough, you will all get a chance tonight, in between bulling your boots and laying out your lockers again, for tomorrow's inspection. Now, if you turn around, I have one more lesson to give you, prior to your evening meal.' The recruits all did a casual about turn and, for the first time, noticed the table at the end of the room. On it were placed a number of items. Creggan walked around the table, so that he was facing the recruits. 'The next thing we are going to learn is how to shape a beret. The shaping of a beret is a very personal thing. Some people like to look smart, others like to look like a farmer and some fuckwits just want to attract helicopters and other aircraft. Whatever your style, we all shape our berets in the same way. For this demonstration, I have one beret, one bowl of hot water, one bowl of cold water and a number one, mark one head,' he indicated each item as he announced it.

Ensure your beret is a correct fit. The band should sit approximately one inch above the eye and should sit level around your head. The cap badge is to sit above the left eye, approximately one inch above the band. Once fitted, tie a double knot in the cord running through the band, do not cut.' He placed the beret on his head and adjusted it as he spoke. 'Some people remove the lining at this stage. This makes the beret easier to shape and ensures a closer fit to the head. Whatever your preference, take great care not to cut a hole in your beret or damage any of the stitching around the band. The Quartermaster (QM) will have your balls, if he finds you have done this. Holding the band, submerge the top of the beret in hot water, being careful not to get the leather band wet.' He removed the beret from his head and dipped it into the bowl, containing the hot water. 'Mould to head. Ensure the cap badge is over the left eye and pull the excess to the right and back.' Manipulating the beret between his hands, it slowly took the familiar shape that Richard had seen a thousand times. 'Still holding the band, submerge into cold water, again being careful not to get the leather band wet.' Creggan transferred the beret from his head to the cold bowl, holding it by the band. 'Mould to head again and repeat the steps that I have just gone through about three or four times. Mould to head and keep it on for a minimum of twenty minutes, shaping and moulding as necessary.' Taking the beret carefully off his head, he finished the lesson by saying, 'Remove from head and allow to dry naturally. Has everyone got that?' As he ended the lesson, he looked around to see all facing him nodding their assent. 'Good, evening meal starts in fifteen minutes, until then, your time is your own.' He grinned at them and strode out of the door.

The room dispersed to their own bed spaces, some flopping onto their beds, others making themselves busy, rearranging their locker layouts. After five minutes or so, Steve strolled across to Richard.

'You coming for some scoff, then?' he asked.

'Aye, why not?' Richard replied.

The pair of them collected their green mugs and knife, fork and spoons (KFS) from their lockers and made their way to the cookhouse. Once again, as they walked, they chatted about the day's activities and how each of them had thought things had gone. Richard had come to like this loveable, though rough, Scotsman. He hoped their friendship would last well after they had finished their training and gone their separate ways. He had found out earlier, on their return from the gym, that Steve was joining The Royal Scots Dragoon Guards, formerly The Royal Scots Greys, the Scottish Cavalry Regiment, famed for the white horse Charge at Waterloo. Although they would be in different Regiments, there was a high probability they would bump into each other, either on training courses, operational tours or even by chance, if they were garrisoned in the same town. A number of Cavalry Regiments were stationed in Germany. This was part of the British Army of the Rhine, which had been set up at the end of the Second World War. Their primary purpose was the defence of Europe against the Soviet led Warsaw Pact.

After the two friends had replenished their energy levels with a three course meal in the cookhouse, they returned to the accommodation. As they walked along the corridor to the room, Richard decided he would check the 'Block Job List', to see what task had been assigned to him for the following morning. As he ran his eyes over the document, he finally found his name. He had been assigned to brush and bumper the corridor. He looked across the list and saw that a member of the neighbouring room had also been assigned to this. 'Well, at least I will have company,' he thought to himself. Taking note of the name, Richard wandered into the room opposite his own.

'Do we have a Fred Diner in the room?' he asked, looking about at the six guys, who were either sitting on their beds or folding clothing. No answer was forthcoming, until a voice from the far end called:

'I think he is still at tea.'

'Who is still at tea?' came a voice behind Richard, as a small, powerfully built, dark haired, handsome young man entered the room, smiling.

'This bloke from next door was looking for you,' the voice from the far side of the room replied.

Richard turned round to face the newcomer, who stood in front of him, grinning like a Cheshire cat.

'I'm Fred, what can I do you for?' The amiable young man threw out his right hand, which Richard took. He was, at first, surprised by the firmness of the grip. Taking into account Fred's stature, it was totally natural. He came across, straight away, as friendly and easy going. He was the total opposite to Steve, not one blemish adorned his skin. He had looks any male model would die for. From his accent, Richard guessed that he was from the South somewhere, but could not place the area exactly.

'I'm Richard, looks like we have been paired up to do the corridor, for the inspection tomorrow.'

'I haven't even checked the list, yet. What time do you want to make a start?' Fred replied, enthusiastically.

'Say, in about an hour's time? I want to get started on my locker layout. Then, if we crack it in an hour, it will give me time to spend half an hour on my boots.'

'Sounds like a plan. I will give you a shout in about an hour, then.'

Fred moved towards his bed space and Richard left the room, to begin working on his locker. On entering the room, he noticed that everyone was there, except Justin Taylor-Forbes. He seemed to be making a habit of disappearing when work needed to be done.

'Where's the posh twat?' Richard called out, to no one in particular.

'Saw him going into the NCOs office when I was coming back from tea ,' Steve replied.

'The food is probably not up to his high standards, along with everything else;' Richard called out, sarcastically.

The entire room fell about in fits of laughter. Taylor-Forbes had not endeared himself to anyone in the Troop. The Army can be a lonely place, when you are not a team player. The joking over, they set about formulating a plan on how they would divide up the cleaning of the room. It was agreed that two of them would begin applying polish to the floor, while the rest carried on with their personal admin. After fifteen minutes, they would change over and do this until the cleaning was complete. Those who had been assigned block jobs were given extra time for their own kit. So, after spending an hour on his locker, Richard was disturbed by a call from the doorway.

'You ready, Richard?' it was Fred, bare chested in a pair of shorts.

'Be right with you, mate!' Richard called back, placing a PT vest into his locker. Fred's physique was not unlike that of Creggan. He had obviously taken care of himself and had been pumping iron over the last couple of years. There was not an inch of fat on him and his wide shoulders tapered down to a tiny waist. He looked like an inverted pyramid. His abdominal muscles were so defined, he looked like he had come out of the mould of a Greek classical hero. The pair of them entered the corridor and took the polish, bumper and brush from the cleaning cupboard. Fully equipped, they began the process of transforming the floor into a thing of beauty.

After about an hour, they reached the end of the corridor, looked back at their results and congratulated each other on their efforts. As they made their way back to their rooms, Richard was bumped from behind by Justin Taylor-Forbes, who made no attempt to apologise and stormed straight into the room.

'He seems a bit of a dick,' Fred grinned.

'You're not wrong there, buddy,' was all Richard could say, shaking his head.

Moving into the room, Richard saw Taylor-Forbes, throwing clothing into the open suitcase laid on his mattress. 'This is an interesting state of affairs,' he thought to himself. Not saying a word, he walked over to one of the others polishing the floor.

'Do you want me to take over for a while?' he asked.

'No, mate, you're okay. Get your admin done, you have done your bit out there.

The bond among the room's occupants was growing and teamwork was forming. All, of course, except a certain individual, who continued to throw things into his suitcase, muttering to himself at the same time. The roommates did not pay him much attention and continued with either bumpering the floor or sorting out their lockers. Taylor-Forbes finished packing his suitcase and proceeded to strip down his bed. As he carried on with his muttering and packing, they were joined in the room by Creggan.

'Right, you lot, if you were wondering why Taylor-Forbes is packing his suitcase, he has decided that military life is not for him. I want two of you to help him return his bedding and military equipment to the QM's.' Creggan looked around the room, until his eyes rested on Shep.

'Sheperton and Angus, give him a hand' he ordered.

Both recruits dropped everything they were doing and moved across the room to help remove Taylor-Forbes' equipment into the army issue suitcase and holdall. After ten minutes, they were complete and loaded up with bedding and equipment. Creggan escorted them out of the room and they made their way to the QM's block. It did not seem more than fifteen minutes and the two returned to the room. It was drawing near to 'lights out', everyone made up their beds and climbed inside. For the next ten minutes the room was alive, debating the reasons for the stuck up prick leaving. Richard did not really care and he closed his eyes, as the bugle sounded for the end of the day.

Chapter 9 – Battle PT

Richard splashed water on his face, clearing the remnants of the shaving foam. He began to clean his teeth, as the call for Reveille rang out across the camp. Other members of the Troop were stumbling into the wash rooms, bleary eyed and half asleep. He acknowledged them with a smile and a 'good morning'. After placing his wash things in his bag, Richard returned to the room. He checked the timetable for the day and confirmed that the dress for PT this morning was lightweight trousers, PT vest and boots. He entered the room and, unlike yesterday, everyone was up. They were either scratching their scrotums or collecting their wash kits from lockers and heading to their ablutions. Richard placed his wash bag in his locker and started to dress. After lacing up his boots in the prescribed fashion, using one end with the laces horizontal to the eyelets, he wrapped them round the top of the boot and tucked them underneath. He remembered the tale his father had told him, when he had enquired why he laced his boots up in that way.

'Well son, in the Second World War, when the Ghurkhas were fighting against the Japanese, it is said that, at night, they would feel the boots of an unknown person in the dark jungles. If the laces were criss-crossed, they knew they were the enemy, because this was how the Japanese laced up their boots, whereas the British laced theirs horizontally. There is also a train of thought that it is easier to slit the laces with a knife, when they are tied horizontally. This may save precious seconds, if a soldier was injured and required immediate attention.'

Richard mused on this, as he picked up his puttees, to wrap around his ankles. These were long strips of khaki coloured cloth, wound spirally round each ankle for protection and support. The word 'puttee' came from the Hindi word 'patti', meaning band or bandage. He had never seen these before, as his father had always worn black leather 'gaters', or high patrol boots, which supported the ankle. They had briefly been shown how to wear them by Creggan on their first day, but he was struggling to remember the correct way. As he finished, Steve and Shep entered the room.

'Coming to breakfast?' Richard called out to them.

'Two minutes,' Shep replied.

Once the three friends were dressed, they quickly made their way to breakfast. Within five minutes, they were joined by the rest of the room. They chatted about their fears for the day ahead. The block and room inspection should at least go better than the day before, they assumed. They were becoming adept at finishing their meals in quick order. In the space of fifteen minutes they cleared their plates and were returning to the room. Looking at his watch, Richard saw that they had 40 minutes, before the inspection at 07:30. Those who had been given block jobs left, to go and make a start.

After Richard had returned his mug and KFS to his locker, he decided to go and look for Fred, so they could give another quick sweep and a bit of a buffer to the corridor. On exiting the room, he found that Fred was already removing the cleaning equipment from the cupboard, in readiness.

'Great minds and all that,' he said, smiling.

Fred was once again bare chested and his perfectly formed torso flexed as he swung the heavy weight with the blanket underneath. They were frequently disturbed by members of the Troop, walking down the corridor to clean the ablutions block or to pick up litter, around the block. The floor gleaming, they decided between them to return to their rooms and ensure their bed spaces and lockers were ready for the inspection, intending to return ten minutes before the inspection to give the floor a final buffing.

With five minutes left to spare, all the rooms completed their allotted tasks, cleaned their bed spaces and arranged their lockers. They assembled themselves at the end of their beds, in preparation for Sergeant Portwood and their room NCOs' grand entrance. They could hear a commotion coming from next door and once again, the sound of beds being overturned. This was to become the 'default setting' of morning inspections. After the NCOs finished with the inspection, the rooms were littered with bedding and clothing. Having given the first bollocking of the day they commanded the Troop to fall in outside. Here, they were once again inspected on their turnout. Richard cringed, as Portwood stopped in front of him and looked down in the direction of his boots.

'Who the fuck dressed you this morning, you horrible fucker?' Portwood screamed.

'I did, Sergeant,' was his timid reply.

'Why the feck have you got your puttees on upside down, you brain dead twat?'

Not knowing what to say, Richard just looked blankly at the enraged NCO.

'Corporal Creggan, sort this piece of shit out will you?' he said looking in Creggan's direction not expecting an answer.

Before Creggan could chastise Richard, the squad was turned to the right and set off, at the double, towards the gym. They were greeted there, once again, by Corporal Francis, who ordered them to turn to the front, while he addressed them. This time, because word had been spread round, they all wore red PT vests. The PTI quickly moved through the ranks, making sure their dress was to his satisfaction. Once he was happy, he made his way to the front of the squad.

'This morning's lesson will take the form of battle PT. However, before we begin any lesson, as we did yesterday, we need to warm up. So, start jogging on the spot…Go!' he barked.

The squad did as they were commanded and it wasn't long before the heart rates began to rise. They spent the next fifteen minutes carrying out the various warm up exercises they had been shown the previous day. Perspiration was starting to show on most of the recruits. Richard looked across at Fred, who hadn't broken sweat. Obviously, Fred had been in training for some time, prior to his enlistment. Richard wondered why they were still outside and not warming up in the gym. He noticed that, to one side of the building, there were large, brown, oversized 'basketballs'. Next to these were wooden poles, approximately a hands width in diameter and around six feet long. Beside these lay what looked like cut down telegraph poles, around ten inches in diameter and ten to twelve feet long. His thoughts were interrupted by the PTI, who called out;

'Class steady….stop!' He waited until there was silence, then continued. 'Right, C1, this morning's lesson is an introduction to battle PT. This will involve using the various bits of equipment, located against that wall.' Francis pointed towards the items Richard had noticed moments before. 'I will shortly be dividing you up into pairs or groups, for the different exercises.' With that, he started to split the class.

After being shown how to perform each exercise using the different pieces of equipment, they were given two minutes on each. Once that time was complete, they moved on to the next exercise station. Richard began with the round balls, which he had thought were oversized basketballs. Francis explained these were called medicine balls, without any explanation as to why. As Richard picked one up, it became apparent that the balls were heavier than they looked. When the first two minutes came to an end, his arms were already starting to ache. From there, he moved to the next station, as did the rest of the Troop, in a clockwise motion. This time, Richard and his group faced the reduced sized telegraph poles, simply called 'logs'. They had to raise the log among six of them, starting by lifting it onto their left shoulders, raising it above their heads, then taking it down to their right shoulders. Again, after two minutes the recruits were sweating profusely. The lesson progressed until everyone passed through every exercise.

'Class, steady….halt!' barked the PTI. Some of them immediately drooped forward the last fifteen minutes' exertions. 'Stand up straight and suck it in, you pussies, we have just started!' The members of C1 just looked at each other in disbelief. Francis lined them up in one rank and began moving down, six men at a time. As he did this, he commanded them to dress off one of the 'logs' they had been exercising with. Once everyone had been assigned to a log, he addressed them again. 'Okay, guys, we are going for a little wander with your new friends. On the command "Pick up the log", you will bend forward and grasp the log like this.' He demonstrated the action. 'I will then give you "lift up," and you will raise the log to your waists. On the next command "Shoulder logs," you will lift them onto your left shoulders.' He paused, before issuing the first order. 'Listen in, pick up the log.' He waited again for the action to be completed and carried on, until every group was standing with the logs on their left shoulders. 'Standby, double march!' Francis called out and the groups set off.

The Troop headed off, following the PTI, who jogged in front of the lead team. They did a circuit of the drill square, before heading past the accommodation and up a slight incline. At the top of the small hill, they passed through a gate, out of the perimeter of the training centre. The footpath they now trudged along was to become familiar to them. Every couple of hundred metres, Francis called out for them to move the logs onto their opposite shoulders. This was not an easy, task whilst moving, but gave some respite to their shoulders. After approximately five minutes, they reached the bottom of a steep slope. Francis halted them and allowed them to catch their breaths.

'Right, we are going to do a bit of a shuttle run,' he said, grinning. He lined the teams up, facing up the hill. 'On my command, you will set off, up the hill. When you reach the top, you will turn around and make your way safely back down. The last group down will give me twenty press ups!'

The groups moved the logs into a comfortable position and awaited the word to go. After the command was given, they set off. It became apparent very quickly that the ground was not as firm as the track they had been running on. It was made of sand, which made it difficult to get a foothold. Some of the groups slipped. Mayhem ensued. They resembled out of control dodgem cars, as they collided with one another. Once they had completed the first ascent and descent and the last group had been given their punishment, they were ordered to go again. This went on for ten more minutes. They thought it was never going to end. Finally, due to time restrictions, the PTI lined them up, once again, in a single file; they set off in the direction from which they had just from. As Richard looked around, he noticed that around 90% of the guys were dripping sweat. There were only a couple who still seemed quite fresh, one of these being Fred. He was giving words of encouragement to his team members, as they trudged back into camp. Fred obviously thrived on the physical side of things, as Richard had thought, when he noticed his physique the night before. They finally arrived back outside the gym. After laying down their logs, they carried out ten minutes of stretching exercises. Once this was complete and Francis had congratulated them on, 'not a bad effort,' one of them was assigned to lead them back to the accommodation. As they jogged back, Richard could feel his legs really heavy and his breathing laboured. He had never felt cut out for running although he had been very sporty whilst at school and had been captain of the rugby team. This was a different type of fitness altogether and one he would have to work at, if he were to pass through the gates and join his Regiment.

Chapter 10 – A trip away to Renney Lentney Camp

The training continued over the next eight weeks, and each PT and drill lesson got harder and more complex. They were however making good progress on cleaning their rooms, and locker layouts. They were down to maybe one person from each room, either getting his bed tipped over, or his locker contents thrown around the room. The room NCOs were becoming a little friendlier, and the Troop had been reduced by eight for various reasons. They were starting to 'gel' as a team, and friendships had grown. The Troop itself had a large number of recruits who were to be badged to the Royal Military Police (RMP). Richard remembered the conversations he had with his father over this body of gentlemen. It seemed no matter what Regiment or Corps you were from, everyone had a severe loathing of these 'Red Capped' individuals. However Richard had found almost all of them to be considerate and team players. This transformation may take place when they went to Chichester after they had passed off from the Junior Leaders Regiment (JLR). This was where they would complete their Military Police Training, and turn them into complete bastards. Richard could not see Fred being changed in any way shape or form. However he did not know what a cruel mistress fate could be.

The recruits were told at the beginning of the week that they were going away for a couple of weeks. This was to carry out various types of training that they could not do in camp. It all seemed rather vague, and Richard did not have a good feeling about it. The evening before they were due to travel, the rooms were a hive of activity. Guys were sorting out their rucksack (Bergen's), with all the equipment and clothing they would need. This had been given to them by the room NCO, in the form of a kit list. The time flew by and before they knew, it was time for lights out. They all clambered into bed and in no time at all were fast asleep.

As usual the dawn was greeted with the bugle call for Reveille. Richard and Steve and a few others in room had already showered and shaved. The remainder had risen and were setting about doing their own ablutions. By 07:00 the whole of the Troop had finished breakfast and had the daily block jobs sorted. The last hour could now be spent ensuring they had everything they need for the trip down to the south Coast. The place they were going to was a place called Adventure Training Centre at Renney Lentney near Dartmoor. Here the young soldiers would spend two weeks of each 14 week term, taking part in outdoor activities such as potholing, sailing, rock climbing, orienteering and cliff rescue. They boarded the bus along with the Troop Instructors for the three hour journey to the Devon coast. The journey was uneventful and they passed their time tucking into their packed lunches or 'scab packs' as they would later be called.

As the bus entered the camp, Richard felt the atmosphere change when they saw where they were going to be staying. There was just a series of huts with corrugated steel roofs, which looked like they had been built during the war. These they were later told were Nissen huts. The story went that they were haunted, and of course sixteen year old young men believed that. They clambered off the coach and collected their Bergen's from the stowage areas. The Instructors called for them to be fell in and Portwood addressed them.

'Right guys, welcome to Renney Lentney Adventurous Training Centre. You will be living in those huts over there' he pointed with his thumb over his shoulder. 'You will find they are compact but cosy. I will call out the roll and let you know which hut you will be staying in.' for the next couple of minutes he went through the Troop, assigning them a hut. As he did so, each NCO led them away to their new accommodation.

As they entered the room Richard observed that they were sparse to say the least. The furniture what there was of it, matched the age of the huts. On each side were lined six steel tube beds, and a metal locker. In the centre of the room was a cast iron stove. It reminded him of the huts that prisoners of war were kept in on films like 'The Great Escape'. Putting this information to good use, he made his way to a bed closest to the stove. Of course he was thinking this would be the warmest place in the room. The recruits unpacked and made themselves as comfortable as they could. Creggan who had been assigned to their hut gave them the timings and dress for the next day. It was a 06:00 start in swimming trunks, lightweight trousers, boots, PT vest and towel. He looked around the hut and saw the look of apprehension on their faces. This done he then gave them directions to the cookhouse and the meal timings. He left the room and the recruits babbled amongst each other. After their evening meal they retired back to the huts and relaxed for the evening, before turning into bed. It seemed strange not to hear the bugle sounding for lights out, but they were now disciplined enough to know that they needed their rest.

At the allotted time, they arose made their way to the ablutions which were located in another hut in the centre of the camp. The morning was brisk and Richard shuddered to think what was in store for them. Shit, showered and shaved the Troop made their way back to the huts and dressed themselves for the parade. With towels under their arms they fell in outside in three ranks. The Instructors were already waiting for them dressed in lightweight trousers, PT vests and boots. Portwood greeted them in his usual sarcastic manner.

'Morning campers, did we all sleep well?' he waited for a reply

At the top of their voices the recruits shouted.

'Yes Sergeant!'

'That's good because we have a little jog this morning, followed by a dip in the sea just to make sure your awake. All turn to the right listen in to my words of command. By the front double march!'

One of the Instructors was at the front of the squad and would be setting the pace. The familiar sound of boots on concrete rang out, as they followed the NCO. They made their way past some old gun emplacements on a winding path towards the cliff edge. On passing the emplacements the track wound its way down from the cliffs to the shoreline. They had to lean back to prevent themselves from tumbling forward. The descent only took a short while, and in no time they were on the beach. The sand was soft as the tide had not yet come in. With every pace they took, they sunk into it by a couple of inches. It wasn't long before their legs were starting to burn with the exertion. In approximate one mile the Troop were halted and allowed to regain their breathing.

'Now that you are all warmed up split up into pairs' Portwood bellowed. 'We are going to carry out a few 'Firemen's lifts', look in for my demonstration.

Creggan moved to face him and he took his right wrist and heaved him across his shoulders. Keeping hold of his wrist allowed his free hand to be used as a balance. He then began to jog with him. Turning around after a few paces he placed him back down on his feet.

'Ok gents pick up your partners like I have just shown you' he waited until everyone had their partners across their shoulders. 'I want you to carry them as fast as you can to Corporal Ross, who you can see waving at you, approximately one hundred metres down the beach. Once you reach him swap over and return to this point. The last pair back gets fifty press ups. Stand by …go!'

The pairs set of towards the waiting NCO. The going was extremely tough under the weight of their partners. Some were obviously better off than others. Richard had chosen Steve and after a few paces was regretting it. He thought his lungs were going to burst, and his quadriceps burst through his lightweight trousers. He finally made it but there was only three other pairs behind him. They quickly swapped over Steve throwing him easily over his shoulders, he set off at a lightning pace. By the time they had reached the start point there were only two pairs already finished. Richard had made the right decision after all, and they leaned forward rubbing their thighs and inhaling large gulps of air.

'Fucking good effort mate' Richard gasped to Steve who just smiled back at him.

As each pair crossed the line they turned to give words of encouragement to those still to finish. As the last couple fell over the line, they were immediately given their punishment of fifty press ups. The remainder were instructed to strip down to their swimming trunks. Once the pair had finished their penalty, they too removed their boots' light weight trousers and vests. As the morning shore breeze touched their naked sweating flesh they at once recoiled, and began to rub themselves.

'Right guys I want to see the last man in the water fully submerged….Go!!' Portwood screamed at the now shivering Troops.

The whole Troop set off at a sprint regardless of their fatigue. This was more to warm themselves back up, than the need not to be last. As their skin made contact with the cold sea water they flinched. Looking around they were trying to gauge who was going to be first to take the plunge. As soon as one had submerged himself the remainder did so. Once the Instructors were happy that they were all ok. They ordered them to swim out to the orange buoy, which was around fifty metres from the shoreline. Richard now realised why they had been required to attend swimming lessons every Saturday morning since they got there. It was obviously preparing them, so that they were all at an adequate level to be able to complete this exercise safely. The water was a mass of thrashing arms and legs as they proceeded to make their way to the buoy and back. As each of them climbed out of the water onto the beach they were given twenty press ups, before being told to dry themselves off and get dressed.

This they all did gladly, and quickly put back on their clothes. As soon as everyone was ready they were fallen in, and made their way at the double the mile back to the bottom of the cliffs. The ascent up the winding path was not as easy as their descent. On their arrival at the top they were told to double on the spot. The reason for this was that a few of the Troop had fallen a little behind, so they needed to wait for them to catch up. With the squad complete they set off back to the huts.

Arriving back in front of the huts, Portwood fell them out, informing them that once they were showered they should parade in an hour's time. This time the dress was to be track suits. The guy's bomb burst to the huts to retrieve their shower gel and a fresh towel. They spent the next thirty minutes carrying out personal administration prior to parading outside again in their track suits. They were met once again by all five instructors who marched them off to another Nissen hut which had been setup as Quartermasters store. The only difference with this one being that there was no military uniform on show. The shelves were stacked with climbing ropes, helmets, waterproofs and anything you would require for adventurous training. Each recruit was issued with various pieces of equipment and clothing. After an hour they all assembled in another hut, here they were given a briefing what would be happening for the rest of the week. It all sounded really exciting with things like canoeing, pot holing and something called the bridge jump. This last one caught their attention, and it would become legend for anyone who had been through the Junior Leaders Regiment of the Royal Armoured Corps.

The lecture finished and the rest of the day was spent, either showing how to wear the various pieces of clothing and equipment. They were introduced, how to tie various knots that would be used in abseiling and rock climbing. As they rotated through the various activities and demonstrations that had been set up for them the time flew by. Before they knew it, the end of the working day was coming to a close. They were dismissed by their NCOs and given the evening off to relax. After the evening meal the room was full of banter, with guys taking the piss out of each other, or playing cards. As they had not completed their first term at the Junior Leaders Regiment, they were not allowed to wear civilian clothing. Another thing that was forbidden up to this point was alcohol. Even though they would not be allowed this luxury until their final term, it did not stop some individuals partaking once they were allowed off camp. Friendships had blossomed over the last number of weeks, not only from the occupants of rooms but the Troop as a whole. One of the guys that was to be badged to the RMP was called 'Sooty', and Richard had sparked up a relationship with him. This was due to the fact that in conversation, they had mutually realised that they were both as sexually depraved as each other. It seemed that whatever one of them had experimented with the other would always go one better. On this particular night 'Sooty' turned to Richard and said

'Have you ever tried putting your knob on the television screen and felt the static off it?'

'Can't say I have' replied Richard rolling about the floor in fits of laughter.

The rest of the room just shook their heads at the pair, this type of conversation had become the norm for the two. Before long it was time to get a bit of shuteye ready for the day tomorrow. They had been told it involved a bridge jump and a spot of rope work. They had no idea what it exactly entailed, but the experience would live with them for the rest of their lives. It was with these thoughts that they started to drift off to sleep. The last thing that was uttered before they succumbed to peaceful rest was.

'Sooty will you stop wanking!' which caused the whole room to snigger before falling asleep.

Chapter 11 – Bridge jump, Gunners Lake and Ropes.

Richard shivered as he sat up in bed, the sun had just risen and the room was like a fridge. Others in the room were also stirring and complaining about the heating. One of the guys with a blanket wrapped around him, made his way to the stove in the centre of the room. He began loading it up with wood and coal that they had in two buckets. They had decided from day one, to draw up a rota for this job, having experienced the same thing yesterday. The stove began to roar as the fire took hold, smoke and fumes travelled up the pipe to the outside. The roommates made off to the ablutions in drib and drabs. By the time Richard returned, the room was toasty warm. After dressing, the recruits made their way to breakfast to fuel themselves for the day ahead. The December wind cut into them as they walked through the camp. This was not the sort of day that was conducive to playing around near water, Richard thought to himself. After breakfast the Troops paraded as usual in their lightweights, boots and PT vest. They had been told the evening prior they would not need their swimming trunks on this occasion. They were however to take them, when they left for the day's activities.

On their return from the morning run, they quickly showered, got dressed, and packed their Bergen's with the clothing they required for the day. This had been posted on their timetable for the week. There was no excuse for a recruit to turn up with the wrong clothing or equipment. For anyone who transgressed this, they were given an appropriate punishment. This was what the Troop had now come to expect, and accepted it as such. The only time it was not acceptable, was if it impacted the whole Troop. This had happened before, and the individual who had caused it, was quietly taken to one side and given a 'gypsies warning' by the rest of the guys. This had happened on more than one occasion to Shep, who was still finding it difficult to follow simple instructions. Some of the blokes were starting to get somewhat agitated with him. There were mutterings that he was close to the line of being given summary justice by his peers. This justice could range from anything depending on the crime committed. Shep was on his last strike at the moment, any slip up during their time there could have consequences.

At the time they had been given, they all paraded outside their rooms and were marched to the small parade square. Here three Bedford four tonne trucks stood with their engines idling. They were divide up into two groups as the trucks could only carry approximately twenty people. The other truck was already loaded with ropes, carabiners, harnesses' and hard hats. These were the equipment that they would be using for today's activities. As they climbed onto the trucks they fought to get to the front nearest the drivers cab. Here they had learnt, was the most comfortable place to be, whilst travelling on these ageing beasts. They took their seats and tried to make themselves as comfortable as possible for the journey ahead. As they left the camp gates the truck that Richard was travelling in hit a pothole. This caused the Troops on the rear half of the truck, who were sitting over the rear axle, to cry out in unison. Richard chuckled to himself, as he had managed to get a seat closest to the driver's cab, so the jolt was less noticeable. The journey continued for the next ninety minutes only interrupted by shouts of pain as they encountered yet more pot holes.

As the vehicles pulled into a car park, the driver slammed on the brakes, causing the occupants to slide towards the front of the truck.

'Okay guys debus, and fall in three ranks' came the cry from outside as the tailgates were lowered and the Troops began to jump off. Lining themselves up they awaited the next instructions from the waiting NCOs who were stood drinking from flasks of tea. On a table by their land rover was a table with two green containers, some cartons and a bag of sugar. The container was known as a 'Norwegian' and would become a familiar welcoming sight to them.

'This morning we will be performing some exercises on high ropes which will be followed by a death slide across a lake.' Portwood grinned as he said it. He liked to see the looks of apprehension and fear in the recruits due to his sadistic nature. 'Before we start though, if you make your way over to the land rover, you can grab yourself a quick brew.

The recruits fell out and gathered their black mugs from their Bergen's. They filled them from the Norwegians, those that smoked sparked up, inhaling deeply the much needed nicotine rush. They chatted for the next ten minutes before they were once again fell in, and marched off to the first activity of the day. On turning a corner after approximately five hundred metres into the wood, they came across a series of ropes suspended between trees high up in the canopy. Richard did not have a fear of heights but this looked daunting to say the least.

'This gentlemen is not just a test of strength and fitness, it is a mental test also. You will notice there are ropes set at varying heights. You will begin at that point there' Portwood indicated a ladder that was set against a tree, ascending to a platform. Here a rope was suspended between two trees, with a rope just above head height also. 'You will attach yourself via the carabiners to your harness. Use your arms to suspend yourself and walk across the ropes. Once you reach the other side you will ascend the plank to the next level. On reaching the next obstacle which is a double roped parallel to each other you will 'Leopard crawl' across to the next obstacle. Rather than me talk you through it, one of the Troop Corporals will now demonstrate the full course.

With that one of the NCOs jogged off to the beginning of the course, and proceeded to make short work of the obstacles. Richard had not been timing it, but the NCO had finished the course in the space of about ten minutes. He returned to the watching recruits hardly out of breath. He obviously had done this more than once Richard thought to himself. The fact was that all NCOs who were responsible for recruit training, had already been through the Junior Leaders Regiment Training Centre. Once they had completed a number of years in their various Regiments they could apply as a training NCO at Stanley Barracks. This also was considered favourably on their yearly Commanding Officers reports. Those that had completed a two year stint here, were ear marked for promotion into the Warrant Officers and Sergeants Mess. They took their responsibilities seriously, and trained hard on their physical abilities as well as their turnout.

'So it's that simple, who wants to start us off then?' Portwood threw open the question to the open mouthed recruits. There was silence, as no one really wanted to be the first to look a fool. 'Okay, as there are no volunteers, you' pointing directly at Pete 'get your arse to the start. Once he has navigated the first obstacle you will follow him. Now line up behind him now!' Portwood bawled at them.

They nervously made their way across to the beginning of the course. Pete looked back over his shoulder at Richard, who tapped him on the shoulder as a recognition of encouragement. No words were spoken as they were not needed, and Pete began to climb the wooden ladder. On reaching the platform he secured himself from his harness to the top rope. Taking hold of the rope he edged onto the bottom rope which moved from side to side. As soon as it settled, and he had his balance he made his way across. With only a couple of wobbles, he safely made it across and the next recruit began to climb the ladder. By the time it came to Richard's turn, their attention had been drawn to Steve who had frozen half way between obstacles. The directing staff were calling up to him, asking if he had a problem.

No reply was forthcoming, and for what seemed like an age he hung there with his legs shaking. This was the first time that he had shown any sign of weakness. Without warning his fingers released the rope he was holding and he plummeted down a couple of feet. His safety harness took up the slack and he was suspended above the crowd. With words of advice, the NCOs managed to talk him through regaining his footing. After a short time he regained his composure and set off once again. Richard's stomach churned as he took his turn climbing the ladder. He found it not as difficult as he had thought, and had settled into a steady rhythm after the first two obstacles. Everyone in the Troop had completed the course in around ninety minutes. That is not to say that there were no hesitations, more than once some of them required words of encouragement from both the directing staff and the guys who had already finished. As the last of them climbed down from the final obstacle, they sighed a collected sigh of relief. Some of them who had an intense fear of heights had conquered it, which instilled a great sense of achievement. They were surprised to receive compliments not only from the Corporals but Portwood himself. You could see them visibly grow in stature on hearing this.

The morning had just begun and there was always time to slip up. They moved from the high ropes down a track which terminated on the edge of a cliff. This overlooked a lake which was suspended a metal cable from a tree, at an angle of around thirty five degrees to the opposite side of the lake. From the wire on their side was a pulley with a 'T-bar' attached, with two leather straps forming loops. They were asked to gather round in a semi-circle, as the instructors set about testing equipment. Portwood quickly ran through what was going to happen next.

'Gents the aim of this exercise is to travel from this side of the lake to the other. Your mode of transport will be this zip line. Look this way while I demonstrate' turning round he deftly attached his harness to the T-bar, which had a metal loop attached to it. Testing it was secure and without a word he launched himself off the edge. In no time at all he had reached the centre of the lake. He must have exceeded speeds of seventy mile and hour Richard thought. When he was around thirty metres from the other side one of the training staff applied a break to bring him to a gentle halt. Unstrapping himself he gave a thumbs up the Troop on the other side. On receipt of this signal one of the NCOs began to pull on a rope which brought the T-bar back across the lake to its start position. One by one they attached themselves to the contraption and made the journey across the lake. It all seemed to be going to smoothly, when suddenly the brake man on the other side had to hurriedly apply the brakes. He had lost concentration and the recruit was almost fifteen metres from the other side before he managed to get the brakes on. This caused the young Troopers legs to fly above the horizontal such was the force of it. The remainder of the recruits made it safely across without incident. The morning activities over, they broke for lunch, before once again boarding the trucks to their next destination.

Pulling once again into a public car park, the young soldiers assembled and awaited their next brief. The low winter sun had already begun to sink low in the sky. The temperature had visibly dropped as the recruits stood there in nothing more than a pair of coveralls and boots. Richard recalling the timetable for that day knew that this was the bridge jump. They had spoken about it the previous evening, each of them offering their own opinion on what it might entail. No matter what their thoughts were on the subject, the experience would live with them forever.

'Right Troops the final stand for the day, is something that all Junior Leaders past and present must complete. It will be an experience that you will speak about for the rest of your military careers on into your old age' Portwood said the words with pride, firmly believing in what he was telling them. 'It takes the form of stepping off that bridge' he nonchalantly jerked his head backwards in the direction of the humped back structure spanning the river. 'You will make your way from here to the centre of the bridge. At the centre of the bridge you will place yourself in between the two NCOs. These will be marking the exact centre of the bridge where the river is at its deepest. After being directed to step onto the parapet, you will wait until you are given the order to take a pace with your left foot. On entering the water it will take your breath away. As soon as you surface, you will shout out your name, rank and number. This is so that you fill your lungs with air and try to compensate for the shock. For your safety we have placed two members of staff downstream. These will be either side of the river with a rope should you get swept away. Are there any questions?' Again a silence amongst the apprehensive young men shivering in anticipation. No questions offered, they were fallen out and awaited for their names to be called. This they were told, was going to be done alphabetically. So Richard worked out that there would only be six before his turn came round. From where they were situated they could not see the river, or gauge how fast flowing it was. What made it worse they could not see how each person entered the water or the look on their faces. The only clue they had to what was going on was the sound of each of them in turn calling out their names and numbers. Richard did not even have time to question those that had completed it because before long his name was called.

He took a deep breath and slowly made his way to the start of the bridge. Looking to his right over the wall he could see the last recruit being helped from the water by one of the directing staff. He was spluttering and unsteady on his feet, which did not sit right with Richard. In the distance he could see the two Corporals marking the centre of the bridge. He felt like a condemned man as he trudged towards them.

'You ready for this?' one of them addressed him.

'As I ever will be' Richard lied.

'Okay when you're ready, step onto the bridge and give us the nod when you feel comfortable' the NCO said in a soothing manner.

Taking a deep breath Richard climbed onto the edge of the bridge. He briefly looked down into the swirling river. For the very first time, he saw that it was indeed fast flowing as Portwood had explained. He could see boulders breaking the surface in the shallow areas next to the banks. However he knew that the Instructors would not allow them to do this if it had not been tested prior. With this thought in his head, he nodded to one of the Corporals. Having been given the assurance that he was ready the Corporal barked.

'One step forward….march!'

Closing his eyes, he took a confident step with his left foot into the unknown. Although the bridge was only thirty feet above the water, he seemed to be falling for what seemed an age. Before he knew it his body entered the water with a resounding splash. All of his senses were heightened, as the heat from his outer skin rushed inwards to keep his core insulated, he found it difficult to think. All he could see was bubbles and white water surrounding him, as he kicked for the surface. He breached the water's surface, and immediately drew in a deep breath. His head ached and he fought to call out his name and number. On the second attempt, he managed it luckily, as he was being carried downstream. He was caught by one of the cut off guys, who helped him out of the water. Still breathless, he made his way up the bank to join the rest of the blokes that had finished.

They were busy towelling themselves, and getting into dry clothing. Once they had done this, they made a brew which had once again been laid out for them. With their mugs full, they chatted amongst themselves until everyone had returned, and had dried and clothed themselves. The directing staff got a couple of recruits to tidy away the brew area before falling them all back in. After congratulating everyone on a great first day, they were ordered back onto the transport. The journey back to Renney Lentney was just full of stories of the day, every person had conquered some fear or another. They looked forward to the next two weeks, little did they know what the last day would bring.

Chapter 12 – Escalation

For the next eight days, the recruits took part in outdoor activities, such as potholing, sailing, rock climbing, orienteering and cliff rescue. Richard enjoyed some more than others, the potholing was not an enjoyable experience for him. At one point, while squeezing through a very narrow gap, he became stuck and panic set in. It took the calm and professionalism of the Instructors to coax him through. Richard had always had a fear of confined spaces, which was strange for someone who was joining a Regiment, where living in a confined space was part of the job. However, like his peers, he persevered and was a better man for it. The military called this 'character building'; it made young boys into young men.

The penultimate evening arrived and the Troops gathered in the dining hall for their briefing for the next and final day. On a board, at the front of the hall, was pinned a map, which showed a detailed area of Dartmoor. On the map a red line had been drawn, which was broken up by various circles. Above the map was written the word 'Escalation' in bold, black marker pen and underlined. The room was full of the sound of voices, some subdued, others excited. They were all anxious and eager to find out what awaited them. They would not be kept long before finding out. The sound of the door banging announced the arrival of Sgt. Portwood, as he strode down the aisle which divided the seats set out. He seemed, for once, to be in a good mood; as he made eye contact with some of them he even smiled. Reaching the front of the hall, he walked towards the map, turning toward the expectant faces. Portwood picked up a pointer, which looked like a small snooker cue, and addressed them.

'Good evening. The final exercise is "Escalation". It takes the form of a twelve mile dash across Dartmoor. We will be leaving by 4 tonner at 07:00, to go to this point here,' he indicated an area on the map, with his cue, 'it is a car park, where the rest of the equipment will be waiting. You will be in teams of six, listed on the board over there,' again pointing to a white sheet of paper, on the left hand side of the board. 'The equipment itself consists of a 50 gallon barrel filled with water. This is attached to a Land Rover axle, with a T-bar at the front. In your teams, you will navigate this course;' he followed the red line on the map. At various points, Portwood stopped and described terrain features, checkpoints and medical posts. The briefing was detailed and took around 30 minutes to complete. After answering any questions or concerns the young Troopers had, Portwood dismissed them for the evening. His parting words were delivered with the sardonic smile, which had become his trademark. 'Make

sure you get your beauty sleep, ladies, it is going to be an interesting day.'
With that and a scraping of chairs on the cookhouse floor, the Troops dispersed.

The room was alive with chatter and men sorting out their dress for the next day. Others were attending to their feet, some popping blisters they had accumulated over the ever increasing PT sessions. Others were wrapping them in bandages or tape to prevent friction burns. Gus sauntered up to Richard and, in his broad Glaswegian accent, greeted him warmly.

'You ready fae this, pal?'

Richard looked up from taping his feet. 'Think so, buddy, but I reckon it's going to be a tough one.'

'You're fucking right there, pal. Just look at it this way, in 24 hours it will all be over. Just a week before we go on leave,' his reply gave Richard some comfort and a goal to set, in his mind.

The dawn broke, with the sound of rain lashing against the corrugated tin roof of the hut. Richard turned over, not wanting to leave his nice, warm bed. The stove had already been lit and some of the room were rising, making their way to the wash rooms. With a gargantuan effort, Richard hauled himself out of bed and pulled his wash kit from his locker. He was normally an early bird, but this morning, he was not feeling as energised as normal. The Troop had been excused PT for the morning, so once they had shit, showered and shaved, they moved together to the cookhouse. Knowing it was going to be a physical day, everyone was loading up with as many calories as they could. The tea and coffee urns were doing overtime, as the recruits consumed as much sweet tea as possible. The chefs started to clear away the hotplates, indicating to the Troops that breakfast was over. Richard glanced at his watch and saw they only had fifteen minutes, before they were to parade.

The one hour journey to the edge of Dartmoor was an uncomfortable one, for Richard. He had not been quick enough to grab a seat near the driver's cab and was positioned directly above the axle. As they trundled along, he felt every bump in the road. He felt slightly envious of those at the front of the truck, quietly dozing. It was a welcome relief, when they finally reached their destination at the car park and spilled out, to form three ranks. All were wearing their lightweight trousers, boots and PT vest, covered by a camouflage jacket. Although the car park was sheltered, with trees around it, the winter wind cut through them. The directing staff were all gathered around one of the contraptions, which Portwood had mentioned the night before. It was a rusty coloured frame surrounding an axle, on which two Land Rover tyres were attached. At the front, sticking out like the bow of a ship, was a T-bar, which would be used to either push or pull the beast. In the centre was a black, cylindrical barrel, attached by cargo straps, of the type used by heavy goods vehicles.

'Right, guys, form a semi-circle around here,' Portwood beckoned them with a movement of his head.

Gathering around the directing staff and the equipment, the Troops awaited further instruction.

'Before we set off, the instructors are going to show you how to manoeuvre the equipment,' and with that, he nodded to the NCOs, who went through a complete demonstration of how to push, pull and turn the equipment. The car park was made of gravel and was flat, so the contraption was easy to control. The Troop would find out this would not be the case, once they entered the moor. 'Grab yourselves a brew and be ready by your carts in ten minutes. We will be setting off at 08:30;' with that he turned away and began to converse with the directing staff.

The young Troopers headed for the brew area and quickly charged their mugs with hot, sweet tea and coffee. Some of the teams had already gathered together, to discuss tactics. Richard's team consisted of two weaker members of the Troop, but was bolstered by Gus and Fred. Pete had been assigned to another team, also of mixed ability. This was not by chance, but by design, Richard mused to himself. The tea and coffee quickly consumed, they gathered around the carts. Richard's first stint was to be on the T-bar; he winced as his skin touched the freezing cold metal. Portwood had made his way to the entrance of the car park, to ensure there was no traffic coming. Satisfied he could see clearly down the road, he called to the Troops to make themselves ready.

'You have a maximum of four hours to complete this, so let's see your best efforts. Stand by….Go! Portwood screamed across the car park.

The teams took up the strain on the carts, the two on the T-bar pulling, while the remaining four pushed from the rear and the side. The tyres took a grip and soon they were motoring at a comfortable speed, towards the entrance of the car park. Exiting, Portwood had positioned himself in the centre of the road, with another NCO, to stop any traffic. He pointed to a track on the opposite side of the road, which the teams were to take. They acknowledged the instruction and the race began.

The first mile was not bad, as the ground was firm, and the teams made good progress. Richard could see a right hand bend in the track, but trees obscured what was around it. As they navigated the turn, the track began to ascend on to the moor itself. Conditions underfoot were heavy and the effort required to keep the carts moving was doubled. Gus, who was at the rear of the cart, called for the team to change positions. He was a natural leader and had taken on the responsibility, without being asked. Richard was glad, as he knew that he was not as physically strong as Fred and Gus.

The change made, they continued on up the incline and looking over their shoulders, they saw they had moved ahead of the others. The NCO assigned to them was shouting words of encouragement and seemed pleased with how they were performing. This was in stark contrast to some of the directing staff in the teams bringing up the rear.

As they reached the summit of the incline, the moor spread out before them. It undulated and, at first glance, did not look too bad. The ground, however, was waterlogged and the tyres were starting to stick. Sweat was running down Richard's forehead and into his eyes. His quadriceps were burning and his hands stung from his efforts on the T-bar. The two weaker members of the team were starting to flag although they were only three miles into the exercise. In the distance, Richard could see a fluorescent yellow vest, which must be one of the directing staff, at a checkpoint, he thought to himself. As they approached the man, he pulled a container from the back of his vehicle.

'Fill up your water bottles before you set off again, guys, you're making good time,' he greeted them.

The team halted, thankfully, in front of him, took out their water bottles and drained them, before refilling from the container. Their thirsts quenched, and having had a little respite, the team swapped around and set off again. The group behind them was now only 100 metres to their rear. Feeling lifted by their short stop, they set off with renewed vigour, but shortly afterwards, Richard slipped and his leg became trapped under the wheel. It took a great effort to reverse the cart off him. He rolled about on the ground and was soon joined by the team's NCO. He quickly examined Richard, asking if he could move his leg and whether was he able to carry on. Richard nodded his assent, gingerly taking up his position and they set off again. They were over halfway now and the rain had started to lash down, driving into their faces. At the next checkpoint, a medical stand had been set up, with a qualified medic on hand. Richard's team took a short, five minute break, as the medic went round the team, checking for injuries. They had been joined by the team following them. After they had adjusted clothing, and again swapped over on the cart, they set off together.

There were only two miles to go, now, and the weather had started to change. The sun was breaking through and their spirits, if not their bodies, started to lift. The ground started to firm up, as they began to descend to lower ground. The two on the front, who at this point were Fred and Gus, had to lean back and dig in their heels, to stop the cart running away. Every part of their bodies ached, and Richard could feel the taped blisters rubbing against his boots. Some time back, they had gained their second wind, but they were now really starting to feel the impact of the gruelling run. One called Blake had already vomited a couple of times and was dangerously close to being dehydrated. The team's NCO was repeatedly asking if he was all right to carry on. To his credit, Blake just nodded his head and plodded on. Richard thought he would never do anything so physically demanding as this, ever again.

As they reached the bottom of the hill, they entered a track comprising firm, fine gravel. Their speed increased and their muscles were allowed to relax slightly. They were running parallel to a road and Richard recalled the route. This was the last stretch before the end, in about fifteen minutes it would all be over. They were joined, out of nowhere, by Portwood, who jogged alongside.

'Good effort, lads, keep it going, just half a mile to push. The team behind you are catching up, so you'd better get a shift on,' he laughed.

Taking a quick look over their shoulders and ignoring the pain they were in, they picked up the tempo. Richard was starting to feel faint, his head was spinning and his vision was strained. The last half mile was just a blur, and as they turned right, as directed by their NCO, they could see the entrance to the car park. Crossing the road with one last effort, they sprinted into the car park. Crossing the line, they immediately let go of the cart and collapsed to the ground. Richard's chest was heaving from the exertion of the past two hours, fifteen minutes. They were oblivious to the next team crossing the line, only thirty seconds behind them. A full 30 minutes elapsed before the last team came in, just ten minutes before the cut off time. Once everyone had rehydrated and recuperated, they were called together by the directing staff. Some of the Troop appeared dead on their feet, they swayed in the wind, like saplings. What was to follow was like a death blow to them.

'Gentlemen, I would like to start by congratulating you all for finishing the course. We have lost only two individuals, due to injury, so well done.' Portwood genuinely sounded pleased with the effort shown by the whole Troop. 'What I omitted to say during the briefing last night is that we will not be returning to camp tonight.' He waited for his words to sink in and looked at the disbelief on the young faces before him. 'In around twenty minutes, the chefs will be turning up with tonight's meal, which will be a stew. I hope you have all brought your mess tins with you, as laid down on the kit list. Those who haven't will be eating it out of their hands,' he smirked, sarcastically. 'After evening meal, return here and I will brief you on tonight's exercise.'

Demoralised, the Troops drifted away and awaited the arrival of the chef's truck. The mood was solemn and the elation of having completed the course had faded. All they had to look forward to was a cold, wet night.

Chapter 13 – Escape and Evasion

The hot stew was a welcome distraction from their bedraggled state as well as a much needed source of energy. The Troop emptied the 'hay box' in which the stew was contained. They had also demolished six loaves of bread, to soak it up. Once the meal was finished, and the chefs had departed, the recruits drank tea and smoked, waiting to be called forward for the final briefing. Everyone, to a man, was aching or carrying some injury or another. Even Fred and the other super fit guys were feeling the strain of the previous three hours. Chatting among themselves, they each voiced their own opinions on what the night held for them. Richard sat contemplating this fact, not his usual boisterous self. The course had completely destroyed him, he was still feeling physically sick. Noticing this, Pete made his way over to him.

'You okay, mate?' he said trying to sound upbeat.

'I'm absolutely fucked, Pete,' was the only reply Richard could muster.

Before they could engage in conversation further, Portwood called them over, for the briefing.

After everyone had gathered round the map that had been set up, and they had all settled down, Portwood began.

'This exercise is the final push, gents. I know that you are all tired, but you need to focus over the next twelve hours or so. The exercise will take the form of escape and evasion. This is to simulate your being cut off behind enemy lines,' the assembled Troops looked at each other, some smiling, others fighting to stay awake. The idea of the scenario given appealed to Richard and, with a new found interest, he began to dismiss the aches and pains. 'You will set off in your teams again, with two minute intervals between each. Here is your position. You are to make your way, by whichever route you choose, to this point here,' he said, using a twig as a pointer. 'Each of you will take turns at map reading. However, you must, at some point, visit this location here,' pointing once more with the twig, he circled an area on the map. 'This is HMP Dartmoor, near the village of Princetown. We want you to make a sketch map of the layout of the prison. Points of interest are likely escape areas or security flaws. You are to take note of any vehicle or security routines that you observe. On your return, one of you from each group will give a presentation on your reconnaissance.' Waiting for the point to sink in, Portwood then continued. 'However, you will not be alone out there, some of the directing staff and others will be on the moor, trying to locate you. If you are found, there may be some mild aggression shown towards you, and you will be moved five miles nearer to this location. The distance as the crow flies, between point A, here, and point B, your final destination, is around twenty miles. 'You must make the final rendezvous (RV) by 06:00 hours, tomorrow. If you are not there at that time, it is a long walk back to Renny Lentney. Has anyone any questions?' The usual silence prevailed, Richard was not sure if it was because everyone understood what the task was, or whether they were too tired to ask.

The next 45 minutes was spent relaxing, waiting for last light. The teams were then called forward, one at a time, to the start line. They had been equipped with torches with red lenses, to protect their night vision, when reading their maps. Everyone had a compass, and they would be putting into practice the lessons learnt during the orienteering they had taken part in, earlier in the week. Richard's team were to be the last to leave, so after eight minutes from the start time, they were called up to the start line. With Fred leading from the front, with map and compass in hand, they set off.

The route they were going to take had already been decided by the group, in hurried conversations held since the briefing. The terrain they were to cross did not appear too hilly, judging from the contours on the map. They chose to follow the contours of features such as Tors, rather than go over them. This would add distance to the overall journey, but they would expend less energy by travelling this way. During the Orienteering phase, they had learnt how many paces it took for them to cover 100 metres. This was to prove invaluable, when moving at night, when no visible light was allowed. Richard knew that his pacing was 117 for the 100 metres, but this differed for each member of the team. Fred, who was leading them was shorter so his stride was also shorter. He required to take 122 paces to cover the same distance. As they made their way away from the main road and any built up areas, it steadily got darker. After half an hour of walking, they could not see the person in front. At the head of the team, Fred stopped suddenly and called them forward, quietly.

'By my pacing, we should reach a track on our right, where we need to bear right.' They all nodded their acknowledgement and set off slowly, letting Fred count his paces. Within two minutes, he stopped again and as he had said, a track was bearing off to the right. He passed word down the line that they were changing direction. As they moved further up the track and onto the moor, they began to climb slightly. After climbing for around fifteen minutes, they started to bear left and make their way around the contour of the feature, which Richard knew was a Tor. The ground became increasingly sodden and the men felt unsteady on their feet. Not knowing where to place their feet caused their pace to slow, as several started to stumble and curses broke the silence. On top of the feature, lights could be seen and raised voices rang out across the moor. This suggested that a group ahead of them had been discovered. The team immediately took cover, waiting for the commotion to die down. Richard crawled forward after a short while and whispered to Fred that he would take over the map reading duties. Creggan, who had been assigned to them for the evening, also made his way towards Fred.

'Are you happy where you are and the direction you are taking next, Hunter?' he asked Richard

Richard simply nodded his head in assent and took a bearing with his compass, from the map. Once he was ready, he motioned for the team to stand up and he led them off.

By Richard's reckoning, in the next hour they covered around three miles. They were off pace, hindered by their inability to see the terrain, beneath them. Glancing at the map, Richard knew that they would need to climb the feature that they were circumnavigating. This would bring them to a position where they would be able to observe HMP Dartmoor, which lay in the valley beyond. Indicating with his right hand and asking the next person to pass it back, they changed direction and began to climb. It was only a matter of 200 metres, but the uneven, marshy ground was sapping their strength. Finally, Richard crested the rise and took great care not to silhouette himself against the skyline. He whispered to the man behind him that they had reached the summit, and that they were to join him, but not cross the skyline. Lying on their stomachs, they crept forward to the lip of the rise. In the valley below them, stood the prison surrounded by floodlights, which lit up the area surrounding the Victorian building. It reminded Richard of the line, "Dark Satanic Mills", from the hymn *Jerusalem*. Taking the pair of binoculars they had been given before the start of the exercise, Richard began to survey the area. Gus started to draw a sketch map and marked the areas that could be vulnerable. They noticed a couple of the spotlights were not working; and there was an area of wall that was not covered, which could be used as a means of concealment. They also noted any vehicle movement in and out of the facility. In the distance, they could hear the distinctive sound of a Land Rover engine. Scanning the roads, Richard watched the vehicle, making its way off the road and across country, in their direction. It was agreed they had gathered enough intelligence, so the men slowly began to withdraw, behind the hill. Moving off to the dead ground, another member of the team took the map and led them away from the area.

For the next six hours, they stumbled in the darkness over their chosen route. They had to make a couple of detours, as they missed the waypoints they had marked to keep them on track. At last, wearied, they came across a disused farm building, marked on the map, which they had chosen as their last waypoint. From here, a bearing was taken for the last mile and a half to their destination, another car park, behind a pub. By this point, they were almost dead on their feet and the lack of sleep was beginning to impact on their concentration. Little stumbles became major issues and tempers were starting to fray. As usual, Gus was the calming influence, giving words of encouragement and reminding them it would soon all be over. He was proven right, as after fifteen minutes, they spotted several headlights moving along what must have been the road leading to the village, where the pub was located. They crossed the road one at a time, after first ensuring no cars were coming. They made a wide arc around the village and entered the pub car park from the rear. As they came into the car park, they saw that there were two Bedford trucks, with their engines running. One group had already arrived and were swilling mugs of tea or coffee and smoking. Richard looked at his watch; it was 04:45, they had made it, with good time to spare.

'Well done, lads, grab yourselves a brew and rest for ten minutes. I will see you over by the Land Rover, then, for a briefing on your reconnaissance report.' Portwood said, almost sympathetically.

The team made their way, wearily, over to the brew area and found a spot in which to relax, for a while. During this time, they found out that one of the members of the first team home had been taken to hospital, with a suspected broken leg. It had happened while that team was crossing some boggy ground, making an escape from a group of directing staff. The team member had placed his foot in a hole in the moor and his body had twisted, in the opposite direction. This had caused the injury and he had been casualty evacuated by Land Rover. Once they had finished their brews, the group gave their recce briefing to Portwood, who seemed pleased enough with their findings. It was approximately 06:30 by the time the last team finished and delivered their report. The whole Troop were then debriefed by the instructors and ordered on to the trucks for the journey back to Renny Lentney. On the journey back, the noise of the heavy vehicles broke the silence of the morning. In the trucks, was the sound of snoring from the sleeping, young men.

Chapter 14 – Leave and final term

Back in Renny Lentney, the Troop was given a couple of hours to shower, have breakfast and clean their rooms, before handing in any equipment they had taken out for their time away. The camp was a hive of activity for the next couple of hours, as huts were inspected, handed back and equipment returned. They all boarded the buses which had arrived to take them back to Stanley Barracks. On their return, they were told there would a room inspection that evening. If the NCOs were impressed by the standards demanded, the Troop would be allocated a period of leave.

Refreshed after sleeping through the journey from Renny Lentney, the room-mates got stuck into giving their accommodation the full military make over. At 20:00, they were all standing by their beds, awaiting the inspection. The Instructors inspected their allocated rooms, and, apart from the odd little point, the exhausted men passed with flying colours. They were told to parade outside, the following morning, in civilian clothing, for transport to the station. Before the bugle called Last Post, every bed was occupied and the men fast asleep. It had been a long 36 hours.

Dawn broke over Stanley Barrack. The recruits were busy, showering and dressing, in anticipation of their leave. Richard had invited Fred to stay with him and his parents in Germany. Fred had jumped at the opportunity, as he had never been outside the UK. At 09:00 the young, junior Troopers paraded outside the block in their civilian clothes, carrying suitcases. The room inspection that morning had been a formality and had lasted only five minutes. The instructors seemed to have switched off for the day, obviously looking forward to their two weeks off.

'Good morning, Troops' Portwood addressed the group. 'I would like to say, on behalf of the training staff, a big "well done" for all your efforts in your first term. We started with 40 of you and still have 32 remaining. That is the number I expect to see here, on your return, in two weeks. During your leave, enjoy yourselves and relax. However, do not get into any scrapes or trouble with the police. If you do, it is your duty to report the matter, on your return.' With that, he dismissed them and they made their way to the parade square, where the buses were waiting to take them to the train station.

The journey back to Germany was uneventful. The three friends, Pete, Fred and Richard, put away a few beers on the train to London. They chatted about the past twelve weeks and about various members of the Troop. The main topic of conversation was the directing staff, in particular Portwood, who had seemed so formidable on their first meeting. Over the last few weeks, he had mellowed slightly and the Troops were warming to him. From London, they took a train to Luton Airport. Here, they waited to board a service chartered plane to Hanover in Germany. There, they were welcomed home by their families and Fred was introduced to Richard's parents.

Over the next few weeks, the three met up regularly with Ivan and Steve. Invariably, the nights ended with the lads swallowing much more beer than was good for them. Ivan and Steve heard blow by blow accounts of everything that had happened to their friends, from arrival at camp to the end of the first term. One drunken night, they were involved in a disturbance, in a local pub, which resulted in them being arrested by the local RMP and detained for a couple of hours. Richard's father arrived and defused the situation, by explaining the tanked up lads were on leave, after which the matter was dropped. Little did they know the impact this small altercation would have.

The leave flew by and it wasn't long before they were once again boarding the flight from Hanover for their return to JLR. The mood was sombre, as they sipped the last alcohol allowed to them for the next few weeks. Back at Stanley Barracks, they were received by the training staff, who were glad to see that everyone had made it back.

Over the next six months, the training intensified, as they were taught field craft, drill, PT and given scholastic education. Before long, they were in their final term and on the home stretch to 'passing off'. This would entitle them to wear the yellow flash, with the white line on their epaulettes. It marked them out as being almost the complete article, ready to join their Regiments and Corps. Although they were trained in mainly military duties and adventurous activities, other subjects were taught. To support these military and technical subjects, part of the training was given over to military studies, in which subjects such as trade science, communication skills and military affairs were taught. As in all work of the Regiment, emphasis was placed on the development of leadership qualities. One of their Instructors from the Army Education Corps (AEC), was a Major Bradbury. The first time they met him, he made an impression. Standing at six feet four, he sported a rather fine moustache. On this initial meeting, Richard had noticed that the Major wore a set of parachute wings on his right sleeve. However, he knew that these were not normal wings, but those of the Special Air Service (SAS). Bradbury resembled the character Basil Fawlty, portrayed by John Cleese, in the television comedy 'Fawlty Towers'. He had a natural gift for imparting knowledge, due to the respect in which he was held by the young soldiers; and they learned quickly. Richard was particularly keen on military affairs and thrived on the subject. He had always been interested in military history and would listen intently, as his father told him stories of conflicts throughout the world.

In their final term, they were taught radio communications and gunnery. Richard hoped to make the former his career path, after joining the Regiment. He found the gunnery phase a little more challenging, but enjoyable, nonetheless. One of their Instructors was from the 'Life Guards', a unit of the Household Cavalry, who not only operated as an operational armoured unit, but also performed ceremonial duties for the Queen. On State occasions, they accompanied the Sovereign, mounted and resplendent in red tunics, breastplates and white plumed helmets. This mountain of a man had the rank of 'Corporal Major' a rank unknown to Richard. It equated to a Sergeant Major or Warrant Officer Class 2 in other Regiments. He was called Townsend and was the personification of a gunnery Instructor. His turnout was immaculate, from the highly polished cap badge in his beret down to his gleaming boots. Their first meeting was not a good one for Richard. It was a normal day, and the Troop had just finished a gruelling hour of battle PT. They entered the classroom, where they were to receive a lecture on gunnery techniques from Townsend. The room was dark and stuffy, with no windows for ventilation or light. On each table was placed an upturned piece of metal, approximately two inches thick, which was formed into a bowl. As the men sat, they were told these could be used as ashtrays. This was self-evident, as some were almost overflowing with cigarette butts. The men were informed that the structures were HESH scabs, formed when armour was hit by a high-explosive squash head shell. This resulted a shock wave, causing the armour to fracture inside. The fragmenting scab then zipped around the inside of the turret, destroying anything its path, from equipment to human tissue. As the lecture went on, Richard could feel himself starting to drift off. Due to the physical exertions of the PT lesson earlier, he was finding it hard to concentrate. Then, he made the fatal mistake of closing his eyes for a split second. He could not have done so at a more inopportune moment. Townsend had seen it, and launched into a frenzy of abuse.

'Am I boring you, Hunter, you fucking horrible creature?' he screamed.

Richard jumped, hearing the comment directed at him.

'No, Corporal Major.' he replied, feebly.

'Then, why the fuck are you taking a nap in my lesson? What I want you to do is pick up that ash tray and place it on your head,' he said, with some malice.

Richard winced, as he reached for the HESH scab, half full of cigarette ends and ash. He was surprised to find that it took some effort to move it. It must have weighed around six to eight pounds, Richard reckoned. He lifted it and placed it, upturned, on his head. The ash and fag ends cascaded onto the desk and into his hair, which caused amusement among his classmates.

'Now, I want you to sit with that on till the end of the lesson,' Townsend smirked as he spoke.

The lesson continued and Richard could feel his neck sinking lower towards his shoulders. He was really uncomfortable, but ensured that his concentration was focused. At one point during the lesson, one of the Troop answered a question with a really stupid response, which was punished by the culprit being given a practice HESH round, full of concrete. He was ordered to "double" around the parade square five times, holding it above his head. To add insult to injury, he had to shout out, 'I am a fucking numpty,' as he did so. The lesson came to an end and Richard was allowed to remove the 'ash tray' from his head. His neck slowly began to stretch back to normal. He felt relieved that it was over and did not wish to repeat the punishment in future. All the way through their gunnery training, Townsend made their lessons enjoyable, however, the Troop knew never to lose focus.

In this final term, the young soldiers were allowed to drink alcohol in a bar that was set aside for them. Some of them had gained promotion. Richard reached the dizzy heights of Junior Sergeant and Pete was promoted to Corporal, although this would pale into insignificance in his later career. The Troop also boasted that they had the Junior Regimental Sergeant Major (RSM), who was to be badged to the RMP. He had been identified at an early stage for his turnout, drill and leadership. It would be his responsibility and honour to take the pass off parade in a couple of weeks.

Evenings were spent mostly bulling their boots, in preparation for the big day. They were inspected, daily, by the room NCOs and constantly reminded that more work was needed. Richard could not understand how he could make his any better, as they seemed to shine like mirrors. He had worked in tins of polish and copious amounts of bees wax on them. He regularly wore them, walking up and down the room, to make sure that they did not crack. Where they did, he filled in, with more polish and bees wax.

The men in the Troop were now being paid directly into their bank accounts, which they had set up the previous term. Before then, they had been paid the princely sum of £10, over the table, every week. The remainder of their money was put into savings, which they received, prior to leave. Most of them spent it wisely, but others, Richard included, made full use of their new found privileges. Weekends were spent in the seaside towns of Bournemouth or Weymouth. It was on one of these trips that Richard and a mate decided to have tattoos done. They had gone to a bar first, for some Dutch courage. After sinking several pints, they made their way to a tattoo artist, well known for not asking for proof of age. None of the Troop would reach their eighteenth birthday until shortly before, or after, they had joined their Regiments. They egged each other into the studio and began to leaf through some designs. Richard chose a geisha girl to be inked on his right forearm. And, to curry favour with his parents, a rose and two hearts design, with a scroll bearing the words 'mum' and 'dad'. The sitting lasted around an hour, and Richard had never experienced pain like it before. The tattoos became an addiction, and before he left JLR, he had another two added. The tattoos covered up, the friends went to the nearest pub to celebrate. It was not long before they realised that they needed to be heading to the station, for the return train. Although they had been given this privilege, they were still expected to be in their beds by lights out. By the time they were nearing camp, it was already getting close to this time. Not wanting to draw attention to themselves, they avoided the main gate. Both knew there was an unmanned gate, to the rear of their accommodation, where they could gain entry. As it came into view, they saw a mobile sentry patrol nearby, so they went to ground and waited for it to leave the area. Dashing through the gate, they quickly entered the accommodation, just before the bugle called Last Post.

The weeks passed very quickly, most of the time spent practising for their pass off parade. Their drill was, by now, to an excellent standard, but Drill Sgt. Rudd demanded perfection. Even big Mark Newbottle had transformed himself from not knowing his left from his right, to a standard most Guards Regiments would have been proud of. The Junior RSM, Keith Crouch, had the parade format firmly fixed in his mind. All the Troops who were passing off from each of the Squadrons were brought together twice a week, to practise the whole parade. Prior to the big day, they had an adjutant's parade, to ensure their uniforms and drill were up to the required standard. They were all thankful that they passed; had they failed, they would have to do it all again on Saturday.

The final evening arrived, and the rooms were full of activity. Some were making the final preparations to their boots, others were pressing their No2 dress uniforms, with razor sharp creases in the trousers and arms. As they all had different accompaniments to their Regimental dress, some had more work to put in than others. Richard and Pete, for example, had a brown belt with a large brass buckle. This needed to be highly polished and a cap badge inserted in the centre. Even the pins that secured this badge, and the ones on their collars, needed to be polished with Brasso or Duraglit. Attention to detail was what the inspecting officer and the directing staff were looking for. The men worked into the night, making sure everything was just right. As they cleaned, pressed and polished, they chatted among themselves. Out of the original 40 who had started, only 28 would be passing out the following day. They had suffered and laughed in equal measure, over the past twelve months. The experiences they had shared would last them their entire lives. Richard thought back to the time with Ivan and Steve outside his parents' house in Germany, prior to him and Pete leaving, to join up. The bond the young soldiers had formed was the same, if not stronger, than the one between the four school friends.

Morning came and was heralded, as usual, by the sound of the bugle playing Reveille. The Troops busied themselves; washing, showering and shaving, before heading off for their last meal at the Training Centre. They ensured they ate heartily, as no one wanted to feint on the parade. If you did, and it was found that you had not attended breakfast, it was a chargeable offence. As the young soldiers left the cookhouse, they noticed the arrival of some of the parents, wandering round the camp, taking photographs. The soldiers had been given a short time to meet with their parents at 10:00. The parade would start at 11:00, which gave them time for this, and to make sure that their dress was sorted.

Returning to the accommodation, they made the final touches to their uniforms. Polishing the peaks of their caps, so that no finger marks were present. They also finished off their boots, by bulling them with water. The time was nearing 10:00 and the instructors were moving round their respective rooms, checking their charges. When it was time for the soldiers to meet their parents, they checked each other over, one last time. Creggan informed them they would only have fifteen minutes and were to be fell in outside at 10:15 for a final inspection. They gathered outside and took some personal photographs of each other. Some of the parents were already waiting, Richard's and Pete's among them. After a quick chat with them and showing them round the accommodation, they bade them farewell, until the end of the parade.

Portwood and the rest of the Instructors had also changed into their best uniforms. They called the Troop together for a last few words of congratulations, wishing them good luck in their future careers. This finished, they then arranged them into three ranks. The first rank was seated with their fists clenched on their thighs. The remaining two ranks lined up, in order of height, from the tallest on the outsides, to the shortest in the centre. The photographer had already set up his camera, and once satisfied, took a number of pictures. This was a tradition every pass off Troop complied with. Once it was over, Portwood ordered them all to fall in, on the road, in their three ranks. One, who had reached the rank of Junior Sergeant Major, was to take the squad. After they had fallen in, the Instructors took a row each, inspecting and making final adjustments to dress. This complete, they stood back and handed over to the Junior Sergeant Major.

'Squad...squad... shun! Move to the right in threes....Right...turn!'

The Troop stepped off and made their way to the parade square, where the lonely, solitary figure of the Junior RSM waited, patiently. As the squadrons converged on to the square, he halted them, when they reached their designated spots. After advancing them, he had them do an about turn, and presented them to the inspecting officer. The inspecting officer returned the salute and made his way, with the Commanding Officer of the Training Regiment, through the ranks.

The inspection over, the Troops then marched past the dais, giving an 'eyes right' in slow and quick time. The circuit having been completed twice, the Junior RSM then advanced the whole pass off, in review order. They presented their weapons in a General Salute and awaited the salute in return. The RSM then marched forward and asked for permission for the assembled Troops to pass off the square. This was given and the RSM did a smart about turn and gave the command for the Troops to shoulder arms. In his loudest voice, he announced that the pass off Troops, for that year, would now march off. As one, the young men, who had started off as young adolescent civilians, marched off proudly, towards their new careers as fully formed soldiers.

Chapter 15 – The Regiment

Richard sipped on his brandy and coke. He started to feel light headed, as his father had been re-filling his glass all afternoon. It was Christmas, and only two weeks until he was due to start with the Regiment. They chatted about what he should expect on his first few days and weeks. The most important advice his father gave him was, although his new Squadron would already know who his father was, never be tempted to drop Tommy's name into conversation.

Tommy had arranged to have Richard's clothing issued by the QM's department, prior to starting. Richard had noticed although these storemen were not as miserable as the ones at training, they were cut from the same cloth. They gave the impression it was their clothing and equipment being issued. From the QM's department, his father took him to see his new Squadron Quartermaster Sergeant (SQMS). Here, he was issued with his bedding and Squadron equipment. As D Sqn was on leave, Richard was able to go to his new room, make his bed up and place his clothing in his locker. The rest of his leave was spent relaxing and drinking, mostly with Pete, Ivan and Steve. Before he knew it, the leave was over, and on the Sunday before he was due to start, his father dropped him off at D Sqn accommodation. This would be his new home for the next six months.

As he entered the block, he came across people milling about the corridor, idly chatting among themselves. The Squadron had obviously started to return from leave, and he drew some inquisitive looks, as he made his way down the corridor. Acknowledging them with a nod of his head, Richard decided not to say anything, recalling his father's advice not to speak, unless spoken to. He tried the door to his room, which was unlocked and went inside. On the far side of the room, a man of average size had his back to him. On hearing the door close, he turned round to face Richard.

'Hi there, lad, you must be our new roommate,' he said, in a friendly manner.

'I am, buddy, the name's Richard.' He extended his right hand, which the amiable guy took.

'I'm Tom Hardgreaves, mate, good to meet you,' he released Richard's hand and continued, 'Bubba is just having a shite, he should be back shortly and we can go for a pint in the Squadron bar, if you like?'

'That would be great,' Richard agreed to the invitation. He guessed that 'Bubba' was his other roommate, as there were three beds. He knew from conversations, with his father that most rooms housed two or three people.

All Corporals and the occasional lucky Lance Corporal were given their own single rooms. They did not have to wait very long before the door opened once again, the doorway filled with a huge figure, with a magazine under his arm. Richard wondered how the fuck this giant managed to fit into a tank. Tom immediately made the introductions and they shook hands. The pleasantries over with, the three made their way from the room. They left the block and walked across to an opposite Barrack Block, which Richard recognised as where the SQMS stores were. On their arrival, they travelled down the stairs into the cellar. A short distance along the dark corridor, Richard could hear voices, coming from an open door.

He followed behind Tom and Bubba, who strode into a room, on the left, full of cigarette smoke. The occupants were either standing at the bar, chatting, or playing darts. As they approached, the barman, who Richard later found out was one of the Troop Corporals, greeted Tom, warmly.

'What can I get you, mate?' he asked.

'Three Paderborners, please, Kevin,' Tom replied, without asking the other two.

The barman reached under the bar and produced three small, brown bottles. He expertly removed the tops, which were a kind of ring pull. Handing them over, Kevin addressed Tom.

'That's one Deutsche Mark 50, marra,' holding out his hand for payment.

Richard had forgotten how cheap the alcohol was in Squadron bars. As he took a sip of the amber liquid, he noticed that his presence had attracted the attention of the others in the bar, who turned away and seemed to be whispering to each other. This made him feel slightly nervous. It was like being the new kid at school. The three new roommates chatted among themselves. In the space of five minutes, Bubba had finished his beer and returned to the bar, to buy another round. The barman, Kevin Webster, noticed that Richard seemed a little nervous, so decided to try to put him at ease.

'Don't mind some of these guys, they're not used to new blokes, you will get used to them. What Troop you going to, then?'

'I think it's second Troop,' Richard answered, thankful for the reassuring words.

'He's going to be Robbo's gunner,' Tom piped up.

This caused a wide smile to break over Kevin's face, 'Good luck with that. I'm in third Troop. I'm sure we will see each other over the coming weeks,' he said, mysteriously.

They were interrupted by a man wearing stay press trousers, complete with braces, a Fred Perry T-shirt and close cropped hair. He looked as though he had stepped off the cover of a SKA album. He was missing only the pork pie hat, to complete the ensemble.

'Fancy a game of arrows?' he asked, in a broad Yorkshire accent.

'Why not?' Tom replied, on behalf of Richard.

They made their way over to the corner, where a dart board was hanging at the regulation height. Tom introduced Richard to the others, already there. After half an hour, Richard started to relax, the ice had been broken. This was due largely to the fact that they had consumed four Paderborners in the space of an hour. They had, in fact, begun their fifth, and Richard was feeling the effects. He like a drink or two, but was never comfortable drinking at other people's pace. However, on this occasion, he did not want to appear to be as young as he really was. He had not yet reached his eighteenth birthday, which was two months away.

After numerous games of darts, they retired, once again, to the bar, where Tom ordered a round of brandies and coke. Richard was mindful that he had an interview with the Commanding Officer the next day, welcoming him to the Regiment. This was a normal occurrence for all new members and Pete would be there too. He did not want to bring this up in front of the others, as it may appear he was trying to wimp out on his first day.

At around 23:00, the door to the bar opened and a uniformed man walked in. He was greeted with the sound of hissing and booing from the rest. He laughed it off, went to the bar and ordered a soft drink. Richard was informed by Bubba that this was the Night Orderly Sergeant (NOS). Although he was only a Corporal, he carried the rank, and every Squadron had an NOS on duty every night. They were responsible, among other things, for closing the bars, seeing there was no trouble and ensuring the living in Troops were wakened in the morning. He sipped his drink for about fifteen minutes before announcing last orders, which was met by a series of groans.

After ten minutes, they were asked to finish their drinks. Those in the room all complied. Richard prepared to leave, but was surprised when Tom asked Kevin if he could buy a carry out. Kevin looked at the duty NOS, who nodded his assent. The barman handed over a box of Paderboner, which Tom gratefully accepted. They made their way from the bar back to the accommodation. The block was full of sounds of different types of music being blasted out from high powered sound systems. This was a different world to training, where lights out was at 22:00. It was after midnight and it looked like the party had just begun. Richard cringed to himself, not sure how much longer he would last.

The box of beer was opened and the three roommates sat chewing the fat for the next hour or so. They went through the characters who were in second Troop, highlighting any good points, bad points or idiosyncrasies that they may have. Tom gave a full description of 'Robbo', who was to be Richard's new commander. He came from the Lake District area of

Cumbria and was one of the Squadron Gunnery Instructors. This was not good, Richard thought to himself, as his standards would be very high. He cursed his luck, to be assigned a gunner's seat on the commander's vehicle. The box of beers was now empty and Richard crawled into his bed. As he stared at the ceiling, the music still continued to blast out from other rooms. This did not prevent him from getting to sleep. As he started to drift off, he felt something stir in his stomach. The beer mixed with the brandy was trying to make a second appearance; he flung the sheets off and dashed for the door, covering his mouth with his hand. This drew raucous laughter from both Bubba and Tom, who found it highly amusing. Dashing down the corridor, he made the washrooms just in time, as golden liquid erupted from his mouth and into the bowl of the nearest toilet. Wiping his mouth with a paper towel, Richard splashed water on his face. On his return to the room, Tom asked if he was alright, to which he mumbled that he was. Crawling once again between the sheets, Richard closed his eyes and slipped into a deep sleep.

Chapter 16 – Commanding Officers Interviews

Richard was awoken by the sound of music, once again being played from the room above them. Deep Purple was not his preferred choice as an alarm clock. He threw back the sheets, gingerly swung his legs over the bed and winced as his feet made contact with the cold floor. His head was aching and his mouth felt like Ghandi's flip flop.

'Feeling rough?' Tom called over, from his side of the room. He was already dressed and was busy polishing his boots.

'A little, yeah,' Richard replied, sheepishly. 'I need to sort my shit out, I've got my CO's interview at 09:00, and I need to water bull my shoes, and run an iron over my barrack dress.'

'The ironing board and iron are over there,' Tom pointed to Bubba's side of the room. 'Are you going to breakfast?'

Richard looked at his watch, it was already 07:30. He knew he would need at least an hour to make sure his uniform was up to standard, so declined the offer. As he did so, Bubba entered the room bare chested, his ample stomach entering the room before the rest of him. Richard was not used to seeing physiques quite like this, and wondered how he passed the annual fitness tests. He would soon discover there were many who didn't. Their punishment would be extra PT in the morning and lunchtimes, until they did. He nodded a welcome, which was returned. Before long, Tom and Bubba grabbed their mugs and left the room for breakfast. Richard was left alone to prepare for his interview, and first, he headed to the washrooms for a shower and shave.

Once he finished washing and shaving, Richard returned to the room, to find both Tom and Bubba had returned and were preparing to go to work. They said their goodbyes, acknowledging they would see each other, either sometime that morning or at lunchtime. Richard continued to press his clothing and put a last deep shine on his shoes. Checking himself in the mirror, he left the room and headed towards Regimental Headquarters (RHQ).

On his arrival at the building, he could see the back of Pete, who had just begun to climb the stairs.

'Hope you have a headache as bad as mine!' he called out. Pete turned around and laughed when he saw Richard.

'Did they drag you into the Squadron bar as well?' he answered, confirming that he had been subjected to a similar first evening.

'Yep, I hope to fuck it's not like that every night,' was all that Richard could come up with.

The two friends continued up the stairs and through a set of double doors. To their left, along the corridor, were two well-built individuals in barrack dress and slashed peaked hats. On their right sleeves they wore arm bands with the letters RP. These, Richard and Pete knew, were Regimental Police. They were bawling at a young man dressed in khaki No2 dress uniform. From a room opposite, strode a short man with a huge badge on his lower right arm. Although small in stature, he carried himself with an air of authority. He spotted the two friends and immediately coaxed them over with twitch of his head.

'You two here for interviews?' he asked, in what sounded like a Cockney accent. Both Richard and Pete recognised the RSM, Kevin Bottelli. He was a close friend of Richard's father and had met Richard on numerous occasions, when he had accompanied his parents in the Warrant Officers' and Sergeants' Mess. The RSM showed no signs of recognition or favouritism, he simply asked them to stand to, on one side of the corridor. He went on to explain the format of the interviews. This done, he called both of them up to attention, so he could give them a quick once over. Richard raised his right leg parallel to the ground and a flash of colour caught the RSM's attention.

'What the fuck are those?' he screamed, pointing to Richard's socks.

'Socks, sir,' came Richard's answer.

'Fucking socks, sir! White fucking socks! How dare you parade for interviews wearing civilian clothing? Get the fuck out of my sight and be back here in five minutes wearing regulation green socks, you cunt ... Move!' Botelli yelled in Richard's face, and Richard could feel the spittle cover him. Startled into action, he quickly turned to his right and beat a hasty retreat towards his accommodation block. Although it was January, he was sweating by the time he reached his room. He hastily opened his locker and took out a pair of green army socks. Discarding his shoes, he swapped the white tennis socks for the green ones, quickly tying the laces of his shoes. He shot off, back across the square, to RHQ. Bursting through the double doors, he came to an abrupt halt, next to Pete. The RSM was not in sight and Richard whispered to Pete.

'Not a good first impression.' Pete nodded his acknowledgement, grinning. The RSM, having heard Richard's return, came out of his office. With a stern look on his face, Botelli asked him to raise his barrack dress trousers. Satisfied that he was now correctly dressed, he brought the pair of them up to attention and marched them into the CO's office.

The Commanding Officer looked up from the paper work on his desk and waited until the RSM had halted both Pete and Richard, three paces in front of his desk. The CO was wearing a heavy duty green army pullover, with his rank on his shoulders, a five pointed star of the garter with a crown above it. He greeted both of them warmly and asked how they thought their training at JLR had gone. The pair gave their honest opinions of both the good and the not so good parts of their training. The Colonel waited until they had finished and informed them, that, being ex Junior Leaders, they stood a good chance of promotion within three years or so. The two looked at each other, genuinely surprised at the CO's remark. Nonetheless, they were pleased that the rigours of the past twelve months could pay dividends in their chosen careers. For Richard, it would take a little longer than the three years the CO intimated.

The interview complete, the RSM turned them about and marched them from the office. After halting them, he gave them a few words of advice, before dismissing them. They could hear the unfortunate soul they had seen earlier, who had been dressed in No2 dress, being marched at lightning speed into the CO's office. They were later to find out that he had been on orders for being absent without leave (AWOL). He had been handed 28 days in the Regimental jail. As they left the building, they burst into fits of laughter, regarding Richard's earlier run in with the RSM.

'I'm just popping over to A Squadron to see me dad,' Richard informed Pete. The pair walked together across the square, as this was Pete's new Squadron. Pete carried on to his room, while Richard headed toward his father's office. Tommy Hunter was the Squadron Quartermaster Sergeant of A Sqn and was responsible for the administration of the accommodation, clothing and feeding of the soldiers. Richard would not be paid until the end of the month and had spent his final pay from JLR over Christmas. With nothing left to live on, he thought he would ask his father for a loan, until he was paid.

He walked into his father's office, this time not only as his son, but as a member of the Regiment. His dad's head was bowed, engrossed in paperwork. Looking up, he smiled at Richard.

'Morning, dad, I was after a favour. You couldn't lend me some money until pay day, could you?' Before his father could reply, the door slammed shut behind him. Looking over his shoulder, Richard saw Ian McKelvie, A Squadron Sergeant Major (SSM), standing there. McKelvie had heard the sound of conversation prior to his entry into the room.

'Dad! What the fuck, its SQMS, you fuckwit! You're not at home now, you piece of shit! Get the fuck out of my block!' For the second time in the space of half an hour, Richard had received a bollocking. As he beat a hasty retreat, he heard the sound of laughter behind him, getting fainter as he ran down the corridor. Arriving back at D Squadron, Richard opened the door to his room and flopped on his bed. Staring up at the ceiling, he thought to himself that the morning had not been a good one. Hopefully, it could only get better, from here on in.

Chapter 17 – The Tank Park

The rest of the day, after meeting with his Troop Sergeant Major (TSM), Jed Monkhouse, was spent doing personal admin and relaxing. Richard had been told that he was expected on the tank park at 08:30 the next day. As he had washed and prepared most of his uniform during his leave, he spent the afternoon lying on his bed. He had called his dad's office earlier and asked again if he could borrow some cash until he next got paid. His father had thought it rather amusing, that Richard had been torn off a strip by the SSM, but told him that it was only in jest and was to give him a wakeup call. Richard understood this, but it had still been an embarrassing situation. It explained the sound of laughter he had heard while getting the fuck out of there. His dad agreed to the loan but advised him to spend it wisely and 'not to piss it up against the wall.' He would drop it off later in the afternoon, or if Richard had time to pop round now, he would give it to him right away. Deciding that he did not want his new Troop members seeing his father handing over cash to him, he set off to A Sqn block. Luckily, no one was about, so after taking the money from his father, they chatted for a while. His dad wanted to know how Richard's first night had been and how his interview with the CO had gone. Richard spoke frankly, but did not have a great deal to offer, except that he had received a roasting from the RSM. Tommy just laughed and told his son there would be many more of those to come. Hearing voices approaching, he bade his father farewell and headed back to his own Squadron.

The rest of the day was uneventful, after Tom and Bubba returned from work, they quickly showered and the three went for tea. Heads looked up as they entered, and Richard, feeling the centre of attention, surmised the other members of the Regiment, not recognising his face, began chatting about him. He wondered if the rumour had gone round that Tommy Hunter's son had joined D Squadron. After an uneasy evening meal, they dropped off their plates in a serving hatch, which were collected by a soldier dressed in coveralls, but without a belt and beret. Richard had no idea why someone from the Regiment was collecting plates. He asked the question to Tom, who replied, simply.

'Cookhouse duties, mate, otherwise known as "pan bash". Don't worry, you'll get one in before long.' Grinning, they continued across the grass, back to the block.

The evening was spent sipping beer from a carry out Bubba had provided and playing cards in the room. Richard explained that he was short on cash, but promised to get a crate the following evening. He saw a pattern forming, mostly revolving around alcohol. From the size of Bubba, Richard hazarded a wild guess that the big man did not visit the gym in his spare time. The evening passed quickly and they retired around 23:00, which, Richard was told, was an early night for them.

The sound of Tom moving around the room woke Richard and he sat up in bed. He felt a hundred times better than he had the previous morning. After saying, 'good morning,' to Tom, he dragged himself out of bed and down the corridor to the washrooms. There was no bugle call sounding Reveille, this had been replaced by the NOS walking round, knocking on doors. Richard was learning quickly that this was nothing like training, the soldiers were now treated as adults. There was no one to hold your hand; if you were given a time to be somewhere you ensured that you were there five minutes beforehand. He returned to the room and removed a green T-shirt and a pair of coveralls from his locker. As he did so, he noticed that by habit, he had laid out his locker as he had been taught in training. Although the standard might fade slightly over the years, this would stay with him his whole career. He glanced at his watch and was reminded him that he needed to parade on the tank park in 45 minutes. The three roommates calculated they had enough time to get breakfast.

After returning, Richard gave a last application of polish to his boots, then put on his black gaters. These had replaced the puttees worn in training and had been given to him by his father. He looked across at both Bubba and Tom, who were wearing high length boots. He asked where they acquired these boots and was made to feel like a new boy when they informed him that they were issued on their last tour of Northern Ireland (NI). Richard wanted to ask what the tour had been like, but decided to keep it to himself; he was sure that he would hear this, and many other stories over the coming months and years.

Suitably dressed, they set off from the accommodation, towards the tank park. Richard knew where it was located, as a youngster, he had accompanied his dad on many occasions, to look around the tanks. He, of course, kept this to himself and happily tagged on to the other two, letting them lead the way.

After a ten minute walk, they arrived at the hangars, where other members of the Squadron where hanging about, smoking and chatting. TSM Monkhouse was already there, organising the opening of the hanger doors for 2nd Troop. Acknowledging Richard's arrival, he made his way over to him, shaking him by the hand.

'Good morning, young man, welcome to 2nd Troop,' he said, warmly. 'Once all the lads are here, I will introduce you.'

Richard took the offered hand, it seemed that his new TSM was genuinely pleased Richard was joining them. As the hangar door opened, he saw three tanks, lined up in their own bays with their guns rear. He was later told the vehicles were always reversed in like this, so that the engine oil levels could be checked, prior to any work commenced on them for the day. This was known as a 'first parade', as it was the first assembly of the Squadron for the day. On a Monday morning, the whole Squadron paraded in their separate Troops. The SSM would bring the Squadron up to attention and they would move into open order. He would then hand over to the Sqn Second in Command (2ic). This done, the Sqn 2ic would fall in the Officers, who took their positions in front of their respective Troops. Richard's Troop was the only one without an officer. The others all had Lieutenants (Lt) or Second Lieutenants. These were a different breed altogether from the normal enlisted men. Many of them in the Cavalry were from well-off families or even nobility. When they first arrived from Sandhurst Military Academy, they were like young boys, yet expected to lead a Troop of twelve men. This was never allowed to happen, as, for their first year or training season, the Troop Sergeants took command, guiding them through the various aspects of running a Troop.

By the time the TSM had explained all this, the rest of the Troop had arrived. Richard could feel butterflies in his stomach, as he knew that he would soon be put in the spotlight. All eyes were on him and the TSM, as they strode over to the front of the Chieftain tanks, where everyone had gathered.

'Morning, guys. I want you to meet the newest member of the Troop, this is Trooper (Tpr) Richard Hunter. He has recently completed his training at the Junior Leaders Regiment.' This remark caused some of the Troop to shake their heads. What Richard had never been told was that some members of the Regiment, who had joined as adult soldiers, did their training in Catterick. This training lasted only three months, unlike the twelve months that Richard had had to endure. They did not take kindly to young soldiers, with perceived airs of grandeur. 'You may recognise his face, as his father is SQMS Tommy Hunter of A Sqn. That is not to mean that he will receive any special treatment.' He said it as a warning, but also of his own intention. Richard was later to find out that Monkhouse had served with his father in Aden, and he had a deep respect for him.

The introductions over, he was taken to meet his new crew. The Troop Corporal, Pete Robinson, was by the front of the tank, designated 42B. He looked immaculate in his extremely starched coveralls with sewn-in creases. He sported a moustache, highly waxed to two points, in line with the corner of his lips He was the archetypical Gunnery Instructor and looked as if he was at the Gunnery school in Lulworth, ready to begin a lesson. He eyed Richard up and down, almost with a look of disdain. Richard's mind went back to the previous day and how he had got off to a bad start. 'Well,' he thought to himself, 'it doesn't look as if things are going to get much better.'

Leaving Richard in the capable hands of 'Robbo', the TSM marched off towards his own vehicle. Richard was then briefly introduced to his new crew by his Troop Cpl. Their driver was called Ian and came from a rough area of Leeds. He seemed friendly enough and welcomed Richard with a shake of the hand. Their Loader, who operated the radio equipment and loaded the gun, was Tommo. He, too, was from Leeds, as were around half of the Troop. He was a quiet, unassuming character, powerfully built and Richard thought that he would be handy, in a bar brawl. After meeting the crew, Robbo showed him round the vehicle. He highlighted the tasks that Richard would be expected to do on a daily basis. They all seemed straightforward and Richard couldn't wait to get stuck in. However, the first task that he was assigned was not at all he expected.

'The first thing I want you to do is come with me,' Robbo started to mount the vehicle, by placing his foot on one of the towing bollards, at the front of the vehicle. Pulling himself up by the headlight guards, he climbed on to the vehicle's glacis plate. This was the sloped armour surrounding the driver's cab. The word takes its name, in military engineering, from an artificial slope as part of a medieval castle or in early modern fortresses. Reaching the top of the turret, he waited for Richard to join him. Once Richard reached Robbo, he noticed various implements, laid out at his feet. They consisted of a container with some liquid in it, a hard brush, soft brush and amounts of cloth. Looking at Robbo, he awaited his instructions. Opening up the double split hatch, where the loader was situated, he beckoned Richard forward. Squatting down, he waited for Richard to do likewise.

'If you look inside, young man, you will see that the turret floor is in need of a good clean. We have an inspection in a week's time and I expect it to be immaculate by then. You will need to take up the turret floor and get rid of any mud that has accumulated from our last exercise.' As Richard peered inside, he saw the enormity of the task and knew that this was going to be some job. 'Also, you will need to remove any ammunition racks, so that you can clean underneath them. You will use this brush, initially,' he said, picking up the wooden brush with stiff bristles, 'to get rid of the big bits. Once you have done this, you can use the softer brush to remove the dried up pieces. When you have reached this stage, you will need to use the final steel wire brush and this receptacle, which contains white spirit, to really get in there. After you have completed that, you can use the remaining white spirit and rag to wipe it down. Only when I am satisfied, will you be allowed to paint it, using the silver paint at the back of the hangar. Have you got any questions?' he asked in a way that Richard knew didn't require an answer.

'No, Corporal,' was his submissive reply.

As he climbed inside, Robbo handed Richard down all the equipment he would need. Taking them from him, he bent down to place them on the turret floor. As he did so, he heard the clanking of metal on metal, as the split hatch closed, and he was in darkness.

'I don't want to see you till lunchtime!' Robbo shouted, jumping down from the vehicle.

Realizing he would require light in which to work, Richard fumbled in the darkness for the switch for the interior lights in the turret. He had spent many hours in the gunnery simulator in Bovington, so in no time his fingers found what he was feeling for. Flicking on the switch, he observed three shiny metal objects on one of the ammunition racks. 'These must be the tools I need to remove the turret floor and ammunition racks,' he thought to himself. So, as instructed, he began the slow job of removing the turret floor plate and ammunition racks. Although this was not a hard job, it was time consuming. He placed the retaining nuts and bolts in a handy receptacle, so that he would have them to hand, when he needed to reassemble.

Taking the stiff bristled brush, known as a 'track brush', he began the arduous task of removing the caked-on mud. Following the process he had been given, he worked away, oblivious to the time. It was not until sometime later, Richard started to feel light headed. The lack of air and fumes from the white spirit were starting to take their toll. He began to feel physically sick and struggled to fight back the nausea. He did not want to appear weak on his first day so refrained from calling out. He needed a breath of fresh air. Despite turning the handles of the hatch and pushing up, it did not give way. 'It must be stuck,' he thought to himself. So, using all his strength, he tried to force it open, but to no avail. It was then he realised, the other sound he had heard must have been a padlock being inserted through the loop on the split hatch. Robbo obviously had no intention of Richard leaving till he was good and ready.

Trying not to panic, he took large gulps of air to try and compensate for the nausea. Settling down, he continued with the job at hand. Before he knew it, he heard the sound of boots on the turret and the jangling of keys. Looking up, he saw the hatches being lifted, and he had to squint in the glare of the hangar lights. Looking down at him was the grinning moustached face of his Troop Cpl., who was certainly enjoying having a new member on his crew. He poked his head inside and looked around at Richard's work.

'Not bad at all, marra, you've made a good start. Get yourself up here,' he extended his right hand to assist Richard from the turret. Taking it thankfully, Richard clambered out and immediately felt the clean air fill his lungs. He swayed unsteadily on his feet, but Robbo seemed to ignore this.

'We are down the Light Aid Detachment (LAD) this afternoon to have a new radiator fitted. Get yourself away for some scoff and be back here for 13:15.'

Glancing at his watch, he noticed that it was already 12:15. He had been locked up inside the turret for over three hours. He made his way, precariously, down from the turret, via the glacis plate. Bubba and Tom were there waiting, with sympathetic looks on their faces. Off they went, together, on their way to the cookhouse.

Chapter 18 – Practical Jokes

Feeling slightly better after forcing some food down, Richard made his way back towards the tank park. He arrived just as Ian was climbing into his driver's cab. Robbo stood in front of the vehicle and turned, as Richard approached.

'Jump up, get the gun kit on and put it on stab,' he directed the order at Richard.

'No problem,' he replied and began to mount the tank from the front. As he clambered up the slope of the turret, he was relived the lessons he had been taught on the Gunnery phase at JLR. He climbed into the gunner's seat and started the gun equipment, in sequence. He gave a sigh of relief as the metadynes sprang into life, confirming the equipment had started. As a last check, he attempted to move the turret, using the duplex controller on his right. He depressed the grip switch and heard the clutch bite, moving it to the left. But nothing happened. He was perplexed as to what could have gone wrong. Had he missed something? Richard climbed back up to the turret by way of the commander's seat and shouted down to Robbo.

'The turret won't traverse, Corporal' he shouted, embarrassed.

'Try taking out the crutch, you clown!' was Robbo's very quick comeback. Glancing over his left shoulder, he saw that the gun barrel was, indeed, still secured in the crutch. Feeling slightly stupid, he made his way over the back decks and began to detach the crutch. This completed, he jumped back into the gunner's seat and confirmed that the gun equipment would traverse freely. Satisfied everything was in order, he once again popped his head out of the turret and gave the thumbs up to his Troop Corporal.

'Get your arse down here, you numpty! You need to learn how we move tanks out of the hangar'.

Not wanting to say that he had already learnt this in training, Richard joined Robbo and Tommo, who were positioned to the left and right of the front of the vehicle. Robbo quickly explained to him that you should never stand directly in front, when guiding a tank, or any other vehicle, for that matter. This sparked the memory of a tale from his father of an accident on the tank park. There were occasions when a tank would not start, due to battery or electrical problems. It was then necessary to attach a second tank, using a cable called a 'slave lead'. On this particular day, Tommy's driver had been guiding another tank towards his own, to perform this action. He had been at the front and as the large vehicles closed on each other, the nervous driver of the other tank hit the accelerator, instead of the brake. The tank lurched forward and sandwiched his dad's driver between the two glacis plates. It literally cut him in two, but it took several minutes before he died. This story had always stuck with Richard, and he knew the advice he was being given was sound.

With the aid of Tommo, Robbo expertly manoeuvred the vehicle out of the hangar. Once it was clear, he led it off the tank park, towards the LAD, walking about ten paces in front. The distance to the LAD from D Squadron hangars was approximately 500 metres, it took around ten minutes to make the journey. On their arrival, Robbo halted the vehicle by giving the necessary signal with his hand. He entered the hangar and after a few short moments, one of the giant hangar doors began to open. After it had reached its full height, Robbo returned outside. Getting the attention of the driver, he pulled him forward, and as he drew level with the opening, he raised his right hand. This conveyed to the driver that he needed to pull his left tiller or stick. This caused the left track to slow, while the right gathered speed, causing it to turn in the required direction. Once the rear of the Chieftain was roughly in line with the hangar bay, Robbo began to guide the driver back. When he wanted the right rear of the vehicle to move he put up his right hand, briefly. This indicated to the driver that he was to pull his left stick, the opposite when moving forwards. With minimum effort, the tank was parked exactly in the position it needed to be. Before getting Ian to turn off the Generating Engine Unit (GUE), he asked Richard to power down the gun kit. The GUE was required for the powered gun equipment to work. As soon as Ian heard the metadynes power off, he almost instinctively began to throttle back the GUE and close down. The hangar seemed unearthly quiet, except for the banging of metal on metal. There were four tanks in separate bays, each with its back deck open. A pair of legs could be seen protruding into the air from the engine compartment of the vehicle next to theirs. Ian climbed from his cab and went directly on to the back decks. With very little effort, he lifted up the armoured decking covering the radiator which required to be changed. Robbo and Tommo were busy talking to two blokes, who Richard assumed to be mechanics. Not knowing what to do with himself, Richard made his way on to the back decks, to see if Ian needed any help. He was simply answered with a shake of the head, but Ian asked him instead if he would top up the road wheel hubs, as they had been slightly low, that morning. Happy to help, Richard jumped down and made his way to the driver's bin, which contained the tools he would need; a 'combination tool' and a bar.

Methodically, Richard started from the front on the left hand side and loosened each filler cap as he went. Checking each one, he closed those that were at the correct oil level. Returning to the driver's bin, he removed a small silver can, which had rag inside it. Removing the rag, he filled it with OEP 220 oil and topped up the hubs which were low. Securing the filler caps, he put away the silver can into the driver's bin. The whole process only took him about fifteen minutes, so he climbed back up on to the back decks, where Ian was busy removing some bolts from the radiator. 'Anything else I can do to help?' he asked, helpfully.

Ian thought for a moment, before replying.

'Robbo mentioned the other day that the Tank Laser Sight (TLS) was running low on reticule ellipses. You couldn't pop into Tech Stores over there and get a bag, could you? Also, if you ask for a long stand, we need one for this radiator.'

Richard thought for a moment before answering. His dad had told him of the jokes played on new members of the Regiment and the comment about a 'Long Stand' rang a bell.

'Nice try, Ian, I'm not that stupid,' he grinned.

The smile spread across Ian's face, confirming that his ruse had not worked. He wiped the oil from his hands and stood up.

'You're not thick, are ya?' he chuckled. 'Come with me, there is a job that you can do for me. It's a bit time consuming, but it's a favourite that gets picked up by the REME on our annual inspections.' He jumped down on to the hangar floor from the back decks, beckoning Richard to follow him. Walking to the driver's bin, he removed a red can with a long nozzle.

'This is a "Wesco",' Ian explained. 'We use it for applying small amounts of oil to parts. Look here on the end of this track pin,' he crouched down, pointing to a silver circle around the end of the pin. 'Notice the circlip, as it is called, has a gap at the end. You need to drop a touch of oil in between the gap. There is another one on the inside, if you could do that for me, that would be great.'

Richard nodded his agreement and took the oil can from Ian, who turned and made his way back to the rear of the vehicle. Starting at one end, Richard placed a piece of rag to mark his starting point. He made his way diligently from the front, applying a touch of oil in the gaps on each circlip. The process took around 30 minutes to finish one side. The left hand side complete, he moved around the vehicle, to make a start on the right. As he did so, all he could hear was Tommo, Ian and Robbo laughing and joking, at the rear of the vehicle. 'All right for some,' he thought to himself, as he began to repeat the process on each of the 96 remaining circlips. He was about halfway through the final track, when he was startled by Dave Walker, their Troop Sergeant.

'What you doing there, Hunter? He asked, puzzled.

'Oiling the circlips, Sarge,' Richard replied, proudly.

'Who told you to do that?' Cousins asked, grinning.

'Ian,' answered Richard, wondering what the problem was. It soon became apparent with the sound of unbridled laughter from behind the tank.

'Ian, get your arse round here!' Cousins shouted, in the direction of the laughter.

Ian's grinning face appeared from the rear of the vehicle. Trying hard not to show his satisfaction, he approached the Troop Sergeant.

'What's wrong, Dave?' he asked, innocently.

'You know what's wrong, you little twat,' he said, jokingly.

'I didn't think he would go for it,' was Ian's only line of defence. Richard now realised that he had been stitched up and hung his head in embarrassment. Dave assured him that he was not the first, or would be the last, who had been caught out with this type of practical joke. It was a Regimental tradition for the more experienced members of the Troop to try to catch out new members with this sort of stunt. This did not make Richard feel any better, he thought he would not have been caught out so quickly. It was only his first week, and already he was a laughing stock. They were then joined by Robbo and Tommo, who were still in fits of laughter. Tommo simply tapped Richard on the shoulder, sympathetically. They then went on to list the other type of practical jokes that they and others had played on new boys. These newcomers were given the unenviable title of 'NIGs', which stood for 'New in Germany'. This title hung on them for varying lengths of time, until they lost their rawness. There was a steady supply of less experienced men joining the Regiment, who would then be given the epithet.

The types of jokes played on the guys included sending someone to go to the stores for some tartan paint. Richard thought that you have to be really stupid to fall for that one. Another was to be sent to the LAD for the 120 mm silencer for night firing. Some were also convinced that if they traversed or turned the turret too many times, it unscrewed and would fall off. The list went on, some pranks more credible than others. Richard wondered why some people fell for the obvious ones.

After all the laughter and storytelling had died down, Robbo told them they could start to clear up for the day. The work on the radiator was not yet complete, so they were to meet back here, first thing in morning. After they had all cleaned the oil from their hands using Swarfega oil and grease remover, they began to make their way from the hangar.

'Don't forget to read orders,' were Robbo's parting words.

The crew left the hangar, chatting and laughing about the joke played on Richard, as they made the fifteen minute walk toward the Squadron Office block. It was mandatory for every soldier to read Regimental and Squadron orders, every evening. These were usually posted just outside the Squadron Sergeant Major's Office (SSM). Richard, later in his career, found out it was never a good move to read them prior to 18:00. The reason for this was that if they required a 'fast ball' for someone for guard duty, you were likely to be 'volunteered' by the SSM. On this particular evening, it made no difference to Richard, as he scanned the duties forecast, he saw his name jump out at him. He was to start his first guard duty in two days' time. He had done many of these over the last twelve months in training, so it didn't really bother him.

'They didn't waste any time with you,' came Tom's voice, over his shoulder.

'At least it's a Thursday and not the weekend,' Richard replied, shrugging his shoulders.

'That's true, mate, I will show you what kit you need for it, if you like?'

Richard thanked him and the pair left the Squadron Office block, to return to their accommodation, then shower and go for their evening meal.

Chapter 19 – Guard Duty

The next two evenings, Richard spent his time pressing his combats, which were to be worn on guard duty. Tom had told him that on every guard mount, the smartest turned out bloke was awarded Commanding Officer's Stick Orderly. This was generally referred to as 'Stick Man'. This individual was excused guard duty for that day, although he was not allowed to leave camp or drink, in case he was called to return, if someone were to go sick or if the security state were raised. This was reason enough for Richard to ensure he was turned out as best he could be. A lot of the guys had an extra pair of boots, kept to one side, which were highly bulled. They would wear this pair for the guard parade; if they were not chosen, they would change back to a normal pair. Some also had a best pair of combat dress, ironed with knife edge creases and rigidly starched. As he was new to this, Richard had to start from scratch, so did not hold out much hope that he would be awarded Stick Man status.

Another thing that differed from training was that the guards were required to wear their '58 pattern webbing'. This consisted of their basic fighting order of a harness, two ammunition pouches, water bottle holder and kidney pouches. Tom had shown Richard how to put it all together. It was also to be clean and well presented; some of the men put them in the shower and scrubbed them with a bass broom and nail brush. As Richard had just had his equipment newly issued, it was in almost pristine condition, which saved him at least one task.

The next couple of days flew by on the tank park and consisted of running through the Gunnery maintenance and general cleaning of the turret. It had taken only three days for Richard to bring the inside of the fighting compartment to the standard Robbo was satisfied with. This pleased Richard and he started to feel part of the crew. No more practical jokes had been played on him since the incident with the track pins. He was, however, still wary that he should not be complacent. At the end of the Thursday, he made his way from the tank park to prepare himself for guard duty. Before getting changed, he had a quick wash and grabbed himself a little bite to eat. Looking at his watch, he realised he only had 50 minutes until the guard was due to be mounted. Collecting his wash bag, he ran down the corridor and showered, hastily. Within ten minutes he was showered, shaved and returning to his room. By this time, Bubba and Tom had finished their evening meal and were lying on their beds. They watched with interest, as Richard busied himself getting ready. Once he had put on his shirt, he donned his trousers and adjusted the braces, so that the crease stood out, proudly. He then laced up his boots and put on his 58 pattern webbing, adjusting the straps to fit, as he did. Once he had given his beret one last brush, he placed it on his head, checking himself in the mirror in his wardrobe.

'Very smart, Hunter,' came the sarcastic remark from Tom, 'the perfect stick man, if ever I saw one.'

Richard was not sure if Tom was joking or being serious, he bade them farewell and left the room. As he made his way along the corridor, he bumped into the lad with the Fred Perry T-shirt and stay press pants he had met in the Squadron bar, a few days earlier. He was also dressed in combats and webbing and was checking himself in the full length mirror, situated opposite the main doors. Glancing down, Richard noticed that his comrade's boots were like glass, and immediately gave up any hope of attaining the title of Stick Man. Turning from the mirror, he acknowledged Richard, with a nod of his head.

'First one, eh, mate?' he greeted Richard, cheerfully. 'Looks like it's going to be a cold one, too,' he continued, with great delight, 'you'll get used to them after a while. We normally pick up at least one, sometimes two, a month. That is, if you don't drop yourself in the shit. I'm Noddy, by the way, we can pair up together tonight, if you want'

'That would be great,' Richard replied, thankfully.

They opened the door from the block and negotiated the path around the playing fields, being careful not to step in any puddles or mud, on route to the guardroom. Arriving with twenty minutes to spare before the guard mount, there were already a number of people milling about. The guard consisted of a guard commander, who was usually a Sergeant, with a Corporal or Lance Corporal as his second in command (2ic). The majority of the guard was made up of nine Troopers, two supplied from each of the 'Sabre Squadrons'. These were the tank Squadrons A, B, C and D, with the final two being provided by Headquarter Squadron (HQ). That gave a total of ten men, one of whom would be dismissed, after receiving the position of Stick Man. There would be one person allocated to the main barrier on the gate, while two people would be assigned to carry out roving foot patrols, throughout camp. Each period of either gate duty or patrolling was known as being 'on stag', and lasted for two hours. This expression struck dread into every serving soldier, in the early hours of the morning, when he was woken, to take his turn. Everyone was checking their dress, to make sure all their buttons were done up and their webbing was sitting correctly. One, however, stood out. He looked like he had just climbed out of a skip. His face seemed familiar to Richard, who wondered where he had seen him before. Curiosity getting the better of him, he pulled Noddy to one side.

'Who is that guy there?' he queried, with a nod of his head, not wanting to make it obvious.

'That's Archie, mate. He's a Regimental character, with the emphasis on the mental. He likes a beer or ten and can usually be found in the NAAFI bar or in the Wee House.'

Richard knew the Wee House, as it was a local German pub, not far from where his parents lived. He had visited it on many occasions with dad and his brother. On a number of these visits, Richard had noticed a small bloke in the corner, in the company of a much larger guy. He always seemed well refreshed, no matter what time of day Richard had gone in. He remembered thinking to himself, 'Does this bloke live here?' Now, twelve months later, he was about to go on guard with him. With only ten minutes left until the Orderly Officer was due to turn up, the Guard Commander fell them in outside. He quickly checked everyone's dress, but when he came to Archie, who was next to Richard, he just shook his head.

'Archie, I just give up on you,' he sighed, resignedly. The small guy just chuckled to himself, his shoulders shaking.

'Has everyone got their yellow cards?' the Guard Commander shouted out, looking around at everyone, who nodded in agreement. Richard did not know what he was talking about, so thought he had better say something. Putting up his hand, nervously, he murmured.

'I haven't, Sergeant.'

'Why not, you fucking scroat?' he spat back.

'I only joined the Regiment this week, I didn't know we needed one,' he replied, still not knowing what on earth a yellow card was.

'I'll let you off, bonny lad, seeing as it's your first time,' he said, reaching into his pocket and handing over a piece of yellow card, explaining that it was what every soldier carried when on duty with a loaded weapon. The Army has a series of rules known as the Yellow Card, which guides as to when a soldier can open fire, lawfully. Generally, lethal force was only lawful when the lives of members of the security forces, or others, were in immediate danger. He advised Richard to read the card carefully, before his first patrol, or turn on the gate. Before he could explain more, the sound of metal on concrete could be heard, away to Richard's right. Out of the darkness strode the figure of the Orderly Officer. He was dressed in 'blues', the No1 dress for officers. On his shoulders was chain mail and his blue Service cap had gold braid on the peak. A sash hung from his left shoulder, across his body, with a small bag on his back. On his feet, he was wearing cavalry boots, adorned with spurs. At his side, he was holding a cavalry sabre, in line with the yellow stripe down his blues' trousers. When he was about five paces from the Guard

Commander, this impressive figure halted. The Guard Commander took a smart pace forward with his left foot, slamming his right into the ground.

'The guard is fell in and awaiting your inspection, Sir!' he announced, saluting.

The salute was returned by the Officer, who looked no more than twenty, with not a blemish on his face. Richard wondered if he had even started to shave yet. Starting on the front rank right hand man, he began his inspection. As the Officer came to each soldier in turn, he looked them up and down and moved to the next. As he did, he pointed out to the Guard Commander anything amiss, such as fluff on berets or not enough polish on boots. Richard took a deep breath as the Officer stood in front of him. He nodded his head and congratulated Richard on a good turnout. Richard felt a pang of pride as the Officer stepped to the left, to inspect Archie. He took one look at him and simply shook his head. He had obviously met him before and was not surprised by his dishevelled appearance. He opened one of his ammunition pouches and placed his hand inside. Lifting up his hand, he produced a small bottle of beer. He turned to the Guard Commander, with a wry smile.

'What's this, Trooper Archibald?' he addressed the somewhat bemused Trooper.

'What's it look like, ya fucking NIG?' was Scott's shocking reply.

Not knowing how to respond to the remark, the young Officer simply turned to the Guard Commander and asked him to note the incident down in his occurrence book and to report it to the RSM the next day. This was clearly not something new for Archie, who was well known for being a loveable rogue. He had been in the Regiment for seventeen years and had attained the dizzy heights of Trooper. This was generally down to the fact that he enjoyed drink too much. As the Orderly Officer finished his inspection, he whispered to the Guard Commander. They saluted each other, the Guard Commander did a smart about turn and faced the mounted guard. At the top of his voice, he announced:

'Commanding Officer's Stick Orderly, goes to Trooper Bennett. You may fall out now.'

Richard glanced in the direction of Noddy, who gave a faint smile and fell out of the ranks. Waiting until he had marched into the guard room, the Guard Commander then ordered the Troops to fall out to their duties. Doing so, he reminded them that there was an officer on parade. As they turned to their right, they saluted and paused for two seconds, before marching off for three paces. Once inside the guard room, they were each issued with ten rounds of ammunition. The 2ic of the guard had already drawn up the 'stag list' for the evening. They all gathered round eagerly, to see what they had been allotted and what times they would be on. Richard was paired with someone called Holmfirth, on a roving patrol at 22:00 - 23:59 hours, then again from 04:00 – 06:00. Suddenly, a booming voice called out:

'Who the fuck is Hunter?'

Richard looked across the room, to where a giant of a man was bawling at the 2ic of the guard. The hapless young Lance Corporal pointed over in Richard's direction. Explaining that as he was new, the Guard Commander had asked for an experienced man to be paired with him. The massive man mountain, was known in the Regiment as 'Big H', for obvious reasons. He looked at Richard in disdain and loathing, before storming out of the front office. Had he made another enemy, Richard wondered to himself. He waited a few moments, before he also departed from the room and went to the back of the guard room, where the beds were situated. Seeking out the big man, Richard approached and introduced himself. The ogre just gave a grunt, not taking the hand Richard had offered. It suddenly dawned on Richard, that this giant was the man he had seen in the Wee House with Archie, on more than one occasion. They were obviously drinking buddies and good mates, which was probably why he had taken offence to being paired with a NIG. Finding himself a bed, Richard lay down but was disturbed almost immediately. The Guard Commander had entered the room and asked for everyone's attention. He went through the Security state they were on at that particular time. Also, he warned them not to go wandering into the cell areas which housed the prisoners. He informed them that the entrance to the cells should be locked at all times. There were two prisoners housed at that particular time, awaiting sentencing, which would probably end with them going to the Military Corrective Training Centre (MCTC), in Colchester. They had deserted six months earlier and joined the Foreign Legion but had been kicked out, after being involved in an incident. The previous week, whilst incarcerated, they had managed to walk out of the guard room and had gone into town for a few beers. To that end, each subsequent Guard

Commander had been given explicit instructions from the RSM, to keep a close eye on them. They were to be checked every 30 minutes, to ensure they had not absconded, and the cell area was to remain locked at all times. Finally, he read out the orders for both barrier sentries and roving patrols. After asking if there were any questions, and receiving none, he left the room. Some of the guys immediately entered a room that was attached to the sleeping area. Here, an urn of tea and brew making facilities was set up. The guard were also provided with sandwiches, crisps and fruit, contained in white boxes. Richard recognised them immediately as 'scab packs' the same as he had received while in training. After making himself a brew, he settled down on his bed to read a magazine he had brought with him. He tried to make himself comfortable on the mattress which had a shiny, green cover on it. Its function was to keep the mattress as clean as possible. It was a pity the pillows did not have a similar cover, as they looked like they had been there for years on end. Tentatively laying his head back on them, he began to read. In no time at all, he was fast asleep.

Unsure of how long he had been asleep, Richard was disturbed by someone, shaking his shoulder.

'Come on, we're on stag,' came the attempted whisper from H.

Rubbing his eyes and trying to focus in the semi darkness, Richard swung his legs over the bed. He grabbed his beret and webbing from the end of the bed and followed H out of the room. As he entered the main guard room, he had to blink to adjust his eyes to the bright lights. The only occupant was the Guard Commander, sitting at a desk, writing in a large, open book in front of him. As he noticed the pair come into the room, he stood up, beckoning them over to a map on the wall. There were various coloured lines on the map, with a number beside them. These were the patrol routes, within the barracks area. He informed them, for their first patrol, they were to take route 1. This included the QM's Block, RHQ, A Sqn, B Sqn Armouries and the LAD. They were, at no point, to enter any accommodation. Their briefing complete, he took them outside to a sand pit, surrounded by sandbags, at waist height.

With the command:

'For inspection, port arms,' he waited for them to cock their weapons, before looking inside, confirming they were clear. He then instructed them to, 'Ease Springs', allowing them to let the working parts go forward under control. Finally, he ordered them, 'With a magazine of ten rounds......load!' Watching that they ensured the magazines were correctly seated in their housing and the safety catches were applied. He then turned from them and re-entered the guard room.

Satisfied that the Guard Commander was out of sight, H began to set off, across the square. Richard was puzzled at this, as the route they had been told, just a moment ago, was in the opposite direction. Not wanting to say anything, he set off after H. Reaching the other side of the square, the big man looked around to see if there was anyone about. Happy that they were not being observed, he entered the double doors of A Squadron accommodation, directly in front of them. Feeling pressured, and knowing that this was not allowed, Richard followed on, regardless. They ascended the stairs to the first floor of the block, turning right, they walked along the corridor. Stopping at the second door on the right, H felt in his pocket and produced a key. Turning it in the lock, he motioned Richard in with a nod. The room was toasty warm, compared to the cold, winter wind outside. He walked straight towards a fridge at the far end of the room, in the corner. Opening the door, he pulled out two bottles of beer and turned to Richard.

'Fancy one of these?' he said, in a friendly manner.

Afraid to say no, Richard simply nodded his head, in agreement. H removed the bottle top with his teeth and gave the bottle to Richard, inviting him to take a seat. For the next 30 minutes, they chatted about how Richard was finding life in the Regiment. Richard gave his honest opinion, he was enjoying it so far, even the practical jokes played on him. The big man thought it highly amusing when he heard Richard had fallen for the circlip ruse. Placing the empty bottles in the bin, he put on his beret and motioned to Richard to do the same.

'We had better show willing, I suppose,' he said and they left the accommodation.

For the next hour and twenty minutes they toured the given route, checking security of doors and hangars. They popped into cellars, for shelter from the elements and had a sneaky cigarette break. Richard was aware that it was against their orders, but found it difficult not to join his patrol buddy, when asked. Although he seemed a scary individual, H was really quite pleasant when you got to know him. Looking at his watch, H decided it was time to make a slow trip back, towards the guard room. The cold was now seeping through into Richard's bones and he was looking forward to a nice, hot brew. Before entering the guard room, H tapped on the window, to alert the Guard Commander that they had returned. Hearing this, he immediately came outside and unloaded them in the bay. Making sure that their weapons were clear, he tapped them on the shoulder and told them to get their heads down.

The next three sentries had already been woken and had begun their two hour stint. Richard and H made straight for the sleeping area. The warmth was gratefully received and Richard decided against making a cup of tea. He crashed down on the slippery, green mattress and buried his head in the dirty pillows. It was 00:10 and sleep was not long coming. In just under four hours, he would be woken and they would do it all over again.

By the time first light was breaking, the sentries had completed their four hours each. The Regimental Police (RPs) had turned up and were preparing to take over from the Guard Commander and 2ic. All ammunition had been handed back in and counted. The sleeping accommodation and brew area had been swept and cleaned. All occurrences that had happened through the night were highlighted. Once they were happy, the RP's dismissed the guard. They returned to their own Squadron lines to shower, breakfast and put in another eight hours on the tank park. 'No rest for the wicked,' thought Richard, wearily, to himself.

Chapter 20 – Wine, Women and Song

Richard had showered, shaved and had enjoyed a full breakfast, before returning to his room. Both Tom and Bubba greeted him, as he entered.

'Good guard duty, mate?' Tom said, laughing.

'It was okay,' Richard answered and told them of the couple of beers he had enjoyed in Holmfirth's room. This did not come as a shock to his roommates, as they told him that was normal for H. Giving his beret a brush over, Richard readied himself for the day ahead. 'Where in Civvie Street,' he thought, 'would you do a twelve hour night shift and then go straight to work?' Once all three of them were ready, they made their way down to the tank park.

The day was spent getting the vehicles prepared for an exercise on the Lüneburg Heide (Heath). This area was referred to as 'Soltau', and they would spend two weeks there, at the end of the month. After the Second World War, Canadian forces and units of the British Army of the Rhine had conducted military exercises on the Lüneburg Heath from 1945, as part of their occupation rights. There was, initially, no defined training area. The site of the former German military airfield became Reinsehlen Camp and was used continuously by British armoured units, from 1950.

Each tank had made modifications, according to the preference of its crew. Extra bins had been bolted on, which could be used to carry personal equipment. Ian was busy attaching a green oil can, with the top cut out, to the back of the vehicle. Surrounding its edge was a layer of foam, covered in black tape. Richard had no idea what this was for, so he asked Ian. He gave a simple answer. It was a makeshift toilet. This was one of the many "comforts" that soldiers fashioned for themselves, to alleviate the need to squat while having a dump. It was a practice known throughout the Army as 'going on a shovel recce'. As the areas where they exercised were frequented by animals, including wild boars, it was the practice for soldiers to dig a small hole, defecate, clean themselves and drop the paper into the hole. On completion, they would fill in the hole, thus avoiding any unwanted interest from wild animals. It was also one of the unwritten rules that you were not to 'surface lay', as this was unsightly and unhygienic.

Richard spent most of the morning removing ammunition racks from inside the turret and placing them in the Troop cage, at the rear of the hangar. Space inside a tank, while on exercise in peace time, was at a premium. Once he had completed organising the turret, he joined his other three crew members. They dragged a large camouflage net from the Troop cage and laid it out to its full extent, outside the hangar. Taking two of the corners, they folded it in to the other side. After this, they repeated the process, from the other side. Then, all four of them lined up along one edge and began to roll it into a sausage shape. Once this was done, they carried it towards the front of the tank. Starting from the rear of the turret on one side, they draped it around to the other side. It was then secured to any position available, with elastic cords, called 'bungees'. The work continued all morning, until Robbo was satisfied with their efforts.

It was almost lunch time and Richard was starting to feel hungry. Some of the other Troop members had gathered in a huddle beside the TSM's tank, and were engrossed in conversation. Thinking he could be missing out on something, Richard made his way over to them. Before he could open his mouth, four of them grabbed him and another approached him, with a small green tin in his hand. Richard had absolutely no idea what was going on, as one of the Troop ripped open his coveralls.

'You look like you need a bit of lubrication down there,' one of Jed's crew sneered in his face.

Dipping his hand into the tin, he withdrew it. It was covered in a black substance, which looked like mascara. Richard knew from his Gunnery phase in training, that this was graphite grease or XG 264, a general purpose grease, used by the Army, for leaf springs and lift guides, lubrication and protection of wire ropes, lubrication of small arms and machine guns in hot, dusty condition and heavy rain. It was generally used on tanks, for covering the fume extractor, located half way down the barrel. With two assailants holding his arms still, the ferret faced Trooper known as 'Mex' pulled forward Richard's boxers, from the waistband. In one motion, he plunged his hand down and smeared the dark substance over Richard's privates. Ensuring that he was completely covered, Mex stood back. Next, two more members of the Troop took the handle of a bass broom and placed it through the sleeves of Richard's coveralls. With his arms stuck outstretched in a crucifix form, he resembled a scarecrow. Then, two of the gun barrels on either side of him began to move inward. Once they were in position, four of the Troop raised Richard and suspended him between the conveniently placed barrels. The pain across

Richard's shoulders was uncomfortable, but bearable. His heart sank, however, when Robbo turned round and said:

'Okay, Hunter, while you hang around here, we are going for a bit of scoff. We'll see you in about an hour.' With that, the Troop left the hangar, locking the door behind themselves.

Although the temperature outside was below freezing, sweat had already started to form on Richard's forehead. The muscles in his arms had begun to burn after only five minutes. He thought that he was lucky that he only weighed nine and a half stones. If he had been of a more considerable size, the torment would have been unbearable. Hopefully, the Troop had taken this into account; but he doubted that. As the time passed, Richard began to itch in the area of his groin, where the grease had been applied. This did help to take his mind off the burning sensation across his shoulders and upper back. After what he guessed was half an hour, he was starting to feel nauseous. Reaching the point when he thought he could endure no more, the chattering of voices outside caught his attention. The sound of the rattling of keys in the lock was a godsend. The door creaked open and the smiling faces of Bubba and Tom peered round it. Entering the hangar, they headed straight to Richard and helped him down from between the two barrels. They removed the broom shank from the arms of his coveralls. Richard immediately sank to the floor and stretched himself out, trying to regain the feeling in his muscles. Tom handed him a package, wrapped in white paper. Unwrapping it, Richard saw that it was a polystyrene box. Inside were some chips and liver, with gravy. He thankfully began to tuck in with the plastic cutlery Tom had brought.

As the rest of the Troop arrived back, one after another, they patted Richard on the back. They laughed and joked together, explaining that most of them had received this treatment when they first joined. It was all part of the learning curve, they assured him. Robbo simply smiled at him and, in his Cumbrian accent, asked that once he had finished his packed lunch, he should nip back and have a shower before returning for three o'clock. Richard rushed his lunch and set off back to the block.

When Richard returned, he saw that the Troop had gathered outside, round a 50 gallon oil drum. The top had been removed and into it they were placing bits of rag, soaked in oil. They put a match to it and it was engulfed in flames. Warming their hands on it, they invited Richard to join them. As he approached, he observed that there were two crates of beer, at the feet of the TSM. Taking the beer he was offered, Richard took his place by the fire. For the next two hours, they drank and told stories. Richard did not have much to input and kept to his father's advice of not speaking, unless he was spoken to. Among the topics of conversation was a trip planned for tomorrow, to Hamburg and the red light district, known as the Reeperbahn. Richard was asked if he wanted to join them. Although he only had 200 Deutsche Marks left until the end of the month, he agreed to accompany them. The beer all consumed, the Troop left the tank park, after locking up the hangars for the weekend. Richard felt happy and was looking forward to the trip ahead.

Richard woke the next morning around 10:00; as it was the weekend, breakfast took the form of a 'brunch'. It went on until 12:00 and both Tom and Richard filled themselves, to the brim. It was going to be a long day, starting off, Tom said, in the Squadron bar, straight after brunch. Bubba would not be joining them, as he was skint, as usual, Tom said. It was only 12:15 when they entered the bar and already it was half full. Kevin was again behind the bar, serving, and placed two beers on the bar, without being asked. He was a quiet guy, and mostly kept himself to himself. Richard had seen him every morning, going out for a run with a rucksack (Bergen) on his back. Straight after the evening meal, he would be seen again, either running in the direction of the gym or out of the camp gates. When Richard asked why he was doing it, Tom quietly said Kevin was preparing for 'selection'. Not knowing what this meant and not wanting to look stupid, Richard nodded his head and continued drinking.

The room was filling up and after four hours of drinking, it was decided it was time for the group to leave. The Troop had arranged for two cars to take them to Hamburg and these were waiting outside the block. Lots had been drawn and two unlucky designated drivers took the wheels, grumbling. The others piled in and they set off on the 90 minute journey north, up the autobahn. As they crossed a bridge spanning the Elbe River, the city of Hamburg spread out before them. After taking the exit for Altona, within twenty minutes, they were parking in an underground public car park. This was directly opposite the main German Civil Police Station (GCP), on David Strasse. Richard's companions headed directly into a bar, not twenty metres from the car park entrance. He tagged on behind the rest and was the last to enter the bar. Getting a round of drinks in, they chose a table at which to sit. The conversation ebbed and flowed, debating the route they would take for the evening's festivities. Plans made, they drank their beers and headed out the door, turning right. Some 100 metres along the street, they came to a bar with the word 'Monica's' emblazoned over the door. Entering the establishment, Richard adjusted his eyes to the dim lighting. It was only 18:00, but the bar was already half full. The clientele was a mixed bunch, from young to old. The first thing that Richard became aware of was the large number of good looking females. They were all dressed very provocatively, with a lot of skin on show. He felt himself start to stir downstairs.

'That lass there has the hots for you,' whispered Gareth, the Troop Sergeant's loader, in Richard's ear.

'Do you think so?' he replied, surreptitiously looking in the direction Gareth had intimated.

'Defo, I would steam right in there, mate,' he urged.

Richard considered this for a while. She was definitely checking him out, from top to bottom. He was really quite shy, but the alcohol was banishing his nervousness. 'A few more of these,' he thought to himself, 'and if she still looks interested, I will give it a go.' All around the room, females were engaging in conversation and acts of a sexual nature, with eager males. Richard had never experienced such things in his life and could not believe his eyes. A couple could quite clearly be seen fondling each other intimately, the young woman massaging the middle aged man's penis through his trousers. Richard was becoming more and more aroused, and was coming close to approaching the female who was still showing interest in him. Taking a deep breath, he prepared himself to speak to her. As he neared the tall, voluptuous, brunette she smiled at him, warmly. Asking if she would like a drink, she replied that she would love one. The ice broken, Richard went to the bar and returned with two drinks. They chatted for a while, making small talk. When she found out that he was a British soldier, her eyes lit up. She was originally from the Philippines and stood around six feet tall. Her eyes were at the same exact level as Richard's, and he was captivated by her. Looking over his shoulder, the rest of the Troop were making gestures, encouraging him to take things a step further. Plucking up courage, he leaned forward for a kiss, which was not rebuffed. As they caressed, Richard's left hand started to move up her leg. Moving ever higher, he felt towards the top of her inner thigh. As there had been no resistance, he reached between her legs. It was at that moment that he felt something familiar. He was expecting a warm, moist feeling, but instead, his fingers grasped a pair of testicles. Sharply withdrawing his hand, he stood back, gobsmacked. The room was filled with the raucous, uncontrollable laughter of his comrades. It had all been a set up and Richard felt totally embarrassed and dirty. When the laughter subsided, they explained to him that Monica's was a renowned transsexual bar. It was another tradition to set up a new member of the Troop one of Monica's 'girls'. It was not until Richard examined the features of the young 'lady' that he noticed 'her' Adam's apple. Lustful thoughts and alcohol had made him oblivious to this. Finishing off their drinks, the group tumbled out of the bar on route to their next location.

The next place they were to visit was, to Richard's surprise, an underground car park. Taking the ramp down to the lower level, they strolled through. Strangely, there were very few cars parked there. Instead, Richard looked at absolutely drop dead gorgeous women. They were all in different state of undress, some wearing Basques and suspenders, others wore thigh length boots. As the lads passed, the women asked if they wanted a good time, but were told that the guys wanted to browse and think. It was decided, after a short while, they would look elsewhere. One suggested 'five mark alley'. So, leaving the beautiful looking women in their wake, they returned to street level. To make things interesting, they came to an agreement that each man would put ten Marks into a kitty. Each would write their name on a bit of paper and place it in a bag. One piece of paper would be drawn and the name that came out would win a cheap shag. Quickly scribbling their names down, they gave the papers to Mex, who had provided a makeshift bag. As Richard was the newest member of the Troop, he was given the honour of drawing the name. Delving deep into the bag, he rustled about before drawing out a piece of paper. He handed it over to Mex, who began to unfurl it.

'The winner is....' he paused for effect, 'Hunter!'

'You jammy twat,' was the first reaction from one of the group. Others congratulated Richard, before explaining what they were about to do. The alley was positioned just opposite the Police station they had passed earlier. At each end were high walls, on the wall was a sign in German and English stating 'no women allowed'. As they negotiated the small gap in the wall, before them stood a little street, with houses along both sides. The windows had no curtains and were all around six to eight feet in height. In almost every one were sitting, scantily clad ladies, selling their wares. Richard was told to pick one, and they would then hand over the money. He was like a kid in a sweet shop and after three houses, had already decided on the one he wanted. Armed with 80 marks, he walked through the door. The rest of the Troop made their way to the other end of the street, to a bar, where they had arranged to meet when Richard re-emerged. Taking seats by the window, the Troop drank and waited for Richard to arrive.

It was only twenty minutes later that Richard's innocent looking face appeared, from behind the wall. He glanced across the road and could see the grinning faces of his comrades. Adjusting his tackle, he crossed the road and opened the bar door. He was met with a great cheer, as he sat down at the table. They all fired questions at Richard asking him how it gone, what she was like and how much it had cost. He was eager to tell all and for the next twenty minutes, was the centre of attention. It was at this point that they told him how he had been so fortunate to win the raffle. Everyone in the Troop had agreed earlier to put Richard's name on their bit of paper. So, when he drew out the winning name, they just needed to act surprised. Once the conversation had died down, a couple of the guys disappeared. The rest of the night was spent moving from bar to bar. At the end of the evening, they met up again at the arranged time, at the cars. Richard had slept the whole way back to camp. He had enjoyed his first Troop outing and looked forward to more of the same in the future.

Chapter 21 – Soltau Training Area

The night out in Hamburg was just a fading memory, as Richard packed his equipment to go on exercise. The men were due on the tank park at 06:00, and from there, would travel in convoy to the railhead. The tanks would be loaded on to flatbed carriages, for the journey to Reinsehlen Camp. When they arrived at the tank park, it was already bustling with activity. Crews loaded their personal equipment, extra food and everything they would need for two weeks in the field. The drivers were busy carrying out their 'first parades', checking oil levels, track pads and the other technical issues needed before the trip. Richard climbed on to his vehicle and began to stow his webbing and personal weapon in the rack provided. Tommo had already arrived, and was setting the frequencies on the two Clansmen 353 radios. A communications check or radio check was to be completed, prior to the vehicles' departure. Robbo instructed Richard to get the gun kit started up. Climbing inside, Richard confirmed that the Generating Unit Engine (GUE) was on line. He then proceeded to start the metadynes. He had already undone the gun crutch and satisfied himself that it was secured. He wasn't one to make the same mistake twice and smiled to himself as the gun kit started up. Giving the thumbs up to Robbo who was waiting at the front, the vehicle began to move forward and out of the hangar, under his guidance.

It was now 06:30 and the Squadron was lined up fourteen abreast, as if on parade. All the crews were now mounted, awaiting the communications check. Richard was sitting in the cramped gunner's station, with only his Tank Laser Sight (TLS) as a window to the outside. He was to spend many uncomfortable hours there, over the coming weeks and was not looking forward to it. The chance to prove himself as part of the team helped put these thoughts to the back of his mind. With the radio check complete, the order was given for them to move towards the back gates of the camp. There, they were met by a number of Royal Military Police (RMP), who were performing the duties of traffic control. Richard wondered if any of his friends from training would be there. He then recalled that, once they had passed off from JLR, they had to complete their military police training at Chichester. The vibrations of the tracks on the cobblestones went through Richard's body. Other members of the Troop had mentioned a sensation known as 'convoy cock'. This was what happened after sustained periods of travel in a tank. As they trundled along towards the railhead, Richard felt a stirring in his groin. He grinned to himself, happy that this had not been another wind up.

After around twenty minutes, the Squadron reached their destination and pulled off the main road. All the crews, apart from the drivers, dismounted, after having turned off the gun kits and secured the barrels, in their crutches. The commanders of the vehicles gathered together with a newcomer in a fluorescent jacket. Richard asked what was going on and was told that they had to be briefed by a member of the Royal Corps of Transport (RCT). It was that Corps' remit to see that the vehicles were safely loaded on to the trains. Once they were briefed, the commanders returned to their vehicles. They began to line up the vehicles in preparation for loading on to the flats. Richard's was the sixth to be loaded, and he watched with interest, as the first one began to inch forward. The commander walked in front of the tank until it was on the ramp. He then walked forward on to the first of the flatbed carriages. Turning to face his driver, he beckoned him forward with the acknowledged hand signal. As it drew closer to mounting the carriage, he gave small, quick movements with his left and right hands. This indicated to the driver to pull briefly on a right or left stick. Richard watched in awe, as the commander guided the vehicle the full length of the train, with only inches on each side of the tracks to spare. Richard waited patiently for their turn to load. Whilst doing, so he watched one of the commanders guiding his vehicle. When he was almost at the half way point, he was walking backwards, then suddenly disappeared. Men rushed forward immediately, as they seemed to know exactly what had happened. The commander had not realised how close he was to the next carriage, and had fallen between the two. Luckily, he was not badly injured, sustaining just a few cuts and bruises. This brought home to Richard how dangerous things could be, working these 52 tonne leviathans. The exercise had not started and one person had already been injured.

Over the next hour, the Squadron continued to load their vehicles on to their allotted flatbeds. Once in position, they were given numerous pieces of equipment with which to secure them, a selection of metal chocks, wooden blocks and chains. The metal chocks were placed at the front of the tracks. The tanks were pulled forward, until they embedded the chocks into the wooden carriage. Then, the other two were placed behind the rear of the vehicle, which was then permitted to roll backwards. This, again, caused the chocks to bite into the wood and vehicles then had their handbrakes applied. On each side of the tracks, both front and rear, were placed wooden slats, around four inches wide and four feet long. These were secured into the wooden flat base with four six inch nails. To complete stabilisation, metal chains were attached to the towing bollards, front and rear. They were placed in a criss-cross fashion and tightened until they were taut. Once this had been done, a member of the Deutsche Bundesbahn, the German railway service, inspected each carriage, in turn. His inspection took a further 30 minutes and any criticisms he raised had been rectified. The Troops were then permitted to climb into the passenger carriages, at the front of the train.

Armed with their scab packs and orange containers, holding bottles of beer, the Troops piled into the carriages and made themselves comfortable. Although the journey by road was only about 40 minutes, the train journey was going to take around six hours. This was because they were not seen as a priority and were shunted into siding until the line was less busy. This did not bother the men in the Squadron, as they began to hand round the beers. Richard was in a carriage with his crew and that of their Troop Sergeant, Dave. The topic of conversation was centred on past exercises; Richard listened intently, trying to gain any information that could prove useful, over the coming days.

'Can you remember the time when Molly had that encounter with a drop bear?' Ian posed the question, waiting for a response.

'Fuckin' hell, aye, he proper shat himself,' came the reply from Robbo.

Richard was intrigued; he prided himself on his knowledge of the natural world, but had never come across this animal before. He politely asked what they were and if they were indigenous to Europe. Tommo went on to explain that drop bears were only to be found in that particular region of Germany. They stood about four feet on their hind legs and resembled a small brown bear. They were shy, solitary creatures and had been hunted, almost to extinction. To evade predators, they had adopted the habit of climbing trees and spent most of their time in the canopy. It was a common occurrence for them to drop from the trees on unsuspecting prey. This is how they had gained the name of 'drop bears'. Richard was told if he was ever to go on a shovel recce, to be aware of this. The beers flowed, when a thought suddenly dawned on Richard. Both Robbo and Ian had put away at least half a dozen bottles of beer. He did not envy them having to negotiate the vehicle from the flats, when they reached their destination.

As the alcohol took hold of Richard, he began to drift over; making himself comfortable, he fell asleep. The rhythmic sound of the train wheels on the track acted as a lullaby, until, all of a sudden, he was startled awake. Due to the cramped conditions in the carriage, the blood supply to his legs had been cut off. He sat up, in agony. Rubbing his legs to try and circulate the blood back into them, he noticed that the train had begun to slow down. Others on the train were stirring and beginning to clean out their carriages of the empty bottles, scab packs and debris. As the train rolled into Reinsehlen Camp, Robbo made sure everyone had their belongings and they made their way to the doors, to prepare for disembarkation.

Jumping down from the carriages on to the platform, the Troops made their way to the vehicles. For the next 30 minutes, they worked with crowbars, removing the securing blocks, metal chocks and chains. Once this had been completed, the rearmost tank began slowly to reverse off its flatbed. As it were quite near the front of the train, Richard's vehicle would have almost 200 metres to reverse. This did not seem to bother Robbo, as he expertly guided Ian the full length of the train. Richard could not believe how this was possible, after consuming the amount of alcohol that they had. In no time at all, they exited the flats and lined up, waiting for the move to their location for the night. The order for all call signs to move to a grid reference was given and, in a belch of smoke, the tanks rolled forward.

As soon as they reached the outskirts of the camp, the ground became both undulating and boggy. The sounds of the Leyland L60 engines rose and fell, as the drivers went up and down the gearbox, coaxing the best out them that they could. The rising and falling of the vehicle were starting to make Richard feel sick. He stared through his sight, which was stabilized and, with his grip switch pressed, remained directly in front, regardless of any change in direction. Although the temperature outside was below freezing, inside the vehicle, Richard was starting to sweat. He was wearing three layers of clothing, completed by a big, heavy, drab, olive parka and hood. Each tank passed under a viaduct, after which the ground rose steeply and the drivers had to kick down the gears, to climb it. Once they crested the top, they crossed a bridge, which led on to the main training area. The ground in front of them was barren, except for the odd strip of wood. The Squadron covered the next three kilometres rapidly and, in single file, passed between two small strips of woodland, which extended from north to south. These would become familiar to Richard and were designated 'strip' and 'finger' woods. Passing through the two features, after approximately one kilometre, they began to swing south, into an area known as Bivouac area four or 'Bivvy 4', which would be their home for the next couple of days. Other Squadrons had been allocated different areas for the first week of training. This would culminate in a final exercise, involving the whole Regiment.

Reaching a wooded area, they were met by the Squadron Sergeant Major (SSM) 'Windy' Miller. It was part of his job to recce any night time locations and to ensure they were safe for the arrival of the Squadron. He directed each Troop to their designated area and the commanders reversed their vehicles in. Each Troop ensured that it provided all round defence, with interlocking arcs, where possible. As this was a non-tactical position for the next couple of days, they had been told that they need not erect camouflage nets. As soon as the last vehicle in the Troop had been placed into position, all engines were turned off. A strange silence spread through the wood, broken only by the sound of birds calling. The commanders made their way toward Squadron Headquarters (SHQ), where the Squadron Leader held his orders group. He informed the commanders what he expected from the Troops, over the coming days. Sitting in his green, army, foldaway chair, he reached into the rucksack at his feet. He withdrew a litre bottle of whisky and, unscrewing the cap, crushed it in his palm. A quiet groan came from the assembled commanders, who knew that when Major Redworth did this, no one could leave, until the bottle was empty. He gestured for them to bring their mugs out of their webbing and proceeded to dish out the whisky. The Orders Group, or O group as it was known, lasted around 90 minutes, of which only 30 minutes were spent discussing the week ahead. The remainder of the time, the Squadron Leader, or 'Crazy Red', as he was affectionately known, chatted with his Officers and NCOs about general day to day matters. Macdonald was one who believed in investing in his soldiers and was very good at getting the best out of them. He led from the front and had great respect from everyone in the Squadron. Richard recalled his first day, when he had waited to go in to the Major's office, to be welcomed to the Squadron. Prior to being marched in for a welcoming chat, the Squadron Leader was conducting orders. As the offender was marched out of the office, he was halted, next to Richard. Blood was streaming from his nose and the SSM was giving him words of advice, before dismissing him. Richard's heart sank when he heard the rough voice call out from behind the open door:

'Next!'

The SSM marched Richard in at a more leisurely pace than he had with the previous Trooper and halted him three paces from the Officer

Commanding D Squadron's desk. The Squadron Leader looked up from his desk and greeted Richard with a smile. He was a big man, going slightly bald, barrel chested, with sloping shoulders. The arms seemed to bulge through his pullover. The backs of his hands and wrists were matted with hair and Richard imagined that continued all the way up. He was not the archetypal Sandhurst Officer, with smooth, baby faced, good looks. He had more of a rustic farmer's appearance, which helped to bridge the social gap between enlisted men and Officers. From the conversation they had that morning, Richard could tell that he was not a man to cross but who would do anything to help, if it was in his power to do so.

The commanders returned to their Troops, a little worse for wear. Dave, the Troop Sergeant, began writing a stag list for that evening, consisting of a ground sentry and a radio operator, with each 'stag' lasting one hour. The drivers and gunners made up the ground sentries, while the commanders and operators, the radio watch. The duty of the ground sentry, which was what Richard was required to do, involved patrolling the Troop hide area, the name given to a location where the Troops would lay up and hide from the enemy, when not in contact. Dave went round the Troop, informing everyone the time they were to be on duty. Richard cringed when he found that he was on the death watch stag, from 03:00 - 04:00. This meant his normal 06:00 rise gave him little time to warm up and get sleep. Everyone gathered round the TSM tanks, chatting and drinking beer. The TSM gave a brief outline of what the Squadron Leader expected, over the coming week. Tomorrow, the first item they would practise would be moving into hide locations, in a tactical scenario. Richard did not know what this entailed, but it would all fall into place the next day.

The light had faded three hours ago and most of the Troop drifted off to their bivvies, makeshift tents, made using a groundsheet either draped over the barrel on the back decks or against the side of the vehicle. Some of the drivers chose to sleep in their cabs. Crawling into the bivvy that they had set up against the side of the tank, Richard removed his boots. He took off his parka, placing it under his sleeping bag, to use as a pillow. He also removed the top two layers of clothing, knowing that he would feel the benefit, when he was wakened at 03:00, only four hours away. Ensuring his webbing was handy and his weapon sling was attached to his wrist, he zipped up the sleeping bag. Once his body began to warm up, it was not long before he drifted off to sleep.

It had been a long day and Richard slept soundly, until he was woken by being shaken, roughly, by the shoulder.

'You're on stag, mate,' came whispered words from the unseen face before him.

Mumbling some form of reply, Richard unzipped his sleeping bag and rubbed his eyes. The silhouette at the entrance to the bivvy had disappeared. He began to don his clothing, finishing off by lacing up his boots. He crawled out of the tent, taking his webbing, parka and weapon. Putting on his parka, he put up the hood, to protect him from the biting, winter wind. He finally placed the webbing over his shoulders and secured it by the belt at his waist. Out of the darkness, a hand touched his shoulder.

'I'm off to bed, you need to wake Bubba up, in an hour.' And with that, the figure was gone.

Richard's eyes were adjusting to the darkness and he began his tour of the three vehicles. He stepped slowly, trying to avoid making any unnecessary noise. The first twenty or so minutes went well and his senses were heightened. After this, though, the cold slowly started to seep into his bones, regardless of his three layers of clothing. Richard found himself checking his watch at regular intervals, each time finding the hand had advanced by only a couple of minutes. He still had another ten minutes to push as was passing the Troop Sergeant's tank. Suddenly, a voice screamed out and, from his right, something shot out of the bivvy. The shape resembled a giant caterpillar, but, as suddenly as it had appeared, it stopped, lying motionless. Richard moved forward carefully and leaned over the shape. As he looked down, he saw Tom in his sleeping bag, fast asleep. Shaking him gently, Richard woke him and let him know that he was outside the tent. Still half asleep, he muttered something unintelligible and crawled back inside. Richard's heart rate slowly went back to normal and he continued his final circuit of the Troop. Checking his watch once again, he saw it was almost time for Bubba to start his stag. Locating Bubba's tank, Richard gently woke him and waited for a response. Happy that Bubba was awake, he turned and made his way back to his own bivvy, crawled back inside his sleeping bag and tried to fall back to sleep. This was hard, as his teeth chattered for the next fifteen minutes, but eventually, he drifted off once more.

The Troop were rudely wakened by the TSM, Jed, who was clearly not in a good mood. Once everyone was up and dressed, they were summoned together. It was light and Richard thought that this was strange. As they were supposed to have been wakened at 06:00, it should still have been dark at this time of year. Jed had in his hand a piece of paper and was studying it, intently. Once everyone had assembled, he looked up and eyed each one, in turn.

'Tom, you were on last ground stag, why did you not do Reveille?' he spat out, venomously.

There was a slight pause before Tom replied, sheepishly 'No one woke me, TSM.'

Studying the list again, the TSM asked Bubba, who had preceded Tom, why he had not wakened him. Richard was shocked at Bubba's answer, which was that he, himself, had not been wakened. Richard looked at him, incredulously, but Bubba avoided his gaze. Jed's temper was fast rising and his face visibly changed colour. The veins on his temple were throbbing and he was grinding his teeth. Glancing again at the list, his eyes then fell on Richard, who was still in shock at Bubba's answer.

'Why didn't you wake him, Hunter?' he asked, his demeanour seeming calmer than before. Richard could only splutter out his answer.

'I did, TSM,' was Richard's only comeback.

'Did you wait until he was up and dressed and had relieved you?'

Richard gulped, knowing that he had dropped a bollock and knew he had to come clean.

'No, TSM,' he replied timidly, looking down at the ground.

Picking up on Richard's embarrassment, and the fact that it was his first exercise, the TSM decided to cut him some slack. He repeated the procedure of changing stags, not just for Richard's benefit, but to reinforce this to the rest of the Troop. The lecture finished, he dismissed everyone, but took Bubba to one side. Looking over his shoulder, Richard could see by the poking finger in Bubbas chest that he was on the receiving end of a proper bollocking. 'Serves him right,' Richard thought to himself, 'trying to drop me in the shit.'

The guys returned to their own vehicles and the operators set about cooking breakfast. Tommo asked Richard to hand him down a tin of bacon grill, sausages and beans from the turret. While Richard complied with the request, Tommo started the portable petrol cooker where they would fry the eggs and sausages. Next to that, he started a gas burner, on which was placed a large, square tin known as a 'Dixie', half full of water. Into it, he placed the tins of beans, sausages and bacon grill. As this was all going on, Ian started the GUE and then jumped inside the vehicle, to turn on the boiling vessel (BV). This had also been filled with water and would be used to make brews. After about ten minutes, Tommo removed the tins from the now boiling water. He opened them and transferred the contents to the frying pan. After a further ten minutes, he was dishing out breakfast to the crew. Once they had finished eating and had cleaned their plates with the remaining water, they took it in turns to strip down, wash and shave. The Dixie was topped up again to boil more water for the remaining two crew members. After 30 minutes, they had finished breakfast, washed and shaved. Lastly, they put away their sleeping bags, folded the bivvy and placed it in its storage bin. Robbo walked round the vehicle, making sure they had not left any rubbish behind. Everything seemed to run like clockwork, without any instructions being given. Richard could tell the team had worked together for some time. Once Robbo was satisfied, he gave the order for them to mount up and Richard clambered into his cramped gunner's station. Trying to make himself as comfortable as possible, he waited for the order for the Troop to pull out of the hide area.

Chapter 22 – Hide Drill and Advance to Contact

After ten minutes, the order came over the air for them to move to a particular grid reference. The messages were sent in BATCO, which was short for Battle code. These messages are first encoded into numbers, using one of several vocabulary cards. The BATCO cipher is then used to encrypt the numbers into letters or numbers, which can be transmitted over unsecure channels and the process reversed at the receiving end. When Tommo had decoded the message, Robbo gave the order for Ian to pull forward, to the edge of the wood. The Troop, clear of their hide area, headed across country, in a non-tactical formation, to the specific grid reference. As they moved over the uneven terrain, Robbo rehearsed Richard in keeping the barrel pointing at an imaginary enemy position, traversing on to the target, then keeping the grip switch pressed. Due to the stabilisation and electronic components, the barrel pointed in the same direction regardless of which way the hull moved.

The short journey, of two kilometres to their new location, took them only fifteen minutes. Richard was thankful for this, as he was starting to feel nauseous once again. The ride itself was smooth enough, as Ian had been in the driver's seat for a number of years and had learned how to negotiate the terrain, affording maximum comfort to the crew whilst maintaining speed. The Troop had been assigned its own radio frequencies for the day, so the only messages they received were from each other. The Chieftain was fitted with two VRC 353 Clansman radios, which were fitted into a harness system. The second radio had been set on the Squadron frequency, so the commanders could monitor any messages from SHQ. As they neared a wood, approximately 200 metres to their front, Ian began to go down the gears and slowed down to a crawl. The TSM had explained that the SSM had already done a recce on the hide and that it was clear for them to move into. One by one, the commanders halted their vehicles, just before the wood and dismounted. Walking in front of the tanks, they guided them forward, swinging them round, in preparation for reversing in. They assembled together, to decide where each vehicle was going to be situated, so that they had all round and mutual defence. Coming to a decision, they returned to their vehicles and mounted up, taking their positions in the cupolas. With great skill, drawn from years of practice, they slowly guided their drivers into position. Once they were happy, everyone dismounted.

Richard was thankful to be free of his seat; as he climbed up over the commander's position the cold, winter wind hit him. Ian beckoned Richard over, handed him a shovel and led him to the front of the entrance to the hide. The other two drivers and gunners were already there and had started to disguise the track marks of the vehicles, after they had entered the wood. This, Ian informed Richard, was known as 'track discipline' and was the first thing that was done after entering a hide location. Taking one track lane each, the pair of them worked their way backwards until they reached the front of their tank. Despite the cold, Richard had worked up a sweat, but they were only just starting. Robbo and Tommo detached the cam net from around the turret and laid it out at the front. Securing two of the corners from between two trees, the four of them walked back towards the vehicle. Ian and Richard, who were in the middle, climbed on to the glacis plate, while Robbo and Tommo remained on the ground, at the left and right of the tracks. Under the guidance of both Robbo and Tommo, they slowly made their way from the front to the rear. Richard quickly realised that both he and Ian had been given the shit end of the stick. The cam net was being snagged on every little protrusion and he was finding it difficult to avoid tripping over his feet.

'For fuck sake!' he exclaimed, for what seemed like the hundredth time. He was very rapidly starting to lose his temper, to the merriment of the rest of his crew. He was quickly to learn that there was a knack to this operation and was yet to master it. After around 30 minutes and many swear words, mostly by Richard, they finished. Tommo called Richard to him and asked him to lend a hand, laying comms to the other tanks. Richard was confused and asked why they didn't use the radios. Tommo duly explained that often, when they moved into hides, they went on to radio silence to prevent any transmissions being intercepted. This could lead to directional finding units pinpointing their location. Communications security (COMSEC) was a big part of the war against the Warsaw Pact. So stringent were the British forces about security that operators were taught to use the lowest power setting, to achieve communications. To enable this, they laid cable, called D10, from each vehicle, back to a centralised location. Normally in a Squadron hide location, this would be back to SHQ and allowed them to be able to communicate, without having to use normal radio waves. Richard followed behind Tommo, pinning down the cable to the ground with stakes Tommo had given him. They ran the cable for about 100 metres to the TSM vehicle and connected it up. Satisfied with their work, they returned to their own tank. The commanders had gathered at the front of the hide, looking inwards. After a short while, they called the rest of the Troop to them, and for the next ten minutes they talked through good and bad points, including camouflage, track discipline and the positioning of the vehicles. Although they took the lead in the discussion, they encouraged input from the rest. Richard liked this and felt that he was being involved, not just being told what to do. For the rest of the morning, they practised moving in and out the hide, until the TSM was happy.

After a brew and hastily made lunch, they prepared to move out to practise 'advance to contact drills'. Armoured Warfare or Tank Warfare had not changed much since the Second World War.

It is a major component of modern methods of war. The premise of armoured warfare, rests on the ability of Troops to penetrate conventional defensive lines, through use of manoeuvre by armoured units. Much of the application of armoured warfare depends on the use of tanks, and related vehicles used by other supporting arms such as infantry fighting vehicles and self-propelled artillery. Also the use of mounted combat engineers and other support units. The doctrine of armoured warfare was developed to break the static nature of World War I trench warfare on the Western Front, and return to the 19th century school of thought that advocated manoeuvre and 'decisive battle' outcomes in military strategy. (Wikipedia)

They trained regularly with these supporting Units, which formed a Battlegroup (BG). However, for the next week, they would concentrate solely on their own Troop and Squadron drills. Jed gave a quick overview as to what they were to practise for the rest of the afternoon. Once he had answered any questions, he dismissed them back to their vehicles, to await orders on the Troop frequency. Wriggling into his gunner's seat, Richard checked the gun kit was running and in stabilisation mode. Just as they had made themselves comfortable, Jed's voice broke the silence on the air waves. They were to advance in a westerly direction, towards strip wood. They would be using a formation called 'one up', which was adopted when crossing open country if the threat of an enemy was high. Richard's tank was to lead the advance. They moved forward at a medium pace, with Ian using any 'dead ground' he could find, this being an area of ground that prevented them from being spotted from an enemy perspective. As they had reached around 400 metres from their start position, the revs of the engines started to drop. As Richard looked through his sight, he could only see the ground, rising up in front of him. Slowly moving forward, the vehicle crept up the incline. Robbo was communicating with Ian the whole time, waiting until he could see the ground ahead, over the rise. As they neared the crest, he ordered Ian to stop for a short while. Happy that he could observe clearly, he then asked Ian to crawl forward once more; Richard was to let him know when he could see the ground ahead. Concentrating intently, Richard forced his face into the TLS sight, waiting to give the word to Ian. As the tank crawled forward, Richard could gradually see more of the ground before them. As he could see above the rest, he gave the order for Ian to halt. Robbo then gave the order for Richard to start scanning, left and right, checking for any sign of an enemy. This was known as a 'hull down' position and provided a limited target to any enemy, directly to their front. For up to half a minute, Richard scanned the countryside and reported that it was clear to their front.

'Hello 42, this is 42 Bravo firm now,' came a voice in his headset, as Robbo communicated over the Troop frequency.

'Roger, moving now!' came the reply from the TSM.

Throaty engine noises erupted, as the other two tanks lurched forward, again zig-zagging, using the dead ground as they went. Covering the ground very quickly, as it had already been cleared by 42 Bravo, they slowed, as they ascended the incline. As before, they crept forward, until they were in a hull down position. Confirming that they could scan the ground ahead, Jed gave the signal that they were also firm, which indicated to Robbo that he could move forward, to the next tactical leap, which was called a 'bound'. As the tank lurched forward, Richard's head came away from the sight and then bounced forward again, smashing his forehead against the hard, metal surface. He let out a scream of agony, which was answered by Robbo, asking what was wrong. Hearing Richard's explanation, he laughed and told him to 'man the fuck up'.

Reaching the next bound and taking up another hull down position, Richard observed two tanks facing them, from strip wood. Immediately informing his commander, Richard waited for further instructions.

'Contact tanks, wait out!' came Robbo's reply, over the radio.

Once he had confirmed the grid reference of the two tanks on his map, Robbo sent the positions over the air. These were acknowledged by the TSM, who began to formulate his orders for a quick attack. It took around five to ten minutes for Jed to formulate his orders and for his operator to encode them. After this had been done, Jed sent them to the rest of the Troop, who, in turn, had to decipher them. They were to move into a 'Forming up Point' (FUP), which was the dead ground to the South of 42

Bravo's location. Robbo guided Ian backwards, then set off for the FUP. The rest of the Troop joined them and they awaited the time to move (H Hour). At the appointed time, all three vehicles set off out of the dead ground, in the direction of the enemy position. The outside two tanks covered arcs, from the front, to right and left flanks, as they sped forward, towards their objective. In Jed's quick attack orders, he had included an artillery fire plan, called a 'fire mission'. The artillery rounds were intended to soften up the target, prior to the attack going in and were due to lift, at the last safe moment. Although this was only a simulation, it would be practised for real on the prairies of Alberta in Canada, in the not too distant future. The Troop rolled through the objective, going static or 'firm' for some 200 metres. The TSM switched to the Squadron net and gave an update to the Squadron Leader, who had actually, along with the Second in Command 2ic, been playing the enemy. He then called the other two tanks to form up next to him, and gave a quick debrief on how it had gone.

The briefing finished, the crew mounted their vehicles, once again. For the rest of the afternoon, they practised various formations. The first of these was a 'two tanks up', which was used when a threat level was low. On this practice, the TSM and Troop Sergeant's tanks took the lead, while Richard's call sign remained in reserve. They had again been given an axis of advance but this time, instead of joining the other two call signs when they went firm, Robbo commanded Ian to 'leap frog' through their position, to the next bound. This was a more aggressive type of movement and they covered the ground quickly. On the third bound, Robbo, once again, identified an enemy position, which was relayed back to Jed. As in the previous attack, orders were issued quickly. They formed up again in the FUP and completed a left flanking assault on the dug in position, on the high ground to the north. Richard thought, from his very limited experience, that everything had gone even better than before. Jed seemed to be happy, though, at the next debrief, so the practice continued for the next two hours. By this time, Richard was starting to feel his arse going numb and felt pins and needles in his legs. Every so often, Robbo's feet would make contact with Richard's back. On the plus side, Richard's nausea subsided. It was with great relief that the order came for them to return to their night time location, where they had spent the previous night.

On arrival, they reversed in, as before; however, as they were still non-tactical, they did not put up any cam nets. Again, the commanders made their way over to SHQ for 'Crazy Red's' Orders Group. The remainder of the crews made a start on the evening meal. Every tank took extra rations, which they had purchased in the local NAAFI store. This was to supplement the 'compo' or composite issue rations, issued by the SQMS. These had a tendency to bung the men up and could be quite tasteless. To compensate for this, every tank carried a supply of condiments, such as curry power, red and green sauces, Worcester sauce or anything to spice up the meals. A favourite at meal times was what was known as an 'all in stew'. The tins of vegetables and meat from the main meal were thrown in one pot. They were supplemented by either mashed or boiled potatoes, if any had brought. It was not unheard of for the Troops to enter into competition, to see who made the best stew or curry.

By the time the 'O Group' had finished, tea was just about ready. The lads eagerly collected their plates and cutlery, from the bin on the vehicle. Gathering round the petrol burner, they waited for Tommo to remove the lid and start to dish out the food. It smelled really good and Richard was salivating, in anticipation. It was amazing how being out of doors the whole time gave them such an appetite. As soon as the food hit his plate, Richard began to dig in, mopping up with his share of the ration of a loaf of bread, given to each crew on a daily basis. Tommo had already placed the steamed apple pudding in the tank's BV. The GUE had been running for the past twenty minutes, so he asked Richard to bring the tins down. Richard eagerly complied and removed the lids with the compo tin opener supplied. He gave half a tin to each of his crewmates, the contents consumed within minutes. After lighting up a cigarette, he sat with his back against a nearby tree. All of a sudden, he felt his stomach gurgle and realised he had not been for a shit since they left camp the previous day. Waiting another couple of minutes, he hoped that the feeling would pass. To his dismay, he knew that he was going to have to go on a shovel recce.

Raising himself from his seated position, he made his way to the long bin, to collect a shovel and a roll of toilet paper. Noticing this, the other three whispered amongst themselves, which made Richard slightly nervous. Announcing his intentions, Richard set off, deeper into the woods. The light was fading quickly and Richard tried to adjust his eyes to the darkness. When he a suitable spot, out of sight and downwind of the Troop, he began to dig a shallow hole. Happy that it was deep enough, he began to remove layers of clothing, culminating in unbuttoning his coveralls. Making sure that he pulled the arms forward, he squatted over the hole. Doing so within a short space of time, he began to empty his bowels. The whole process took less than three minutes and satisfied that he had finished, he tore off a strip of toilet paper. Turning to clean himself, he instinctively look down. What he observed knocked him for six, the hole was almost empty; with the exception of a small turf, which stood erect, like a stalagmite. Rapidly cleaning himself and dressing, he set off, back to the Troop, in the hide, where he immediately told them what had occurred. This was met with a barrage of laughter, as the other three crew members fell about, holding their sides. Tears were streaming down Ian's face. Once the laughing had subsided, Ian went on to explain the reason behind this mystery of the disappearing shit.

As Richard had earlier collected the shovel and paper from the bin, Ian had also retrieved another shovel from the front of the vehicle. Following Richard into the woods, at a discreet distance, he had waited until Richard chosen a spot and begun to dig. Getting down on his stomach, he crawled forward, taking great care not to alert Richard to his presence. When he was about four feet away, he waited until Richard had begun to squat. Carefully, he moved the head of the shovel forward, until it lay directly over the hole. As Richard began to defecate, Ian caught most of it on the outstretched shovel. When he thought Richard was just about finished, Ian withdrew it and quietly moved back into the shadows. Returning rapidly to the hide, he hid the shovel, the contents of which had already been discarded on route. Then, the three sat around, waiting for Richard's return. On hearing the explanation, a broad grin spread across Richard's face and he also joined them in laughing at the situation. He didn't feel embarrassed at all, maybe just a little stupid for not guessing what had really happened.

Chapter 23 – Squadron and Battlegroup Training

For the next couple of days, the Troops carried out their own drills. They moved from area to area, so that they had different grounds to assess. The drills were now coming as second nature to Richard, and he was enjoying it. He had even started to feel a little more comfortable in the gunner's seat, if that were possible. At the end of day three, they moved to a hide location, but this time, they were ordered to go tactical. This was the start of a two day Squadron exercise, where all four Troops would be working as one. As light was fading, they crept slowly, without lights, toward their given grid reference. They halted approximately 100 metres in front of the wood and the commanders dismounted. After a brief conversation with the SSM, they returned to their vehicles and guided the vehicles into position. As soon as the vehicles were in place, all engines were cut and the Squadron went on to radio silence. Like a well-oiled machine and without any need for instruction, each crew member carried out his hide drill. As soon as the crew had erected the cam net, Tommo and Richard laid the line back to the centre of the hide, where SHQ was located. The wood was crowded, with fourteen tanks, a ferret armoured car, and a FV432 Armoured Personnel carrier, which was used as an ambulance. Joining them was the REME fitter section, which consisted of another three vehicles, one being a recovery vehicle, used to extricate any tanks which became stuck. To an outsider, this number of vehicles, combined with around 70 people, a certain amount of commotion could be expected. However, Richard was impressed at how quiet it was; people were speaking in whispers and going about their business in a quiet, determined manner.

As usual, the commanders headed off to SHQ for the Squadron Leaders' 'O Group'. There was one difference this time, the orders were more complex and no alcohol was offered. They would be 'dry' for the next two days, until Saturday lunchtime, when all movement was halted on the training area. No tanks could move after 13:00 by German law. Any maintenance that needed hard standing, like track changes or taking out links, would need to be done before this time. The orders group took 40 minutes to complete, then the commanders dispersed, back to their Troops. The evening meal had been prepared and was consumed quickly. The TSM had arranged a Troop brief to go through the Squadron Leaders' orders. As they assembled, Richard became aware that Jed's crew had made a makeshift screen, in shape of a 'U'. This was in order that no torchlights were visible to anyone observing the hide. Jed had taped a map of the whole area on the bazooka plate of his tank. Using part of an antenna, he pointed out various features and markings on the map, such as high ground, direction of advance start lines and boundaries. Next, he went through a full orders brief, which included situation of both enemy and friendly forces, mission, execution, service support and command and signal. Richard was intrigued and thought to himself would he ever be doing this for real?

The briefing over and questions answered, the guys returned to their vehicles, to prepare for the following day. Everyone was wearing their webbing and helmets and carried their weapons at all times. Out of the darkness, came Dave, who had prepared a stag list for the evening, giving the good news to Robbo's crew. Richard had drawn the final stag from 05:00-0600, which meant, at least, he would get a good night's sleep. Ian was on from 02:00-03:00, but this would not disturb them, as he was again sleeping in his cab. The preparations complete, they all turned in for the night.

Richard woke about two minutes before the hand touched his shoulder and shook him and those immortal words were spoken.

'You're on stag, mate,' came the whisper in his ear.

Dressing fully against the elements, he rolled out of the tent. Checking he had everything with him, including a torch with a red lens. This type was harder to observe from a distance than white light and was used in tactical situations. As he was about to begin his patrol, a voice from inside the tent spoke, in hushed tones:

'Watch out for those drop bears.'

Richard had totally forgotten about these creatures, which had been mentioned on the train journey north. As he stepped off into the darkness, he continually looked up into the canopy, keeping a watchful eye for the elusive creatures. He made his way slowly around the Troop location, stopping every now and again, listening for any sound of movement. There was no wind that evening, but the cold bit into him, even through three layers of clothing. His feet were starting to go numb and he glanced at his watch, to check the time. As he did so, a rustling sound, from his right, caught his attention. Straining his eyes in the direction of the sound, he advanced slowly towards it, moving cautiously so as to make any undue noise. He neared the source of the sound, which was becoming louder. As he rounded a large pine tree, he could make out the shape of one large figure and four smaller ones. The larger one stood around four feet high and about six feet long. The smaller figures were only two feet from the ground and approximately three feet long. Richard immediately recognised them as wild boars, having seen one before, in his parents' garden. They were a party of a mother and four piglets, and knowing that the mothers were very protective, he decided to back off and make his way to the relative safety of the Troop hide. His heart was racing, but he thought to himself that at least it had livened up his stag.

With only fifteen minutes to go before the end of his stag, and having to wake everyone up, he toured each tank in turn. All of the petrol cookers had been left out with a Dixie full of water, with tins for breakfast inside. It was the duty of the last ground sentry to light every cooker, so by the time he had woken the Troop, breakfast would almost be ready, apart from frying eggs. Once he had completed this, Richard began to wake the rest of the lads, starting with his own crew. He received a mixed response from each tent, but learning from his mistakes, made sure that at least the commander had acknowledged him and had stirred. Finishing his rounds, he re-joined his crew, who were busy putting away their sleeping bags and dismantling the tent. They had one hour in which to breakfast, wash and shave and decam the vehicle. Once they had put away the tent and their personal kit, Robbo and Ian began to strip for their wash. Richard helped out Tommo, finishing cooking and making the brews. After the other pair had finished their ablutions, they tucked into breakfast. Once Tommo and Richard had finished, they stripped down, washed and shaved. While they did this, Ian and Robbo washed the plates and cleared away the cooker and cooking utensils. This done, and Richard and Tommo once again clothed, they began to remove the cam net from the vehicle. Due to the practice put in over the last four days, they completed the task in around fifteen minutes. With fifteen minutes left until H hour, Tommo climbed inside, to tune in the radios to the Squadron frequency, in preparation for a radio check at 07:00, when they were to be mounted and prepared to move. Grabbing the chance for a quick cigarette, Ian offered Richard one and they chatted together, while Robbo walked off to see the TSM. The bond among the four had grown over this past week and Richard definitely felt part of the team. Although he was still being set up for the odd practical joke, it seemed the Troop had taken to him. On Robbo's return, they climbed into their relevant positions. The radio check had been completed and they all waited expectantly for the time to reach H hour. Then, over the air at the allotted time, the distinctive voice of 'Crazy Red' was heard.

'Charlie, Charlie One, this is Zero Alpha…move now!'

The smell of fuel carried in the air, an occasional misfiring engine was revved slightly higher, emitting a plume of black smoke. All crews were now fully focused on the job in hand as the tanks rolled north, to begin their advance. Moving line abreast, they trundled up to the start line. There, three Troops halted, while first Troop continued forward. As in the orders given the previous night, the advance would move with one Troop 'up', with the other three Troops in reserve. This would continually change throughout the day, according to the threat and ground. The first kilometre was fairly flat, so the first bound was approximately one kilometre. Once they had reached this point, the lead Troop halted and began to scan their arcs. On receipt of 'Firm now!' the remainder of the Squadron rolled forward to join them. As soon as first Troop had been joined and had confirmation that the rest of the Squadron were covering the advance, they moved forward to the next bound.

Richard recalled, from the briefing given by Jed, that they would soon encounter a narrow crossing, in the area of the 'jerry can'. This was a crossing from that part of the area, into a larger expanse, along their main route of advance. Just as Richard was thinking about this, first Troop leader announced that they had reached the edge of a possible minefield, at the entrance to this narrow gap. Since, at this point of Squadron training, they did not have any Field or Armoured Engineers with them, they went through the process of calling them up. One of SHQ was playing the part of the Engineer support and replied to the Squadron Leader's request. The SSM ferret was seen making its way, from the rear of the formation, towards the entrance to the minefield. He was acting the part of the Engineer Recce NCO, who assessed the obstacle. After a period of twenty minutes, he came on air, saying that they would need to call the 'Giant Viper' (GV) forward, to breach the minefield.

*The **Giant Viper** is a trailer-mounted, vehicle-pulled, mine clearance system, designed to be deployed in areas containing land mines. It was developed for the British Army in the 1950s. It was designed to be towed behind a Centurion gun tank, FV4003, AVRE (Armoured Vehicle Royal Engineers); and also the FV432 Armoured personnel carrier.*

The Giant Viper uses rockets to launch a 250-metre-long hose, packed with plastic explosive, across a minefield. Once fallen the charge is detonated, clearing a six metre wide path through anti-personnel or anti-tank mines over a distance of around 200 metres(Wikipedia)

The GV was simulated by one of the SQMS trucks towing a water bowser, moving forward to the entrance. Announcing over the Squadron net that they were firing, a period of time elapsed. Then they confirmed that the breach was successful. The lead Troop crossed the breach and went firm on the other side. Securing the breach, they called forward the remainder of the Squadron, who leapfrogged through their position and took up a holding line, facing east. The Squadron was now ready to continue along their line of axis and, as it was open ground, the Squadron Leader instructed them to go 'two up'. Both second and fourth Troops set off, across the open ground, scanning the terrain, as they did so. At the next bound, they went firm, and first and third Troops leapfrogged through them, for another 400 to 500 metres. The SHQ element followed up, one bound behind the rear two Troops, so as to keep an overview of the situation.

At the area known as the 'Southern Crossing', which gave access on to areas 3A and 3B, the Troops were funnelled in and had to cross, one Troop at a time. As the first Troop crossed, the one behind gave mutual fire support. Once on the other side, they shook out, to form the previous line of axis. To the west, rising up, was a high piece of ground called the 'Kreuzberg feature', which dominated the whole of the southern crossing and any advance west. Second and fourth Troops confirmed they were firm and the second two Troops were about to set off. Richard had continued to scan his arcs, when suddenly he spotted the cupola of a tank on the northern slope of the high ground.

'Contact tank!' he shouted to Robbo.

His commander immediately looked through his sight and confirmed the vehicle was, indeed, a tank. After further scrutiny, he spotted another two, accompanied by some dug in infantry. Pressing his presell, he informed the rest of the Squadron, directing them to cease any further communications on the net. Assessing the exact location, vehicle types and size and composition of the opposing forces, he gave his brief contact report. This all happened within the space of five minutes. Receiving the information, the Squadron Leader began to formulate his attack orders. Robbo had already circled an area on his map, south west of the feature. He tapped Richard on the shoulder and waited for him to turn round.

'This is where the FUP will take place, mark my words, young man,' he said, smiling and pointing at the map.

Richard returned the smile and nodded his head. He knew, because of the limitations of the area, and the amount of times the British Army had exercised on it, there were few places the commanders did not know. The voice of the Squadron Leader broke the silence, as he set about giving his encrypted orders. He paused after a few lines and asked one of the call signs to acknowledge. Once he had received, he acknowledged and repeated the process, until his orders were complete. Tommo had been scribbling with his lumicolour non-permanent pen, on to the quick attack orders template in his operator's folder. It took him about ten minutes to decode the orders from BATCO into plain text. He handed the information over to Robbo, who smiled, as the FUP was confirmed to be the area he had circled earlier. As they were the Troop who had contacted the enemy, they were designated as 'Fire Support'. Ian, under guidance from Robbo, sited the tank in the optimum position to bring down fire. While they were jockeying into position, the remainder of the Squadron were making their way to the FUP.

In twenty minutes, the move was complete and the remainder of the Squadron vehicles sat in the FUP, waiting for H hour to arrive. The Squadron Leader had included a fire plan in his orders, which would bring artillery fire down on the position, prior to them moving into the assault. Checking his watch, Richard knew that the order for the artillery was imminent. As he did so, the silence was broken by Crazy Red.

'Hello Golf three zero, this is Zero Alpha, fire Zulu Tango two three four five!'

'Golf three zero, fire Zulu Tango two three four five, wait out!......Shot over!'

'Shot out!' came the reply, from the Squadron Leader's call sign. For the next two minutes, the fire was adjusted to give the most effective coverage of the target. With 30 seconds to go till H hour, the vehicle engines began to roar and, as it reached the appointed time and in a belch of smoke, the Squadron, as one, rolled out of the FUP. At this point, they were not training with the infantry, so this would be simulated.

Armour cannot take ground, only the infantry can. This type of assault would normally be spearheaded by a Company of infantry, supported by tanks. When the assaulting Troops had reached 500 metres from the objective, the Squadron Leader gave the order to the infantry, to check fire. The assaulting force covered the ground rapidly, simulating engaging the enemy, to their front. As they entered the objective, they rolled on through, going firm a bound plus of it and covered the ground in front of them. Meanwhile, the Troop which had been designated close support for the infantry followed up slowly into the objective, giving suppressing fire to the trench systems. This would aid the attack by the infantry, as they took the ground, after debussing from their armoured personnel carriers.

The whole operation had taken less than an hour from the initial contact report from Richard's vehicle. After about ten minutes, the Squadron leader called second Troop and the close support Troop forward. All commanders were asked to report to his call sign, when he would debrief them on how the attack had gone. The commanders disappeared but were back after only ten minutes. Apart from a few things that needed brushing up, the Squadron Leader had been happy with how the attack had gone. For the rest of the day, they practised moving from west to east in the area they had been given. As it drew close to last light, they received a request from the Squadron Second in Command (2ic) to send their ammunition and fuel states. Although the ammunition number had to be fictitious, as they were not carrying any, the fuel states were genuine. Once every Troop had called in with their states, the 2ic then formulated how much fuel and other administration needs the Squadron required. These figures were then sent back on the 'rear link', which was used by the A1 and A2 Echelons, whose job it was to resupply the Troops, when in battle. As there was a lull in the Squadron movement, Richard's crew took the opportunity to grab a quick bite to eat. Tommo had had the foresight to put a couple of tins of comp in the boiling vessel earlier in the afternoon. He removed them with the aid of some cloth, to prevent him burning his fingers. Removing the tops, he handed them round, for the crew to take some and pass the tins on. He dished out a couple of slices of bread to each and they spooned the contents on to make a sandwich. They never knew exactly when they would get time to make a proper meal, so they ate when they could. Just as they finished and were swilling the food down with a mug of hot tea, another set of orders came over the air. After it had been decoded by Tommo, they learned that it was a replenishment request. They were to move to a location along what was known as the 'Pylon line', a rough, undulating track, well known to armoured Regiments. The name was derived from the pylon lines carrying electricity to Soltau, making radio communications difficult, if non-existent underneath it.

All equipment taken out for the brief pause was quickly stowed and they set off once again, into the failing light. This was always the preferred time of day for replens, as the darkness afforded them some form of cover from the air. The pitch of the engines rose and fell, as they entered on to the pylon line. The drivers, trying to give their crews the smoothest ride possible, gently coaxed their beasts onward. Richard, however, after fifteen minutes moving up and down, began to feel that familiar nausea, and hoped they would reach their destination soon. Looking through his sight, he could see a small, red light in the distance. This was the SSM, marking the beginning of the replen set up by the SQMS Echelon packet. He explained the series of coloured torch lights they would go through, which denoted where in the replen they were. This served as a refresher to the more experienced commanders and crewmen, who had performed this many times before. They passed through the replen, taking on essentials, such as fuel and extra rations. Ammunition was simulated by an empty truck designated for this purpose. The whole process, from start to finish, only took twenty minutes and before long, they were released and moving to their night time location. This was to be a Squadron hide. They were, once again, fully tactical, as would be the case for the next four days. Over this time, they would practice, over and over again, the various attack and withdrawal techniques on different areas. This was to lead up to the final exercise, which would involve all supporting arms.

One of the rules set in stone on the Soltau Luneburg Training Area was that, on a Saturday, after 12:00 there was no armoured vehicle movement. As the Squadron assembled, after their dawn attack that day, they gathered themselves, waiting for the order to move to a location, for the weekend. Richard was to find out that, before they could grab some well-earned rest, the vehicles required some tender, loving care, which always took the form of a maintenance period, normally done in a location which provided hard standing. Tanks that required links to be taken out had level ground to enable the crews to achieve this. Over a period of time driving over rough ground, the tracks became elongated and would, at times, jump from the sprocket, causing a banging sound and the vehicles to become less responsive. It was also a time to ensure the suspensions were greased and all oil levels were checked and were topped up to the correct levels. This would be the last time, before the final exercise, that they would have an opportunity to perform this. As they sat on top of the vehicles sipping tea, the operators remained in the vehicles with their signals folders and pens in their hands, waiting for the order to move to the maintenance area, which they knew was not far from their location. There were only a couple of places in the area that provided this luxury. One being 'Scharrl Crossroads' which was only about two kilometres from where they were situated. Robbo pointed it out on the map to Richard.

Ten minutes passed, then the expected order came over the air. Once Tommo had decoded it, the crew were not surprised to find that it was, indeed, the very spot that Robbo had just pointed out to Richard. Once again climbing into their positions, the Troops moved out, non-tactically, to Scharrl. It was only a short journey at speed and Ian was coaxing every last bit of power out of the beast. As they emerged from the woods, the sight before them looked like a scene from a great tank battle in the Second World War. There were vehicles lined up all along the hard standing, by the crossroads. Some had the mechanics (REME) fitter sections alongside them. A crane attached to an AFV432 vehicle was hastily being attached to the power pack of one vehicle. If the team did not complete the work on it in the next three hours, they would be stuck there for the weekend. Robbo guided the tank behind the last one in the line. As he did so, he ordered Richard to traverse the barrel over the back decks, so that the radiators could be lifted and oil levels in the gearbox and engine checked. Once they were in position and the vehicle engine and GUE had been cut, the crew climbed out. Ian set about checking his running gear, which consisted of the sprockets, road wheels and oil levels in the hubs. Richard had already clambered on to the back decks and had begun to lift them to gain access to the engine compartment. Robbo was busy inspecting the tracks and assessing whether they needed to remove any links. Tommo remained inside, busy preparing a bit of breakfast.

By the time all the oil levels had been checked, Tommo's head appeared out of the operator's hatch. He was armed with a couple of mugs.

'Scran's ready!' he shouted down, to the rest of the crew.

Dropping everything they were doing, they clambered up on to the turret. Tommo handed over the mugs, one at a time. He then began to open the tins, warming in the boiling vessel. Two eggs were frying in a small frying pan on the petrol cooker, next to him. He dished out the first helpings to Robbo and Ian, putting a further two eggs in the frying pan for Richard and himself. Once breakfast was consumed, they used the remaining water in the BV to clean their plates and utensils. Their bodies were energised once more.

Robbo's assessment on the tracks was that they did not need to remove a link, but needed to be tensioned. Ian made his way, immediately, to the long bin on the right hand side. He returned carrying an L-shaped bar, a huge ratchet, a hollow tube and an extension bar. Lifting up the mud flap, he attached the ratchet to the massive nut surrounding a bolt, protruding from the front of the armour. Inserting the L-shaped tool into the bracket, he confirmed it was secure. He lifted it up to the two o'clock position and beckoned Richard to join him. The two pushed down on the bar, then pulled it up to the start position. They repeated this, each time a little more effort required, as the sound of the tracks creaked, as they were slowly tightened. When it was impossible to push the tool down between them, Ian fitted the hollow tube to the end of the L shaped tool. This allowed all four to bring their combined weight to bear on it. They managed another four depressions of the bar, until they thought they could not manage any more. Robbo checked the track tension and asked Richard to climb on to the glacis plate, to give one last pump, for good luck. Richard did as he was told and placed all his weight on the end of the bar. He was hanging, suspended from it, bouncing, trying to tighten it one more time. The last thing he remembered was a searing pain in his skull and everything going black. He opened his eyes, staring up into the faces of Ian and Tommo, who were leaning over him, with concerned looks. Richard's head ached and his vision was slightly blurred. After a couple of minutes, he had come round enough for them to explain what had happened. In his enthusiasm to get one more turn of the ratchet, he had dislodged the hollow extension bar, bringing it crashing down on to his unprotected head. Luckily, it had not broken the skin but a rather large bump protruded from his bushy, dark hair. He was taken to the Squadron ambulance, where the medic checked him over for any signs of concussion. After being given the all clear, he was allowed to return to his tank. Looking a little sheepish and rather embarrassed, Richard approached his crew members, who were in hysterics, recounting the story. It was commonplace for comrades to laugh at their workmate's misfortunes. Would this now become one of these stories to be passed down through the generations, around a camp fire or in the mess?

The remainder of the Squadron completed their maintenance by 11:15 and were mounted, awaiting the order to move to their hide location, for the weekend. The grid was given and the engines burst into life, as, one by one, they departed in plumes of smoke. They arrived at their hide location with fifteen minutes to spare, before the movement ban came into effect. As it was non tactical at the weekend, the crews did not bother with any hide drills. Instead, they began to put up their tents and make themselves comfortable for the next 36 hours. Movement would not be permitted by armoured, tracked vehicles until 00:01 on Monday morning. In the centre of the hide, two 4-tonne Bedford trucks, provided by the SQMS, were sitting, with their engines running. This was the highlight of the whole exercise, a chance for a nice, warm shower and a porcelain 'dump'. Two members of each crew were allowed to depart on the first shower run. As Ian and Richard normally worked together, they were chosen to gather a change of clothing and shower kit, and take the first transport. They mounted the first 4-tonner they came to and took seats as close to the driver's cab as they could. There were already four others on it, and they had taken the best seats. Ian and Richard were, however, not over the dreaded rear axle, where the strongest vibrations were felt. Once the truck was full to capacity, it set off on the bumpy journey to the first available tarmac road; for the 30 minute drive back to Reinsehlen Camp. As they had only managed to catch about three hours sleep over the last 30 hours or so, they slept the whole journey.

They were rudely awakened by the truck slamming on its brakes and were catapulted towards the front of the vehicle. With shouts of abuse to their 'taxi' driver, the Troops picked up their belongings and made their way towards the shower blocks. As they neared the entrance to the block, a group from another Squadron were leaving it. As they passed, one of them called out, to no one in particular:

'I've left you a little present in trap number two;' he said. He and his mates all laughed among themselves.

It was always a race for each Squadron to reach the showers first, so that everything was pristine and smelling fresh. As soon as they entered, the smell of cheesy feet mixed with shower gel and deodorant was overpowering. Richard fought hard not to bring up his breakfast. Having lived outside for the past ten days, he had not noticed that both he, and probably his crew, smelled like a tramp's vest. The aroma emanating from the direction of the toilets was unbelievable. It was the product of the composite rations they had been living on for the last ten days. Some of the Regiment had refused to go on a shovel recce; choosing to wait for the first opportunity to use Reinsehlen Camp. As the previous Squadron had fully unloaded into porcelain heaven, the smell was akin to a Victorian sewer. Richard was breathing through his mouth, trying not to smell the putrid stench. He undressed quickly and dashed towards the showers, housed in an open room, which accommodated around twenty soldiers. The floor was covered in a residual filth, left over from the previous occupants. Richard dashed to the nearest showerhead and quickly turned the knob clockwise, to turn on the water. He took a sharp intake of breath, as the tepid water hit his skin. Starting from his scalp, he massaged the shower gel into his body, removing days of encrusted dirt, which had built up. As he looked down at his feet, he saw rivulets of dirty water running away from him, into the nearest grate. Although the water was only lukewarm, it felt good to be able to wash away the accumulated dirt. The shower room was full after five minutes and Richard was sure that the water temperature had increased.

Looking to his left, he saw one of the guys from fourth Troop, urinating against his leg. Jumping back in shock, he let out a scream.

'What the fuck? You dirty bastard!'

The offender stared back at him and laughed; the whole of the shower room, who had observed it, joined in. This was obviously a trick regularly played on new boys, or NIGS, as they were affectionately known. After the initial surprise had worn off, Richard took the prank on the chin and vigorously scrubbed the affected area. He knew to complain or winge about it was not an option, as this would leave him open to ridicule. It was a man's world, and any sign of weakness was soon jumped upon. As he continued to shower, he wondered how long it would be, before the pranks would stop. How long would he have to serve before he was deemed a regular member of the Squadron? The joke over, the protagonist, who was called 'Bungalow', slapped Richard on the back.

'No hard feelings, marra,' he offered his apology.

'None at all, mate, you dirty fucker!' came Richard's chuckling response.

Having cleansed themselves thoroughly, they retired back to the changing rooms, where they dried themselves and put on a fresh, clean set of clothes. It felt like being reborn, and Richard savoured the fresh smell of the conditioner he had used on his clothing, prior to the exercise. Taking the opportunity to have a porcelain dump, he made his way to the toilet cubicles. Locking the door, he pulled down his coveralls and sat down. As he sat there, waiting for nature to take its course, he was entertained by some of the humorous comments scrawled on the cubicle walls. These had been left by various battle groups over the years, and were a testimony to the minds of soldiers over the decades. Richard could have sat there forever, but was disturbed by the sound of the voice of the SQMS, telling the Troop they had five minutes to get back on the truck. Having cleaned himself, he rapidly put back on his coveralls and exited the cubicle, heading outside, to the waiting trucks, with the rest of the guys.

The return trip took the same amount of time, however, this time, most of them were awake and chatting idly. It was not long before they moved from the road, back on to the Area and they bounced up and down for the next ten minutes. On arrival, the tailgates were thrown down and they disembarked from the trucks. The other half of the Squadron were already waiting to climb aboard. As soon as they returned to their Troops and stowed their kit, they were detailed by the SSM to begin collecting wood. Richard asked Ian what this was for and was given a broad grin and reply of 'Smoker'. Not knowing what this was, he followed behind, picking up any dead wood they could find, then taking it to a central location, where a huge pit had already been dug. A Smoker, Ian explained, was a kind of Squadron barbeque. The SQMS was given fresh rations for this purpose, to feed the boys. He also sold beer at extortionate prices, with all profits, he said, going into Squadron funds. With the amount of people engaged in building the fire and helping the SQMS to set up the BBQ, the work was completed in no time at all. Ian and Richard returned to their vehicle, lay down and, before long, were fast asleep.

They were wakened by the return of Tommo and Robbo, from their shower run. They stowed their bags and called Ian and Richard to them. Robbo informed them that while they had been away, the SSM had drawn the list of sentries and radio stags, from a hat. Before doing this, he had noted down the name of anyone who had fucked up since leaving camp. They had, unknown to them, been awarded 'extras', meaning extra duties. Richard swallowed hard, knowing that as he had been blamed by Bubba for not waking him up, he was certain to be on the list. To his pleasant surprise his name was not called out by Robbo as he went through the list. As Tommo was not a big drinker, he had volunteered to take one of the radio stags, so the rest of them were free for the evening.

'You fuckin' dancer!' exclaimed Ian, who made his way to his driver's cab, where he returned with an orange day glow crate. It was a ten pack of 'Herforder Pils', left over from the supply he had brought. 'Get a few of these down your neck,' he said, offering a bottle to Robbo and Richard, 'before we have to pay the SQMS rip-off prices!'

The crew, apart from Tommo, who was drinking tea, consumed a few sociable beers and chatted about life in general. In particular, they reminisced on Smokers gone by and things that had happened. One of the stories they told was about a new Troop Leader, fresh out of Sandhurst, who had not endeared himself to his Troop. They had waited until the Squadron Smoker and got him paralytic drunk. While he was being occupied by his Troop, one of its members had crept into his tent and shat in his sleeping bag. At the end of the evening, the poor, unsuspecting Troop Leader crawled into it. Although he was absolutely hammered, after five minutes the unmistakable stench got to him. It was already too late, as he had rolled around in it. The sound of his screams were probably heard a couple of kilometres away. Richard pondered on this story and wondered if they had anything lined up for him, that evening.

The light was starting to fade and the Troops began to assemble around the SQMS tent, with their plates and knife, fork and spoon (diggers) in hand. On the menu were beef steaks, chicken, Bratwurst, jacket potatoes and fresh salad. Richard loaded his plate up and collected a case of beer. He took his place around the fire, which had not yet been lit. Other members of the Troop were already seated, tucking into their plates of food. They had deposited their orange handbags of beer into one pile, so

Richard did likewise. For the next twenty minutes, they ate, drank and chatted among themselves. As the evening progressed and the beer flowed, the banter started. Troop rivalry was prevalent throughout every Squadron, each one believing it was better than the rest. These exchanges were mostly friendly, but could escalate into violence, when alcohol was involved. This also happened within the Troops and this night was no exception. Richard observed a heated exchange between the Troop Sergeant of Third Troop and one of his Troopers. It also had not gone unnoticed by the Squadron Leader, who raised an eyebrow. As the debate grew ever louder, the Troop Sergeant gesticulated over his shoulder, with his thumb. The pair turned around and trudged off into the darkness. The Squadron Leader smiled to himself and returned his gaze to the fire. One of the men was pouring OMD 75, the oil used for the main engine, on the fire. This allowed the flames to burn for longer, but at a slower rate. The rule of thumb was that the thinner the oil, the more combustible it was.

Out of the darkness, Richard could see the form of the Third Troop Sergeant emerging. However, he was alone; he made his way silently to the fire and reclaimed his seat. One of his Troop passed him a bottle of beer, which he consumed in one gulp. The Squadron Leader looked over in his direction and smiled. It was obvious that the debate had been settled and the other party had been put to bed. Speaking with Ian after this incident, it became apparent that this was a common occurrence that happened at Smokers. Nothing was said afterwards and the air was cleared. As long as it was done out of sight, the hierarchy turned a blind eye.

The hours passed and the mountain of crates slowly declined in size. It was at this time, the stories which had been passed round were now replaced by a series of songs. Each Troop was challenged in turn to give a song or "show their rings". The challenges were taken up and the singing went to and fro, across and around the fire. When they were bored with this, one of them announced that A Squadron were parked up in an adjacent wood, not 500 metres away. It was decided it would be a great idea to put in an assault on them, on foot of course. Arming themselves with 'Thunder Flash' pyrotechnics and the hollow extension tubes normally used for tightening the tracks, they set off. The distance over the open ground was covered in a short space of time. The small group spread out, so that they encircled the fire A Squadron were sitting around. On the pre-agreed signal they opened up with their pyrotechnics, either throwing them near the assembled Troops, or firing them direct, from the hollow tubes. This was done by ramming one end into the ground and tilting it, striking the Thunder Flash and dropping it into the tube. This acted like a small mortar and forced the projectile out of the tube, in the direction of the Troops. There was a mass of confusion among the A Squadron men. Before they could react, the assaulting Troops withdrew into the darkness, back to the safety of their own hide. When they returned, Richard decided it was time for bed. He had lost count of the amount of beer he had drunk. All he knew was that he had staggered most of the way back, across the ground from A Squadron. He found his tent, after going to three different vehicles, opened the flap and unzipped his doss bag. Thinking back to one of the stories told earlier about the young Troop Leader, he gave a quick sniff, before climbing in. With a contented smile on his face, Richard fell into a deep sleep.

Chapter 25 – Battlegroup Final Exercise

Richard woke to the sound of birdsong. The sun had already risen. Startled, he anxiously looked at his watch. It was 09:15. He rushed to get out of his sleeping bag, but looking across, saw that Tommo and Robbo were still fast asleep. It was then he remembered they had been given a late start. Over the coming days, they would get minimal rest, so they were best to take advantage of it while they could. Richard turned over and it wasn't hard for him to fall back to sleep.

At some point, the smell of frying bacon grill and sausages assailed his nostrils, stirring him from his slumber. Climbing out of his sleeping bag or 'maggot', he dressed and rolled outside. Tommo was already washed and dressed, hunched over two burners, with breakfast on the go. Richard acknowledged him with a polite, 'Good Morning', and asked if there was anything he could do. Tommo asked if Richard could make the brews and make sure that Ian was up. Robbo had been first up and was over with the Squadron Leader, being briefed with the other commanders, on the events of the day. When Robbo returned, they took breakfast and finished their ablutions. They were to be ready to move out, by 4-tonner, by midday. The day was going to be spent visiting various locations, where the supporting arms of the Battle Group would give presentations on what services each could provide. The first stand was only twenty minutes away and was to be a presentation by Support Company of the Royal Regiment of Fusiliers.

On arrival, they were asked to form a semi-circle around the Company Commander, an imposing, powerfully built gentleman. He stood around six feet four inches and his voice, when he spoke, carried easily to the back of his assembled audience. He introduced himself in a professional, well-rehearsed manner.

'Good afternoon, gentlemen, I am Major Mike Myers of Support Company, 3rd Battalion Royal Regiment of Fusiliers. This afternoon, I am going to give a short insight into what we do as part of the Battle Group. The Company is often referred to as Fire Support Company (Coy). It is made up of more experienced soldiers, NCOs and Officers from the Battalion, who have generally spent time in a Rifle Company. Our purpose is to provide a vast array of fire power to the Commanding Officer. We consist of the Reconnaissance Platoon, Mortar Platoon, Anti-Tank Platoon,

Machine Gun Platoon and Snipers. So, you can see, we can bring a potent amount of firepower to bear, if required to do so. To explain each of the Platoon's capabilities, split yourselves up into five groups and you can visit each stand, one at a time. Members of each platoon have vehicles and weaponry set up and will explain everything you need to know and, hopefully, answer any questions.'

The Squadron split into the required number of groups, which was easy, as there were four 'sabre Troops' and SHQ. Each Troop went to a stand, and rotated for the next hour. Richard was taking in all the information presented to him. It was the first time he had learned of the capabilities of other units. For most of the Squadron, it was a matter of refreshing their knowledge and many just paid it lip service. Once they had visited every stand, the Squadron Leader thanked the Support Company Commander and they set off for their next destination. For the rest of the afternoon, they were given presentations from the Royal Artillery and the Royal Engineers.

The Artillery described their equipment, the distance the guns could fire and how many rounds each gun could deliver in one minute. They went into the effects of high explosive on an enemy's defences. They also covered the air defence equipment that provided defence against air attacks. The Engineers presented demonstrations on clearing a minefield by hand and the use of the Giant Viper (GV). It was explained how they spanned various sized gaps using their bridging equipment. Richard was impressed and found it all very interesting how the support arms of the Battlegroup meshed together, to make an effective fighting unit.

The afternoon of presentations finished, the men boarded the trucks for the trip back to their hide location. They arrived back before last light and had time to make the evening meal, prior to going tactical once again. Everyone was walking round, talking in whispers, sentries were posted and at least one person per Troop was listening on the radio. The Battlegroup members were all on radio silence, but this would be lifted, prior to the start of the exercise. The commanders had been given their orders from Crazy Red and they, in turn, briefed their crews. The first phase of the exercise was a Battlegroup route march to the top of the area. This was a distance of some 30 kilometres from their present position. Each Troop was given timings, to which they needed to adhere. They would pass through various check points on route, heading North East. The minutes ticked by until 30 minutes before H Hour, when all crews mounted and sat in their crew positions. Richard was not looking forward to this, as he knew that he was going to be in his seat for some considerable time. Their start time and expected arrival time spanned two and a half hours. With the extra half hour waiting time, his arse was going to be seriously numb by the end of it, he thought.

At one minute past midnight, H Hour arrived and the Squadron, as one, started their engines and the gunners turned on the gun kits. One Troop at a time, they made their way to the start point of the route. Here, they were met by a Land Rover, manned by two RMPs. As soon as they hit the concrete road, the operators attached the orange flashing lights, known as 'winky wanky' lights, to the top of the turrets. This warned other road users that there were large, heavy vehicles approaching, though this was obvious, from the noise and size. Turning in the direction indicated by the military policeman, the tanks pulled on to the main road. They stopped any civilian vehicles, coming from either direction, much to their drivers' annoyance. The military presence on the training area was a hot political subject, but for the time being, they were backed by the government, mainly because of the threat from the Soviet and Warsaw Pact on their borders. The first 90 minutes of the route march were uneventful. As they reached one of the checkpoints, the silence was broken by a message, sent on the Squadron frequency.

'No duff, no duff, road traffic accident on the southern crossing. This call sign has driven into a civilian Mercedes. We require emergency services and police at this location ASAP. Possible fatality...No duff, no duff!'

Richard knew that the code words 'No duff' designated that this was a genuine, non-exercise message. He also recognised the voice as coming from First Troop Corporal Andy Crawley, whose men were some ten minutes ahead. All traffic ceased on the airwaves, giving priority to this incident. The information was passed, up the chain of command, to Battlegroup HQ. They, in turn, contacted Reinsehlen Camp, who got in touch with the local emergency services. The Battlegroup continued on its route north east and Richard felt the tank take a hard left turn as it exited the tarmac road. Although it was dark, Richard could make out the silhouette of the pylons, stretching off, into the distance. For the next twenty minutes, they navigated along it and, at the far end, went through a Battlegroup replen. By the time they had cleared this, they were only fifteen minutes from their hide location. They were bang on time and Robbo was in a happy mood. As they approached the hide, Richard could make out the sounds of vehicles jockeying into their positions. They waited their turn patiently and eventually were given the signal from the ground, to move in. Climbing on to the back decks, with an extension lead for his microphone, Robbo guided Ian back into position. All this was done with the minimum use of lights. As soon as each vehicle was in position, the drivers waited for the gun kits to be switched off. They then cut their GUEs, then their main engines and silence descended on the wood. The crews, by now automatically, went into their hide routine of track maintenance, cam nets and laying line to SHQ. There was a small difference this time, as they had been joined by a couple of platoons of infantry, who were to provide close support. They had dug themselves in at key spots around the Squadron. The drills were carried out, just as they had practised, over the last ten days, and were complete within 30 minutes. The sentries were set out in trenches, with line back to their vehicles, so that they could make contact without leaving their positions. One difference was the inclusion of a Nuclear Biological and Chemical (NBC) sentry, downwind in a trench. He had various pieces of equipment with him, to detect different threats from elaborate hardware to pieces of paper which changed colour when they came into contact with chemicals. Richard remembered the chemical safety rule from training. *'If you experience a bombardment of any kind. Sight any hostile or low flying aircraft. See suspicious Mist, Smoke, Droplet or Splashes. Smell anything unusual. Notice symptoms in yourself or others such as, dimness of vision, irritation of the yes, running nose, sudden headaches, excessive salivation or tightness in the chest. Or hear an alarm. You are to carry out the Immediate Action Drill.'*

Hide drills carried on throughout the night, until first light. Like well-oiled machines, the crews went through their routines and, at first light, mounted up, awaiting further instructions. They left the cam nets up, to hide themselves from any air reconnaissance. At around 07:00, the Commanders were called for by the Squadron Leader. He had just returned in his Land Rover from Battlegroup HQ, where the Commanding Officer (CO) gave his orders. Quickly, he went through the mission he had been given by the CO. After asking if there were any questions, he dismissed Commanders, to go back and brief their crews.

The mission brief was quickly covered by Robbo, and everyone was fully aware of what was required of them. They had been chosen to be lead Squadron in the advance, following closely behind Reconnaissance Troop in their Scorpions, equipped with 76mm guns. They would probe, approximately two kilometres in front of the Battlegroup. As they moved forward, they would report back any obstacles, possible threats or actual enemy locations. The threat level from NBC attack was high, so all Troops had donned their chemical suits, minus their respirators. Although normally uncomfortable to wear, in winter these gave an extra layer of warmth. Extended periods of time in this equipment, though, impeded the soldier's ability to perform their duties to their best. Richard would find this out during his career, both as an Instructor and also whilst taking part in an experiment, assessing equipment and performance in NBC conditions.

On H hour, the Troop moved out of the hide towards the start line. Moving two up, they leapfrogged through each other, as well as the terrain allowed. No reports were coming from Recce Troop, so their progress was swift. Covering around five kilometres in the first 25 minutes, their advance was halted by one of Recce Troops' call signs.

'Contact tanks and dug in Infantry wait out!'

Again, the air went silent, to give precedence to the lead Troops, who had made contact. After receiving the location of the enemy position, Second Troop manoeuvred themselves into positions where they could get 'eyes on' the targets. Taking up a hull down position, Robbo confirmed the enemy position and began to formulate a fire mission. Tommo quickly encoded it and passed it over to him. Robbo sent the fire mission to the artillery, giving grid, direction in mils, a description of the target, what was to be done to it, for how long and when. This was relayed back to him by the 'Forward Observation Officer' (FOO) to ensure all details were correct. Then, after a two minute silence:

'Hello Tango 42 Bravo this is Golf 10 shot two zero over.'

Robbo repeated the message, to confirm he understood that the incoming rounds would be due to land in twenty seconds' time. Looking through his sight, he scrutinised the area around the enemy position. A puff of smoke was seen on the ground, which had been caused by an umpire throwing a Thunder Flash, to simulate artillery fire landing. Using the divisions marked on his sight, he calculated the necessary adjustments needed, to bring the fire on to the target.

'Golf 10 this is Tango 42 Bravo, right two hundred add two hundred.'

'Golf 10, right two hundred add two hundred, wait out!' Again, a slight pause and then the message that the next round was incoming in twenty seconds. Assessing the fall of shot, Robbo asked the rounds to be dropped 100 metres. This would bring the next rounds directly around the centre of the enemy position. The next rounds, simulated by pyrotechnics, confirmed that the adjustments had been correct.

'Golf 10 this is Tango 42 Bravo rounds on target. Record as target over!'

This transmission was to let the gunners know that this targeting could be used in the upcoming attack, to be delivered in the next twenty minutes or so. This was conveyed to Robbo, in the form of:

'Tango 42 Bravo this is G10 rounds on target, record as target. Target number Zulu Tango, three, four, five, six.'

The words were repeated back by Robbo and acknowledged by the Squadron Leader, who would include this in his fire plan, in the orders he would give shortly. The other Troops were busy assessing their maps and the ground ahead, for possible FUPs, and routes to them. The orders came, but this time, once they had been decoded, Second Troop found they were to be close support Troop, for the Infantry assaulting the position. Fourth Troop took up a position on some high ground on the left flank, which overlooked the position to provide fire support. The other two sabre Troops were to go to the left and right flanks of the position, laying down supressing fire as they went and engaging the armour. SHQ Troop would follow up in reserve, co-coordinating the attack. When they reached the FUP, which was being marked by two of Recce Troops' Scorpions, they lined up abreast of each other, with two platoons of infantry to the front. Once everyone was in place, they waited for the appointed time, to launch the attack.

With a revving of engines and in a billow of dense, black smoke, they crossed the start line. The Troops on the left and right flanks immediately began giving situation reports (sitreps) on their engagements. Second Troop followed approximately 100 metres behind the Infantry Armoured Personnel Carriers (APCs). When they were about 100 metres short of the infantry's dug in position, the APCs screeched to a halt. The back doors flew open and the mounted Troops disgorged on to the ground. After they had taken to ground, they began moving forward, in a leapfrog movement, just as the tanks had done. They did this in 'fire teams' of two men, moving at one time, within a section of eight. Reaching the required position, they threw grenades and followed in, behind them. Second Troop in Close Support was laying down supressing fire on the trench systems, with their coaxially mounted 7.62mm machine guns. These were fixed to the side of the main gun and provided a very stable platform. Although no live rounds were fired, they had had blank rounds issued and pyrotechnics, to provide some form of realism. The two flanking Troops fought their way on, through the position, and went firm a bound plus of it. Here, they scanned the ground ahead, for other enemy positions. It was their job to make sure they were not surprised by an outflanking manoeuvre or a counter attack. Once the infantry had fought through and confirmed they had seized the position, this was relayed to the Squadron Leader. He passed this, once again, to Battlegroup HQ, who ordered them to continue the advance. To their right flank A Squadron came across a similar position and dealt with it quickly. They went into holding positions, waiting for D Squadron to do the same. The Battlegroup now continued its move South West.

The Squadrons rolled on throughout the morning, with Recce Troop split into two halves. One half leading D Squadron's advance, while the other did the same for A Squadron. Gradually, the ground ahead was becoming tighter, as the axis of advance was squeezed by 'out of bounds' markers. These were areas where no vehicle movement was allowed, so movement was beginning to be very limited. The CO decided he would reduce the frontage of the advance. Instead of two Squadrons up, he let A Squadron lead the advance. This enabled the following Sabre Squadrons to relax, slightly. They trundled on behind, checking their flanks for any incursions by hidden enemy forces. As they advanced, they were alerted to the fact that Recce Troop had come across a river, which the Battlegroup would need to cross. They called forward the Royal Engineer Recce NCO, to assess the situation. After making his assessment it was deemed necessary that they would have to call forward one of the armoured bridge layers, to span the obstacle. While the lead Squadron secured the bridging site, the remainder of the Battlegroup awaited orders from HQ as to how the obstacle would be crossed. To provide cover for the bridge layer, a barrage of smoke was called down around one kilometre plus of the far side of the river. Richard watched the drama unfold through his sight, while the bridge layer was brought up from the rear. It took no longer than ten minutes for it to span the gap and withdraw from the site. This achieved, the CO gave his orders for the advance to continue, and D Squadron pushed through A Squadron on the near side of the bridge and secured the bank, on the other side. The other two sabre Squadrons and

Infantry Companies pushed through them and lined up, to continue on the axis of advance.

This continued, slowly, for the remainder of the day; it was not until the light was starting to change that Richard noticed they had not eaten since that morning. His eyes felt sore from the continuous scanning through his sight. They had been going for nearly ten hours, without a break. If they needed to urinate, they did it in crew positions into any container, they had to hand. This was then thrown over the side, at the first opportune moment. The Chieftain had an opening at the bottom of the turret, to which a bag could be attached. They could put your backsides against it and defecate, transporting the motion outside the vehicle without having to climb out.

The next two days were spent, slowly travelling back, towards the area from where they had started. They were managing a maximum of three hours' sleep a day and tempers were starting to fray. On the final morning of the exercise, the Squadron was awakened by the sound of metal being banged against metal and the words:

'Gas! Gas! Gas!' being bellowed by the chemical sentry, from his trench, upwind of the hide location.

All the men, instinctively, made a grab for their respirators on their webbing, either being worn or close to hand. They had approximately nine seconds to complete this procedure before becoming prone to any nerve agent attack. Once done, each one checked the man next to him, in what was known as a "buddy buddy" system. The sound of 'Gas! Gas! Gas!' echoed throughout the hide, as each person, in turn, completed his masking drill. They immediately went through their decontamination drills, checking their detection papers, which were worn on the patches of their NBC suits.

The next thing they did was to decontaminate their hands, with a pad, in a "blot, bang and rub" motion, finishing by putting on their gloves. Going under cover, they then decontaminated any exposed areas, such as face, ears, neck and hair. Once decontamination drills were complete, they remained either in their vehicles or under cover. Here, they stayed, until the orders came for the last push back, towards the 'Tank Bridge', which they had crossed some thirteen days earlier. For the next two hours, they remained fully masked up. After the area had been checked by the SSM and a small party, it was declared that the danger from chemical attack had passed and the order was given to reduce the NBC state to medium. This meant they could take off their respirators, which was a relief for everyone. As Richard removed his, he looked inside, it had filled with sweat, even though the temperature outside was only just above freezing point. Recce Troop were already on the move and had come across a sizeable force, defending both 'Strip and Finger Wood' on Area Two. This area was two kilometres east of the 'Tank Bridge.' It was a favourite place for an exercise to finish, as Robbo informed Richard.

Hastily taking the cam nets down, they prepared to move out. Both A and C Squadrons had already moved to the start line, they were going to lead the assault. D Squadron and B Squadron were to act as reserves. Each Troop, once ready, departed from the wood and took their positions, facing west behind the lead two Squadrons. Once the reserve two Squadrons were in position, A and C Squadrons and an Infantry Company moved to the FUP. The artillery barrage had already begun and would be lifted, at the last safe moment. Richard watched the attack go in, but the enemy positions were obscured by the carpet of smoke laid down by the umpires, using smoke grenades. He felt a little disheartened at not being involved in the final attack. He had learned so much over that past couple of weeks and this was a bit of an anti-climax. Fifteen minutes later, the instantly recognisable voice of Crazy Red was heard on the radio:

'Endex, Endex, Endex! All call signs move to the following grid,' and proceeded to send the grid still in its encoded form. There was no need to decode it, as everyone knew they would be assembling just short of the tank bridge. As the tanks moved off to the rallying point, a voice was heard over the air, announcing 'Black Mug.' This, in turn, was repeated by another, then another. Richard turned round and looked inquisitively at Robbo, who obliged with an explanation. It was a tradition at the end of an exercise for some crews to crack open a bottle of whatever they carried and pour it into their Army issued 'Black Mugs'. So, these were the code words used, as a form of celebration, to announce that the exercise was over. As he explained, Tommo pulled a bottle of German Asbach brandy from one of the projectile racks. He poured the golden liquid into four mugs and passed them round. Ian would have to wait until they had stopped before he got his.

Sitting on top of the turret, feeling totally exhausted, Richard sipped on his brandy. He looked round the members of his crew and Troop and felt a sense of belonging. He was stirred from his thoughts by the sound of a bell ringing. In the distance, he observed the familiar sight of a blue Mercedes Benz van. Every soldier, who had spent any time on the training area, knew this sound and sight. It was 'Wolfgang', who was a purveyor of "bratties", chips, chicken breast, currywurst and all other manner of goodies. It did not matter where the lads were situated on the training area, in places inaccessible to military vehicles, somehow Wolfgang would turn up, out of the blue and ring his bell. This had happened eight days ago, before the Regimental exercise had begun. Richard's Squadron had moved into a wooded area, for the evening. They were fully tactical and not a light was observed, nor a sound heard. All of a sudden, out of the darkness, appeared a set of headlights, and the ringing bell was heard. Regardless of where they were, Wolfgang would always seem to find his clientele. Some thought he was a Soviet spy and monitored not only their tactics, but also their radio transmissions. The normal squaddie didn't give a fuck about this, because beer and food came into the equation. They could be seen like lemmings, attracted to the cliff edge, wandering over, waiting to be served. It was no different this time, as the queue stretched around 50 metres, with guys from all the support arms, waiting patiently to be served. Tommo also joined the queue and returned laden with four offerings, wrapped up in pink paper. He handed one each to the crew and they tucked in. As they were just about finished, the call came for them to mount up and head back towards Reinsehlen Camp, but this time, via the wash-down.

The journey from the Tank Bridge to the wash-down, once again transiting under the viaduct, took little less than fifteen minutes. As they approached the entrance to the wash-down, a Squadron was already busy, hosing down its vehicles. They lined up and waited their turn, removing their bazooka plates in preparation. This allowed them access to the running gear, such as road wheels, suspension and top rollers. This was where most mud had accumulated, over the past two weeks. Some of the crews opened bottles of beer and drank, while waiting to be called forward. It was a full hour before Second Troop were given the okay to pull forward. Ian revved the engine and followed Robbo, Tommo and Richard, as they led the way on to the cattle grid, next to a set of hoses, on either side of the vehicle. They had only just started and the Quartermaster (QM) was already haranguing the Troops, telling them to 'get a fucking move on!' They began to attempt to clean down the vehicle, starting at the top and working their way down. All the QM was interested in was that they cleaned the worst mud off their running gear, so that it did not leave a mess on the road to the railhead, which was adjacent to the wash-down. The hoses, which were supposed to be high pressure, spurted out what looked like liquid mud because the water was recycled from the vehicles that had already gone through. For some reason, where water was involved, it brought out childish behaviour in the crewmen, which resulted in them getting more water on themselves than on the tanks! They were only given around fifteen minutes per vehicle and before long, their time was up. They were then instructed to pull up on the other side, behind the other vehicles, already lined up. As they neared the rearmost vehicle, they observed a soldier, naked and clasping his privates with his hands. He was making a dash down the whole line of vehicles around them, then down the other side. They later found out that one of the Squadrons had held a 'kangaroo court'; someone on one of the crews had been stealing chocolate from the compo rations. These affairs were quite funny for all the men, except the accused. A defending lawyer and a prosecutor were nominated; someone was given the post of judge. Others from the Squadron formed the jury and gave the 'guilty' or 'not guilty' verdict, after hearing the evidence. This was normally contrived and weighted heavily on the prosecution side. This unfortunate had obviously been found guilty and was carrying out his punishment.

Richard smiled to himself, as they slowly moved forward, with the rest of the vehicles, towards the railhead. They began the loading process, just as they had done, when leaving camp. This seemed like an eternity ago, and although he was exhausted from the past three days exertions, Richard felt he had achieved something. He had survived his first exercise and grown closer to his crew mates and Troop. He was slightly saddened, though, that he had not come face to face with the elusive 'drop bears'. "Maybe next time," he thought. As he settled comfortably in the carriage, Richard closed his eyes and began to dream of what the future would hold for him.

Chapter 26 – Berlin Bound

Richard removed the projectile rack from its mounting in the turret and placed it to one side. He had already removed the turret floor and the rest of the racks. It had been three months since the exercise on Soltau. On their return, the Squadrons had entered into an intense period of activity. There was only one week until they handed over their equipment and accommodation to the incoming Regiment. "This time next week, we will be in Berlin, as part of the Armoured Squadron of the British Brigade stationed there," Richard thought, to himself. As he did so, he called to mind the reasons why Troops were stationed deep inside the 'Iron Curtain'.

The victorious forces at the end of the war divided Germany into four zones. They also divided Berlin into four zones. Each of the victorious nations controlled one zone and one sector of Berlin.

The Allies (Britain, America and France) ran their zones differently to the areas controlled by Russia. Russia wanted to keep Germany as weak as possible to ensure that Russia itself was never attacked again by Germany. They also took from their zones whatever was needed by Russia so that it could be used in Russia itself. This way, Russia could start to rebuild itself at Germany's expense and the Germans would be kept poor.

The Allies believed that a strong Germany would enable democracy to prosper after the years of Nazi dictatorship. They also believed that Europe needed a strong Germany so that their economies would prosper. To enable their zones to work more effectively, the British, Americans and French decided to amalgamate their zones into one unit and introduced into that one unit a new currency - the Deutschmark. All four occupying forces had agreed to inform one another if changes were going to be made in their respective zones. This the Allies failed to do with regards to Russia.

The biggest problem for Stalin was that the German people of the Russian controlled block could not see the prosperity that was occurring in the other zones - but they could see the difference in Berlin as three of the zones in Berlin were controlled by the Allies and prospered accordingly. Therefore, to Stalin, the Allies being in Berlin was the problem. He needed to remove them from Berlin and have a Russian controlled city as opposed to a segment of that city.

Stalin could not forcibly remove the Allies - he still had to reckon with America having the A-bomb and Russia did not in 1948. He therefore ordered the closing of all rail lines, canals and roads that entered West

Berlin through the Russian sector. This cut off supplies of food and fuel. The only way for the Allies to supply their sectors in Berlin was to fly in supplies. Stalin would not dare to shoot down Allied planes with America's atomic supremacy. Flights into Berlin lasted for 11 months and when it became clear that the Allies would stand firm, Stalin gave in. (http://www.historylearningsite.co.uk/berlin_1945.htm)

The 7th Armour Division (Desert Rats) and 1st Grenadier Guards entered Berlin on the 4th of July, 1945. From 1945 until 1954 the British HQ was located in the Lancaster House in the district of Wilmersdorf. It was then moved to the compound at the Olympic stadium in Charlottenburg. The core of the British Brigade was made up by three infantry battalions and one armoured squadron. The infantry battalions rotated every two years the armoured squadron also every two years.

The first British plane landed on Gatow Airfield on July 2nd, 1945. On August 1st it officially became Royal Air Force Gatow. During the Potsdam conference the Gatow area was traded with the soviets which in turn received the airport Staaken-Dallgow. In 1947 a concrete landing strip was built.

The day finally arrived and the Squadron handed over their tanks to the incoming Regiment. As Richard left his room for the last time, he glanced back and smiled, thinking of the good times he had enjoyed during his first six months in the Regiment. The practical jokes had stopped and he had, at last, been accepted by his Troop and the Squadron as a whole. They would be going their separate ways now, the majority heading off to Catterick in North Yorkshire. There, they would provide the vehicles and manpower for the Training Regiment for the Royal Armoured Corps. A select few from different Squadrons had been chosen to form the Armoured Berlin Tank Squadron. Richard was one of those picked and felt excited, as he made his way, with his belongings, to the Regimental parade square. The remainder of the Regiment had left the previous day, for their flights back to the UK.

On his arrival on the square, Richard saw that the majority of the newly formed Squadron were already there. He made his way to four others from D Squadron, who had been selected, greeting them, as he placed his suitcase on the ground. They entered into conversation, discussing the journey ahead. They were to be taken, by military bus, to the airport at Hanover. There, they would take a military flight, to RAF Gatow in Berlin, which was the only port of entry by air, for military personnel. The other two routes were by road, along what was known as the 'Berlin Corridor.' Those making that journey had to book in at the Western Checkpoint at

Helmstedt, known as 'Alpha', where odometer readings were taken. After passing through a Soviet manned checkpoint, they then made their way along a road, without deviating from it, to checkpoint 'Bravo'. Here another odometer reading was taken, to ensure they had not strayed from the route. The third method was by rail, on what was known as the 'British Military Train' (BMT).

Once the roll had been taken and they had received their movement brief, the Troops boarded the waiting buses. Richard took a seat, next to one of the blokes from his former Squadron. His name was Dave Paris, given the obvious nickname 'Ken' by his mates in Third Troop. He and Richard were to be in the same Troop, when they arrived in Berlin. Ken had been in the Regiment about a year longer than Richard and was also a gunner. They had been given the same job, on different tanks, within their new Troop. Richard asked Ken if he knew any of their new Troop members. Ken replied that he only recognised around 50 percent of the names. The ones he did know, were the Commanders. The Troop Leader was an established Lieutenant, who had completed just over two years in the Regiment. It seemed that most of the Officers, Senior Non Commissioned Officers (SNCO) and Junior Non Commissioned Officers (JNCO) had been chosen for their experience.

They chatted over stories heard about the night life in Berlin, and couldn't wait to experience it for themselves. The two, along with a couple of others, were to become really good friends and would keep in touch, after their careers ended.

The bus journey to Hanover Airport took less than an hour. After a two hour wait, they boarded the military flight to Berlin. The flight took just an hour and, as the seatbelt signs were lit, Richard prepared himself for the landing. Looking out of the window, Richard saw that the aircraft had already begun its descent, through the clouds. It was grey and murky, and it made Richard feel a little depressed. As the plane touched down on the runway at RAF Gatow, all on board realised they were now behind the Iron Curtain. West Berlin was just an enclave of Western democracy, surrounded by the Soviet Third Shock Army. The very name of this formation made Richard's skin tingle. Disembarking, the Squadron made its way to the Arrivals Lounge, to await their luggage. In less than twenty minutes, the cases and bags were unloaded and collected. The Troops made their way outside, where, again, two buses were waiting for them, their engines running. They stowed their luggage in the compartments at the bottom of the buses, and boarded for the 30 minute journey to 'Smuts Barracks', in the Spandau area of the city.

Smuts Barracks was situated on the Wilhelmstrasse, in the district of Spandau. The barracks were built between 1883 and 1886, originally housing a train unit. Also on the Wilhelmstrasse, Spandau Prison had housed seven war criminals from the Nuremburg trials. Now, it only had one inmate, Rudolph Hess, who had the whole prison to himself. The three Allied powers, Britain, the United States and France, along with the Soviet Union rotated guard duty. It was rumoured that when the Soviets' turn came around, they removed any luxuries the previous guards had given Hess. Each nation in charge would bring its own cook, and in the American, French, and British regimes, the prisoner would be fed better than regulations allowed. The Soviets provided an unchanging diet of coffee, bread, soup, and potatoes.

Guard duty didn't appeal to Richard, but, thankfully, he found out that it was just the Infantry Battalions who had the responsibility of providing guards.

As the buses entered the gates, the sentry lifted the barrier, to let them in. They were obviously expected. An advance party from the Squadron, consisting of Officers, SNCOs and JNCOs, had arrived, a couple of days earlier. They had already taken over the vehicles and equipment from the outgoing Regiment, the Royal Hussars. This changeover included taking over the ammunition each tank carried, as they were always 'fully bombed up'. Richard's father had been assigned as the SQMS and had taken over the single accommodation, known as the 'Berlin Hilton'. This was an unusual situation, as fathers and sons were normally assigned to different squadrons. Richard was to find out, however, that there would be no favouritism shown to him during his time with the Squadron. The first time he had evidence of this, was when clothing was issued from the stores. Everyone received brand new coveralls, except Richard, who was given four second hand sets. While they were in very good condition, he still felt a little downhearted. He soon cheered up, when the men were taken to their accommodation. All single soldiers in the Troop were assigned a single room. The rooms came complete with a fitted carpet, wardrobe and a washbasin. This was a world apart from the four-man rooms, which most of them were used to. Each Troop lived on a different floor, which had its own toilet and shower room, complete with washing area. They had also been provided with a kitchen and communal room, with a TV. Richard was pleased that Pete had been assigned to the Squadron, although to a different Troop. That stay would not be for long, as they were to find out in the coming months.

As Richard entered the accommodation, the men were ushered towards a lift. Each of the Troops was on a floor designated by their Troop number. As Third Troop, they would be located on the third floor. Placing their luggage in the lift, Ken pressed the button for the third floor. In a matter of seconds, the door opened for them to exit. Walking through the glass doors ahead, they entered a highly polished corridor. There were six rooms on each side of the corridor, and Richard found his name on a door, second from the end. Ken's room was on the opposite side. Opening the door, Richard could not believe how immaculately clean the room was. He now understood why the premises had been given the name Berlin Hilton, this was like walking into a plush hotel room. Placing his bags on the floor, Richard began to go through the check list he had been left. It was every single soldier's responsibility to check and sign for the bedding and other items in his room. He was, at the same time, to inspect the serviceability of the furniture and note any damage. When he 'marched out' of the room in two years' time, any damage would have to be charged. Richard had received this lecture from his father, so was fastidious in checking his room. All the Troops had been given the rest of the day off, to settle in. They were to parade at 08:30 the next day, on the tank park. The newly formed Troop decided that all those living in would meet in the bar, after the evening meal, in order to get to know each other a little, before the next day. The married guys were busy taking over their married quarters, on Darbystrasse. This was about a twenty minute drive from the camp and where Richard's parents, brother and sister would be living. This meant that the married men would not get to meet everyone, prior to parade, the next day.

Richard decided that once he had put everything away, he would explore a little. Taking the lift down to the ground floor, he wandered around. The first place he came to was the cookhouse. This looked more like a hotel restaurant in the way it was set out, complete with table cloths and cutlery on the tables. The chefs had to cater for the Armoured Squadron and a Squadron of Royal Engineers, 38 Field Squadron. Exploring further, he reached a series of rooms, intended for leisure. The first contained books, magazines and newspapers, the next a snooker and pool table and the third room for table tennis. Just next to this, was a large bar area and a NAAFI shop for all their administration requirements. Everything they needed was contained within the accommodation and there was no need to go elsewhere. Richard had only been there a few hours, and he was already enamoured by it. Meeting up with Ken and ordering their evening meals, his opinion of the place thus far was cemented. All the meals were cooked to order, from a menu for the day. Richard and Ken both ordered medium steaks and waited, as they were cooked in front of them.

'I could get used to this,' Ken commented, as they waited.

'Me too!' was Richard's genuine reply.

The pair sat down and tucked into their steaks. The meat just fell apart as they cut into it and melted in the mouth. They could not fault anything and wondered why it was of such a high standard. They later found out the food supplied to the Allied forces in the city was sold at a discounted prices. The chefs were cooking for smaller numbers than usual and this meant they could deliver higher quality. Richard looked around and wondered why, given the quality of the food, the 'restaurant', as it was called, was so empty. Afterwards, he would find, that due to the abundance of local restaurants, a lot of soldiers would eat out, a couple of times a week. Their meals eaten, the pair returned to the third floor, showered and arranged to meet in the bar, when it opened at 7pm.

The bar was around twenty feet long and was surrounded by a comfortable seating area, directly opposite and around the sides. There were two NAFFI girls working behind the bar, and one of them, catching Richard's eye, asked what he was having to drink. As he pondered, Ken entered the room, asking him what he wanted. Richard ordered two beers known as 'Schultheiss', a local Berlin beer. Over the ensuing two years, more than a few of these would be consumed. Before long, they were joined by other members of the Troop, who quickly introduced themselves, if they did not know each other already. As the introductions came to an end, Richard noticed a group of four blokes in track suits, carrying bags. One of them went to the bar, while the other three sat at the table next to Richard and the new members of Third Troop. It came to light that they were members of the Royal Hussars rear party. They were remaining there until the next day, to provide the 'Alert Troop' for the Squadron. Richard, inquisitive about what this entailed, asked if they could elaborate. The Hussar who turned out to be one of the Troop Corporals, explained that the Squadron had a Troop on high alert for a week at a time. They had to have their kit with them at all times, ready to deploy, if the alarm called 'Pony Express' was given. They had a maximum of fifteen minutes to get to their vehicles, start them and reach the front gates, ready to depart, to designated areas. The record timing was three and a half minutes, however, this was with prior warning. One of the rules for alert Troop was that each man was only allowed a maximum of two beers, during the whole week on alert. For the other four weeks, it was 'party time', they explained. There was an abundance of drinking establishments throughout the city, where you could obtain alcohol 24 hours a day. The four Berlin 'old hands', gave them a few names of night clubs and pubs that were worth a visit. The Hussars were thanked, finished their soft drinks and disappeared.

The drink started to flow and round followed round. It wasn't long before the bell sounded for last orders. Richard dashed to the bar, as it was his turn to get them in. He ordered a full round of brandy and cokes and a crate of beer to go. Passing over the money, he didn't give a second thought about how he would feel in the morning.

As the duty Sergeant ushered them out of the bar, the Troop made their way to the lifts. Just as they approached, the doors were closing but they caught a glimpse of a female draped around a drunken looking Royal Engineer. Over their time there, they would become very familiar with this young lady, who would be given the nickname 'Jenny Mess Tin' by one of the Squadron. Reaching their floor, it was decided they would use the communal TV room, to carry on the party. Over the next hour or so, they got to know each other better, until the beer ran out. As it had been a long day, they decided to turn in for the night. Closing the door to his room, Richard undressed, fell into his bed and within minutes was fast asleep.

Chapter 27 – Berlin the Party City

The sunlight broke through Richard's window, waking him, immediately. His mouth tasted stale, from the beer consumed the previous night. He rubbed his eyes, to remove the sleep from them, then, swung his feet out of bed. It seemed strange not to be looking across at another two bodies, stirring from their slumber. Or, indeed, the sounds of farting and coughing, which had been normal for the past six months. As he gathered his towel and wash kit, he instinctively went to open the door. It was then he remembered that he had the luxury of his own wash basin. Putting the plug in the wash basin, he filled it to the brim with hot water. As he washed and shaved, he thought to himself that this was almost like being on holiday. The sun was shining outside, birds were singing and everything seemed good with the world. It took him only ten minutes to finish his morning routine before he was dressed and ready to go for breakfast. As he opened the door and entered the corridor, he almost walked into a stern looking type, who was knocking on doors, rising occupants from their sleep.

'Up you get, you lazy twats!' He shouted into each room, in his broad South Yorkshire accent. He reminded Richard of the character Casper in the film *Kes*, the story of a young lad in a South Yorkshire mining town who befriended a Kestrel. The only difference was that this loudmouth didn't seem vulnerable. His coveralls were heavily starched and had creases sewn in. He wore the insignia of a Corporal on his right arm. As he made eye contact with Richard, he sneered at him malevolently.

'What's tha' looking at, young man?' he sneered, not expecting an answer.

'Nothing, Corporal,' Richard replied, timidly, feeling like he was back in training. He had seen this NCO about the Regiment and he was always turned out immaculately. He glanced at the name tape, worn by everyone, above their left breast pocket. The name was unpronounceable, but started with a K and ended in ski. Richard guessed that he must have been of Polish descent, as there were a number of brothers in the Regiment with that lineage. He was looking Richard up and down making an assessment of him. Without a word, he turned away and continued to knock on doors.

Once Ken and Richard had finished breakfast, they returned to their rooms. The stern looking Corporal with the strange name was busy organising the cleaning of the toilets and communal areas. 'Nothing changes,' thought Richard to himself, realising this was not a hotel after all. They were put to work scrubbing the showers and mopping floors. Others from the Troop were sweeping the corridor or hovering the TV room. For the next twenty minutes the Corporal toured the floor, checking up that all jobs were completed to his satisfaction. Once he was happy, he dismissed the Troops, informing them that they needed to be on parade in ten minutes time. Richard had forgotten about his slight hangover as he hadn't had time to dwell on it. This guy was obviously a hard task master and Richard hoped he was not his commander.

The Troops began to assemble on the tank park, with SHQ on the left hand side, then the Troops in sequential order ending with Fourth Troop on the right hand side. The SSM marched on to the tank park, with his blackthorn stick under his arm. He was slightly portly, with a waxed moustache. Reaching the centre of the tank park, he halted, smartly. Bringing the parade to attention, he ordered the right hand man to dress the ranks, in open order. Once he was happy, he turned to his left, to await the arrival of the Squadron Leader. As the Squadron Leader approached, the SSM took one smart pace forward, slammed in his right foot and saluted.

'Berlin Armoured Squadron, on parade and awaiting your inspection, Sir!'

The Squadron Leader returned the salute and thanked the SSM, who promptly turned to his right and fell in, at the end of the Squadron. The Officers were then ordered to fall in, and halted in the centre of their Troops and advanced to face the Officer Commanding (OC). The OC then gave a few words of welcome to his new charges, highlighting what would be coming up over the next few months. This was to include Her Majesty the Queen's birthday parade to be held in the Olympic Stadium, an Allied Forces day parade, and the Berlin Tattoo. There would also be a few small exercises thrown in for good measure. It would not all be work though, there would be plenty of opportunities for sports and leisure time. It was his intention that the Squadron would get the most out of their two year posting away from the Regiment. Standing fast SHQ Troop, he commanded the Troop Leaders to inspect their Troops.

The Troop Leaders did an about turn and were greeted by their Troop Sergeants, who led them along the ranks, starting with the front rank. The Third Troop Sergeant was a six feet four giant of a man, with not an ounce of fat on him. He was called Tim Hauxwell, but was known throughout the Regiment as 'Hux'. As he came to each person, he introduced them to the Troop Leader, explaining what position and what crew they would be on. As the Troop Leader came to Richard, Hux explained that he was the gunner of Lance Corporal Grant Mitchell on 43 Charlie. The Troop Leader whose name was Wheelstone, paused for a moment, then asked.

'Hunter, are you any relation to SQMS Hunter?'

'Yes, Sir, he's my father,' was Richard's quiet reply.

'I see the similarity, good to have you on board,' he said, looking down his nose at Richard.

Richard had the feeling that his father had upset this guy at some point or he did not like the fact that he was related to someone of rank within the Regiment. He expected that he would not have an easy time of it over the coming months. Moving on, his attitude changed as he came to the huge bloke immediately to Richard's right.

'How you doing, Lance Corporal Kossak?' he asked, amiably.

'I'm fine, Sir, how's yourself?' his deep Cumbrian twang carried half way across the tank park. They were obviously well acquainted, by the friendliness of their manner. They had possibly served together prior to them being posted to Berlin. Richard was later to find out this was to be his new commander. One of the blokes, called Duggan, was torn a strip off by both the Troop Leader, Sergeant and the immaculately dressed Corporal Kotowski. Corporal Kotowski asked him if he had used shit for toothpaste that morning, as his breath was putrid. He was warned that if he turned up on parade, in such a state again he would be put in jail. Out of a Troop of sixteen, two of them were of Polish extraction, they seemed however to be completely different in their bearing. The Troop inspections over, the Troop leaders returned to the front of their Troops. The Squadron Leader returned to his position and handed back to the SSM. The SSM saluted and gave the command for the Squadron to fall out. After saluting and marching three paces, they headed off to their respective hangars.

Entering the hangar, Richard was taken aback by the pristine look of not only the hangar floors and walls, but the tanks themselves. They looked like they had just rolled off the production line. The commanders called out the names of their crews, to gather round the front of their vehicles. Gathering round the front of their vehicle their new commander introduced himself with his full name, but informed them it was okay to call him 'Albert', as long as there was no one of authority around. He told them that he was a firm but fair man, but not to piss him off by not doing what he asked. They all nodded in agreement, as this sounded fair. He then asked each of the crew to introduce themselves, giving a brief outline of their careers. Richard gave his quick introduction giving his last Squadron and job and how long he had been in the Regiment. The driver was called Solomon Kane (Sol), he came from Bradford, had previously been with C

Squadron and had been in the Regiment for just under a year. Their Operator/loader was a tall, good lucking bloke, from a small village in the country, near Halifax. He was called Paul Holmes but insisted on being called 'H'. He had joined up three years previously, his whole time also being spent with C Squadron. Albert had been in the army for ten years and had spent most of that time in A Squadron, as a driver. So, it was no surprise, that he was an Instructor in Driving and Maintenance (D&M). The introductions over, Albert asked them to empty all the bins and lay the equipment out on the hangar floor. This was to be done as per the 'Complete Equipment Schedule' (CES), a booklet listing all the equipment that was carried on an Armoured Fighting Vehicle (AFV).

The rest of the morning was spent laying out the equipment, as Albert called it out from the booklet. Once they were done and made notes of any deficiencies, each member of the crew signed for their tools. When they finished their posting, and were handing over, anything that was missing would have to be paid for. Every three months the commanders would carry out an equipment check, so that they could keep on top of any missing tools. They would also check the serviceability of equipment every month, known as a 'Board of Survey' (BOS). Any equipment worn, or not fit for purpose, was exchanged for new. After the tools had been checked, the crews did a first parade on the vehicles. All oil levels were spot on and the fighting compartment was gleaming. The running gear did not have one hint of dried mud or oil leak. What would they do with their time, Richard pondered? This question was soon answered by Hux who called them over to his vehicle.

'Okay, guys, that's a good morning's work. The tanks seem to be in good nick, with only a couple of small things to do. The Troop Leader and I, have decided that you can take this afternoon off, to do a bit of local orientation. Try and make sure you don't kick the arse out of it and we will see you back here 08:30 Monday' and with that he ushered them out of the hangar, asking one of the Troop NCOs to ensure they locked up and handed the keys into the Squadron Office. With an excited buzz the single lad's bomb burst back to the Hilton. Richard had not realised that it was the weekend already. They had left their old camp early on Thursday morning. Catching the lift, they headed up to the third floor, a few of them including Richard, Ken, and Sol agreeing to meet in 30 minutes.

Before leaving the Hilton, they popped into the Women's Royal Volunteer Service (WRVS), where a kind, elderly lady gave them information on bus and tube costs. It only cost one Deutsche Mark and 80 pfennigs to catch a bus from the Heer Strasse to Theodor Heuss Platz. From here they could take the tube to Bahnof Zoo, which was in the heart of the city. This could be done using the same ticket, only if you were changing direction did you need to get a new ticket. This appealed to the young soldiers as it meant more beer tokens, as was pointed out so eloquently by Ken. Leaving camp, they turned right and made the short walk down Wilhelm Strasse to the Heer Strasse. Here, they waited for the bus that would take them to the Underground Station (U-Bahn) at Theodor Heuss Platz. Examining the time table they learned the buses ran every twenty minutes. Within ten minutes a bus arrived and, climbing on board the group of six young soldiers purchased a ticket each. Ascending the stairs to the top deck of the double decker, they looked for some seats where they could all sit together. Richard bid good day to people, as they moved along the bus. His German was passable but would get a lot better over the coming months.

The journey to Theodor Heuss Platz along the Heer Strasse took only fifteen minutes. They had not realised that for a city it was quite green, and had a number of lakes, used for recreation. They had passed over one of these, the 'Wannsee' on the way, they would come more familiar with it during their time there. Leaving the bus, they entered the underground system and looked for signs for the Bahnhof Zoo. Sol spotted it and directed them to platform one. Within two minutes they were heading east, into the heart of the city. The carriage was full with young and old people alike, and Richard eyed two pretty girls, engaged in conversation. Plucking up courage, he approached them and asked in his best German, recommendations of decent pubs or night clubs. He felt a wave of relief, when, after conferring, they answered, giving him a list of four or five places to visit. They seemed genuinely interested in him and were giggling between themselves. Richard smiled and thanked them for the information.

'Looks like it could be an interesting night. If those two are anything to go by,' he said, after returning to his seat and addressing the group of friends. They nodded their heads in agreement, after watching and listening to Richard's conversation with the young girls. They were only one stop away from their destination and they assembled by the door, ready to exit, as it pulled into the station. There was no need to rush though, Berlin was a city that functioned 24 hours a day.

Pulling into the Bahnof Zoo, the friends made their way out from the underground, passing beggars and buskers on the way. As they climbed the stairs, the evening sun was still quite warm, and the noise level had risen considerably. Everywhere there were cars, buses and motorbikes blasting their horns. Weaving in and out of the lanes, trying to make the journey to their destinations as short as possible. Richard could tell that like all big cities, Berlin was full of bustle and excitement. Everywhere they looked, buildings were lit up with neon signs. Directly in front of them was a tall, blue building made of glass, directly next to an old church. This was known as the 'blue church' and had been built after the original church was bombed during the Second World War. It was situated on one end of the Kurfürstendamm or Ku'damm, as it was known colloquially. This was one of the busiest streets in the West of the city, which was a stark contrast to the East. It was renowned for its night life, restaurants and theatres. On the opposite side of the road, they spotted a bar. Richard recognized it being one mentioned by the girls on the tube. Looking both ways, and waiting for a break in the traffic, the group crossed the road and headed for the bar. Its name was the Pal Joes and it stood on the corner of the Ku'damm. They secured a table outside and waited for a waiter or waitress to arrive. In no time at all, even though the establishment was almost full, they had been served and were enjoying a round of beers. They surveyed the scene, as scantily clad girls strolled along the Ku'damm.

'This is fucking great!' Sol said, licking his lips and scratching his groin.

The boys were like the crowd at Wimbledon, their heads moving from left to right, not wanting to miss a thing. Richard was like a kid in a sweet shop, and at just eighteen years of age his hormones were going mental. The beers flowed continuously for the next two hours, before they decided to move on. They had heard of an Irish bar in a place called the Europa Centre. Enquiring from one of the waitresses, they found it was only a five minute walk from where they were sitting, just past the blue church. Splitting the bill between them, they left a tip to the pretty young waitress that had provided the directions. Again, crossing the road in the direction they had just come from, they passed the blue church on their left. Approximately 200 metres in front of them, a tall glass building rose up. There was a neon sign saying 'Europa Centre' across its front and a large rotating Mercedes sign on its roof. The group entered the building at ground floor level, and immediately could hear the unmistakable sound of Irish folk music. They followed the sound as it got louder and louder. On a sign 50 metres to their front, was a green sign with cream coloured Gaelic lettering saying simply 'The Irish Pub'. They made a bee line for the doors. Opening them, they were hit by a wave of music and singing. The atmosphere was great and the friends smiled at each other as they headed to the bar. The decor was done out like an authentic Irish pub, and ordering six pints of Guinness the barmaid immediately answered them with an Irish lilt. She had obviously picked up from their dress that they were not locals. As the troubles in Northern Ireland were at their height, the group had already decided that they would not promote the fact that they were

British soldiers. The barmaid asked what they were doing in Berlin. Richard, quick as a flash, came up with the tale that they were builders, working on a contract for the next twelve months. This would give them a cover story for the next time they were in there. Richard wasn't sure if she believed it though, but she smiled, so he was happy enough. As a young lad, his mother had played Irish music on the many occasions when she and his father had returned from a function in the Warrant Officers & Sergeants Mess. This was normally in the early hours of the morning, and went on till daybreak sometimes. He knew most of the songs being played by the live band on the stage. Before long, he was clapping his hands in time, stomping his feet and joining in. The atmosphere was infectious and for the next couple of hours the six of them drank, sang and made merry. It was not until they were about to leave, that Richard noticed that both Sol and the Troop Leaders gunner, a guy called Lofty, were chatting to two girls in the corner. Told the lads were moving on, they said they would catch up. Ken said that they would be checking out the nightclub they had been given a name of. It was not far from the Europa Centre, so they promised to be back in a short while. The two of them nodded their heads, not braking eye contact with the girls' ample top halves.

Leaving the Europa Centre, the four remaining friends walked for about 300 metres before they spotted the sign for the night club called 'Take Off'. On investigation, they deduced that it was still not open, as it was only 21:00. The timings on the door, said it opened from 23:00 until 06:00. Happy that they could find it again, and the realising they were feeling a little peckish, they decided to collect the two from the Irish bar and then find something to eat. Having separated the two love birds from their conquests, the group found a 'Schnell Imbiss' which were littered on nearly every street corner. They ate until they had their fill, ordering bratwurst, currywurst and chips with mayonnaise and ketchup. However, when Richard came to ordering his, he thought he would have a 'Frikadella', which was like a meat patty with onions. He pronounced it in his best German, only to be met with a quizzical look from the vendor. It came to pass, after much gesticulation, that in Berlin these were known as 'Boulette'. Richard felt suitably embarrassed, as the rest of the group taunted him for the next ten minutes. He realised this was the army way and took it on the chin, laughing with them. He would not forget this, making a mental note to remember these local variations, knowing he would encounter other small differences in this German enclave.

Wiping their mouths clean, the friends continued down the Ku'damm, until they came across an entrance to a place called Ku'damm Karree. This was an indoor shopping boulevard, and it seemed to be very busy for that time of night. The friends decided to take a little look around and found that it was littered with little bars as well as shops.

'This is my kind of shopping!' Lofty laughed, as he pointed to one of the bars.

Laughing at this remark, they decided to squeeze a quick one in, before they returned to the night club they had found earlier. As they walked through the doorway, they were greeted by a very friendly, blonde haired, buxom barmaid. She asked them what they wanted, and Richard ordered a round of beers. Each of them taking a stool at the bar they waited the couple of minutes it usually took to pour a German beer. Their glasses filled, and placed in front of them, Ken raised his and with a grin proposed.

'Here's to the first of many great nights, lads,' and with this, he touched everyone's glass with his own. This was echoed by the six friends, and they took a deep gulp of the ice cold beer. They chatted amongst themselves, but Richard's eyes were continuously drawn to the barmaid. Was it his imagination, or was she checking him out every so often? Putting the thought to the back of his mind, he and the others made their plans for the rest of the evening. This entailed leaving this bar and heading to the nightclub where they would dance till dawn. Depending on how they felt, they would either return to camp, for some much needed sleep, or have breakfast and carry on. Richard knew which one he favoured. As they had just been paid, it looked like it was going to be a long weekend. As the group finished their drinks and were ready to head off, out of the corner of his eye, Richard saw the barmaid, looking over in his direction. Thinking that maybe she was interested, he said that he would catch them up in the night club. Ken caught his gaze and simply smiled at him, patting him on the shoulder he bid him farewell until later.

'If you're not there by 01:00 we'll send out a search party!' he joked, as they left the bar.

It was the norm for people not to be left on their own, unless they knew that the single man was going to be safe. Richard waited for the other five to depart, before ordering himself another beer. The barmaid smiled at him and began to pour a glass, holding it an angle of 45 degrees. Once the froth reached the top, she scraped it off with a piece of plastic. Again, waiting for it to settle, she asked Richard in broken English if he was visiting Berlin. He thought for a while, before answering, and, as she appeared to be friendly, he had no reason to deny he was in the British Army. Speaking in his best German, he explained that he and his friends had just been posted there and were stationed in Spandau. On hearing this, she immediately complimented him on his use of German. Not many soldiers, she said, even attempted to learn the basic rudiments of the language. So, she must have come across a few, thought Richard to himself. As the conversation flowed and gathered pace, he found that she was single and five years his senior. She lived in a rough area of the city called Kreuzberg, which was a twenty minute tube ride from the Ku'damm. They were joined by a middle aged man probably in his late thirties. He took a stool next to Richard and ordered a beer. He bid Richard a good day, and said that he had overheard their conversation from his seat at the other end of the bar. He also complimented Richard on his use of the German language. Richard smiled to show his appreciation and asked if the man would like a beer. The German accepted and the barmaid, who Richard had found out was called Annette, obliged and set the beer in front of the guy. The newcomer was called Danny, and had a very flamboyant air about him. He smoked his cigarette in an almost feminine manner, with his fingers outstretched. He explained that he was an actor working in one of the theatres on the Ku'damm. This was his local, and he came here for a few beers after a performance.

As the conversation ebbed to and fro, Richard was really warming to the pair, but especially Annette, who seemed genuinely interested in him. Glancing at his watch, he noticed the time had flown by, and it was close to 01:00. He decided he had better head off to the night club and meet his friends before they came looking for him. Saying goodbye to his new found friends, he promised he would be back either sometime that weekend, or in the near future. Annette and Danny bade him farewell until the next time, and the look she gave Richard caused something to stir. Heading off back down the Ku'damm, it took him twenty minutes to reach the night club and a queue had already formed. Richard took his place and shuffled along with the rest. Within five minutes he had paid his money and been given a stamp on his hand to prove that he had paid. He began to survey the mass of bodies assembled in the huge bar and dance area. On the far side on a raised platform he spotted his comrades and made his way over to them.

'We were starting to get worried there,' Ken shouted over the sound of the music as Richard approached.

'I got carried away with that barmaid. Does anyone want another drink?' Richard replied, with a shit eating grin on his face. They all shook their heads, as it looked as though they had just got a round in prior to Richard's arrival. The evening was passing by and everyone was having a great time. The young ladies who frequented the establishment were used to the presence of soldiers from all three of the Allied Forces in Berlin. There was a mixture that evening of Brits, Yanks and French squaddies in the night club. Due to the number of beers consumed, Richard felt the urge to take a piss. Letting the others know where he was going, he was joined by Sol. Looking for the signs for the toilets, they located them and descended the stairwell, into the basement. On their entry they heard the distinct accents of two Americans, who by the sound of it were worse the wear for drink. Standing side by side, the two friends began to relieve themselves into the urinals. Letting out an exclamation of relief, Richard shook himself and zipped up his jeans. Moving to the wash basin to wash his hands, he saw that the two Americans were eyeing him closely. Sol joined him at the basins and the pair began washing their hands.

'Looks like there may be a bit of trouble here,' he whispered to Richard, who had already picked up the vibe, and simply nodded in agreement.

As they turned to leave, their exit was barred by one of the individuals, who had taken up a stance like a boxer. His compatriot, was stood directly behind him as backup, waiting to see what would occur. Richard moved to pass the rather squat, powerfully built individual. However, he countered by stepping to the side, barring his exit.

'I'm an American Indian, and you will have to go through me to leave!' he challenged Richard, who sized him up, thinking what move he would make. Coming to the decision that this dickhead was not going to budge, he turned his head, as if to retreat. Then, with a lightning fast movement, his head recoiled and smashed on to the bridge of the nose of the Indian. He felt the bone give way under the force and blood spattered his shirt. Not stopping, he stepped over the downed Yank and headed straight for his mate, who was stood frozen now in shock, behind him. He raised his hands in supplication as Richard confronted him, ready to dish out some more of the same. Sol had already knocked down the floored Indian, who had attempted to get back up.

'I'm sorry, buddy, we didn't mean anything by it,' came the cowardly reply from the other American 'fuckwit'.

'Get out of our fucking way,' Richard said, brushing him to one side, and he and Sol climbed the stairs, back to the bar area. Once they had got there, they recounted the story to the others, who fell about laughing. This would not be the last time that they would have a brush with soldiers from the other Allied powers.

Before they knew it, the club was starting to empty, and looking at the clock on the wall, they were surprised to find it was 05:45. Finishing off their drinks, they, too, made their way towards the exit. Opening the door, they were blinded by the bright sunlight, like vampires about to turn to dust. It had been some eight hours since they had last eaten, and the alcohol they consumed had given them a raging appetite. Deciding that they would try and find an establishment open at this time of the morning, they set off in the direction of the Europa Centre. The first café they came to was already open, with people sitting at tables, drinking coffee and eating bread rolls. The friends took a table and started to read through the menu. Richard was surprised to find that everything from continental snacks to steak and chips was available. The only thing missing was an English full fried breakfast. They all decided on steak, egg and chips, apart from Sol, who had an addiction for currywurst and chips.

They received their food within fifteen minutes and after an hour were all sitting, drinking coffee and chatting. Directly opposite them, and next to the Irish bar, was a small German pub they hadn't noticed the evening before. To their amazement people were going in and out of the door, and this was at 07:00 in the morning. Now that they were fully replenished with their breakfast, they came to the decision that they would continue the party, in the bar opposite. Squaring up the bill between them, they left a generous tip for the waiter and headed the twenty paces into the drinking establishment.

The room consisted of a small 'U' shaped bar and a couple of benches in the far corner. There were already five customers, engrossed in drunken conversation. Seeing the five friends enter, the proprietor greeted them, with a friendly 'Good morning'. This was returned by the group, and taking the remaining seats, ordered a round of beers and a schnapps chaser. Surely they could not continue in this manner for the entire two years they would be stationed there? Richard thought to himself. Not only would they seriously damage their health, but their bank balances also. This was quickly put to the back of their minds, as the drinks arrived and they continued the break away from camp. This would be the flavour of the day, but taken at a more sedate pace. They explored more bars, again ending up at 'Take Off', before taking a taxi to Theodor Heuss Platz, and a bus from there at 03:00 to Spandau. Completely exhausted and unable to drink one more drop, they entered 'Smuts Barracks', obligingly showing their MOD 90 Identity cards to the sentry on duty. Although he was totally hammered, Richard could see by the guards face, that he was completely jealous of their condition. They made their way to their respective rooms and fell into a deep alcohol induced sleep.

The following weeks were just a blur. The Troops paraded every morning, invariably in glorious sunshine. The morning consisted of getting the vehicles ready for the upcoming Queens Birthday parade. The afternoons were spent sightseeing and generally enjoying themselves. Richard had stripped the turret right down to the bare bones. He had brushed all dust that he could find on the turret floor, before cleaning it down with white spirits. He had become quite an expert at this, over the last eight months, and took pride in his work. The final stage was to cover it with silver paint, and this was his job for the morning. Sol and H were busy finishing off the first parade on the vehicles oils. Once Richard had completed the turret, they would begin to paint the tank in its distinctive black and green camouflage. As Richard climbed out of the turret to fetch some silver paint, H and Sol were already busy opening tins of green and black paint.

'You going to be long?' H asked Richard, as he passed them carrying a tin of silver paint.

'A couple of hours,' Richard replied.

'Okay, we will start spraying the running gear,' H said, still stirring the tin of green paint at his feet.

Richard had already painted the ammunition racks, which he had taken out the previous week. He had mounted these back into their positions and just needed to paint those parts of the interior of the turret such as the floor, safety guard and anything else that was silver in colour. He wondered to himself, why they needed to be so immaculate? It wasn't as if anyone would see them. That was the Army way, and he just put his head down and got on with it. As he progressed through his career, he would be asked to do many things that didn't make sense. This was just all part of growing up, and accepting orders issued by your superiors. As he meditated on this and other things, he moved his left arm back and forth, in sweeping strokes with the four inch brush.

He thought of Annette, who he would be meeting on the weekend. This had become a regular occurrence, and he had stayed at her apartment on a number of occasions. He would go to the night club with the boys, and would disappear to her bar around two o'clock in the morning. Here he would spend the last hour or so with Annette, and some of the locals, including Danny, who was a regular. Danny would often go to the bar, after he had finished in whatever performance he was in at any given time. He was a very flamboyant character, and quite feminine in some of his mannerisms. Richard found this amusing, but enjoyed his company, none the less. Once Annette had got rid of the die hards at around 04:00, they would lock up and head off to her apartment. The first night she had invited him back, it had come as a surprise to Richard. As she locked up, Richard said goodbye and turned to leave to meet up with the guys once again. He had only walked three paces when she asked him where he was going. On hearing his intentions, she simply smiled and took him by the hand. Not saying a word, she led him down the street, and into the underground. Here they boarded a tube to the area of Kreuzberg, which was a run-down district of the city. They entered her apartment block, and as she turned the key in the door, she looked over her shoulder and smiled at Richard. Dragging him inside, she kissed him passionately, tearing off her t-shirt as she did so. Richard buried his face into her neck and returned the kisses, lingering there for a while. As he moved slowly down her neck, towards her ample breasts, she unclasped her bra, and they fell free. Richard could feel himself growing hard as he nuzzled her nipples with his tongue. She murmured, and gave a sigh of pleasure as he took one of her nipples in his mouth. Sucking on it gently he alternated from left to right, carrying out the same motion on each. She ran her fingers under his shirt and descended past his navel, her nails forced their way down inside his jeans and deftly undid the top button. The top of his penis was already trying to force its way out of his boxers, like a missile trying to break free from its silo. As her fingers found the tip, they slipped slightly on the thin film of pre ejaculation that had been produced by her actions. Working her hand down to the base she caressed his testicles, massaging them lightly. Richard thought he was going to explode with pleasure.

Annette was five years older than Richard, he did not know how many sexual partners she'd had in the past. All he knew was that she knew how to hit the right spot, and had to slow her hand before he came too quickly. Tearing open her jeans, he, too, slid his hand down, until his fingers came across the channel they were searching for. Probing one finger inside her, he massaged the well lubricated area of her labia. Her sighs grew ever louder as the tempo of his fingers increased, and delved ever deeper inside her. She pulled him backwards, not breaking the embrace, into her bedroom. Stepping backwards and continuing to face him, she slid down her jeans to the floor and kicked them to one side. Copying her example, Richard did the same, then the pair of them embraced once more. Their hands explored every inch of each other. The end of Richard penis was seeping visibly with a clear liquid as she massaged it faster and faster. He felt a great relief, as she removed the skimpy panties she was wearing and stepped backwards towards the bed. As they moved, Richard pulled down his boxers and stepped out of them. The feeling of his penis touching her bare skin sent a shiver through him. She held him by his shoulders and did a complete 180 degree turn. She pushed him gently back onto the bed, and climbing on top reached down to grab his now throbbing member. With her legs either side of his groin, she rubbed the tip along the length of her vagina. She whimpered like a chastised child, as she worked it along the length of her labia. She continued this action for about five minutes, until she could not hold on any longer. Guiding his shaft in between her lips, she lowered herself onto him, gasping as she did so. With her hands on his chest, she gyrated her hips grinding his swollen member deeper and deeper inside her. Raising her hips, she let him slide almost out of her, before once again enveloping him with her warm, moist lips. Her motions grew ever more frantic, as she rode up and down on him, using his tool to satisfy herself. Feeling that he was about to come, Richard stopped her, and turning her round so that she was on all fours, withdrew and gave himself a little time to compose himself. With her arse staring at him invitingly, she moved it to and fro like a snake charmer charming a cobra. Not able to contain himself, he move forward and placed his hands on her hips and penetrated her now exposed labia. His rhythm started long and slow until he was pounding in and out of her like a steam piston. Their breathing grew ever more rapid and exited, as they drove towards climax. Just as she was about to come Richard felt his balls tingle and that familiar sensation of his seed pouring out the end of his penis. His thigh muscles stiffened, and his back arched, as he forced every last drop out in short pumping movements. Once everything had been forced out of him, he collapsed, spent, on Annette's back.

For the next two hours Annette coaxed him hard again with her mouth, before the pair of them were at it again like rampant beasts. Richard did not remember how many different positions they tried, but once they were fully satisfied, they fell into a deep contented sleep. As Richard chuckled to himself, he was roused from his thoughts by a face appearing, looking down from the operators hatch.

'You finished yet?' came the deep Cumbrian voice of Albert, as he licked the hair from his walrus like moustache.

'Just about,' came Richard's reply. 'Can you give me two minutes?' He said, indicating a small section he had left to paint. He also would need time for the 'boner' he had accumulated while thinking of Annette, to go down. Nodding in agreement, Albert climbed down from the turret, and joined H and Sol, who were putting back the 'bazooka plates' covering the running gear. By the time Richard joined them, the tank been taped up, or covered in grease to prevent the spray paint covering areas such as sights and the like. Albert had been busy drawing a pattern in chalk, from the top of the turret down to floor. This pattern had been agreed by the Squadron, and every tank would be painted exactly the same. The first part of the process was to spray the tank completely green. They started from the top of the turret, working their way down to the ground. This was so that they did not have to step on anything that had already been freshly painted. They worked in pairs, swapping over every ten minutes or so. The pair who were not spraying were busy, mixing paint with thinners to make it easier for it to be blown through the nozzles, which were fed by compression. By the time lunchtime had arrived, they had completed the whole thing. They stood back to admire their work, and Albert seemed pleased with the results. So much so, that he decided that they would take a 'Sports Afternoon'. This was synonymous in the Army and usually took place on a Wednesday afternoon. It invariably had nothing to do with sports, and involved mostly drinking, or any other activities they wished to partake in. That was not to say that they never had sports that they could attend, there was always some competition or other that required the Squadron to provide a team for. Richard had already signed up for the rugby team and had attended a couple of training sessions. He was happy as not only was he quite good, his father was one of his team mates. He had been the rugby captain at school and had excelled in the sport. It was to play a big part of his life along with boxing in his career. His father had represented the Regiment at rugby, and had boxed as a young man for a local club, prior to him joining the Army.

Emptying any paint left in the spray guns, they gave them a thorough clean with some white spirits. They ensured the nozzles were paint free, ready to be used again the following day. Once they had completed this and were given the nod by Troop Sergeant Hux to disappear, they locked the tool bins on the vehicles and headed off to their rooms, to get changed.

The itinerary for the afternoon was to visit the 'Strandbadwannsee' which was a nudist beach on the Wannsee, one of Berlin's lakes. It had been a very popular recreation area for many years. It was established in the 1920's progressive city politicians, with hot and cold showers both in the facility and on the beach. It was a 'Mecca' for tourists and locals alike. Taking a quick shower, the usual crowd of Ken, Sol, Lofty and Richard, were, this time, joined by H and other members of the Troop and Squadron. By the time they boarded the bus on the Heerstrasse for the twenty minute journey, they numbered twelve in total. They all had towels along with trunks, stuffed into shoulder or grip bags.

Leaving the bus, they walked along the beach, following the signs. As they entered the sandy beach, it came apparent that not all were naked. Richard gave a sigh of relief, although it was exciting seeing naked, nubile, young women, he did not really wish to remove his clothes. At least half of the group were of the same opinion, and they found themselves a space on the beach that was frequented by half clad people. However not twenty metres away, were family groups and young adolescents, running about naked. Some were bathing in the clear lake water, while others were playing games such as badminton, or throwing a Frisbee. Most of the guys in the group laid their towels out and immediately laid face down, with their hands cupping their chins, whilst they surveyed the scene in front of them. There were bodies of all ages, shapes and sizes in various stages of undress. The boys laying on their towels did not know which way to look. Suddenly, one of the blokes from Motor Transport Troop (MT), decided he wanted to play Frisbee with a couple of young ladies. They were completely naked and their firm upturned breasts glistened in the hot afternoon June sun. After a quick conversation and the use of hand signals and gestures, it became apparent that if he wanted to join in he would have to be naked. The beach was divided up into sections, some you had to be completely naked, others you could be partly clothed. The big strapping lad known as 'Lefty' was not shy at coming forward, immediately dropped his shorts and discarded them to one side. Richard could see why, as his member could be seen hanging about five inches below his arse cheeks when viewed from behind. As he threw the Frisbee to the girls and ran and jumped to retrieve it, the assembled group of squaddies were in fits of laughter. As they watched they sipped on cold beers, bought from the beach bar. By the end of the day, everyone was very drunk, and most, including Richard, were completely naked and loving it. As the sun began to set Richard closed his eyes and thought how lucky they were to be stationed in this very Cosmopolitan city, behind the Iron Curtain.

The next morning at work, the word had spread about their antics the previous day at the nudist beach. Albert, who was the biggest pervert in the Squadron was eager to get any information he could about the location. He was almost literally kicking himself for not having accompanied them on their afternoon out. He was a single man and proud of the fact that he had never been with a woman without paying for it. For the first 30 minutes in the hangar, he quizzed Richard, until he had enough information banked for his evening wank, Richard thought. The Troops carried on from the day before this time, ensuring the patterns for the black areas were identical, they began the process of completing the spray job. By the time the bell of the NAAFI van was heard, they had almost finished their vehicle. They lined up, one behind the other, waiting to collect their crispy German rolls of Cheese and Pickle, Ham and German mustard, washed down with a hot brew. This was a tradition throughout the Army and some people even referenced it, when putting down a new guy's length of time in the Regiment. They would say something along the lines of 'I have spent longer in the NAAFI queue than you have in the Army, son'.

As they returned to the hangar, Richard and Lofty noticed that Albert had left his belt on the front of the tank. Lofty picked it up and they were examining the length of it, joking that you could get two people in it. Thinking that it would be a good laugh, Lofty suggested they stood back to back, then put the belt around them. Richard laughed and nodded his agreement. They turned around, both facing outwards. They wrapped the belt around themselves and found that it actually fitted exactly. Just as they had secured the clasp on the front, the enormous figure of Albert appeared from around the side of the tank, rolls and brew in hand. Catching sight of the pair of them, with what he figured was his belt, he realised that he had become the butt of someone's joke. He immediately turned from a gentle, placid type into a raging bull. Richard, seeing the look in his eyes, attempted to release the clasp of the belt. However, as Lofty had already seen the oncoming danger, he had decided to try and get away. This just tightened the belts grip as they tried to move in opposite directions, and it was impossible for Richard to release it.

'So, you think you are funny?' Albert bellowed, as he rushed towards them. He proceeded to knock them around the hangar for the next five minutes. Although Richard's arm was going dead from the amount of times it had been struck, he could not help but laugh. This was infectious and Lofty was doing the same. This, of course, just made matters worse, and Albert increased the strength of punches he meted out to the pair. At last, the two of them could take no more, and they cried out to Albert to stop, and promising they wouldn't do it again. This seemed to placate Albert, he shrugged his shoulders, and returned to the front of the tank, to eat his rolls and drink his brew. Making sure that he was not going to return to punish them some more, Lofty and Richard undid the belts clasp. Lofty returned to his tank rubbing his arm, whilst Richard moved to the front of his vehicle with Albert's belt in hand. He offered it to Albert with a grovelling apology, which was accepted, at once. Richard had found out that it took something really bad to piss the big man off for a long period of time.

Once NAAFI break was over, the crew continued with their paint job and, by lunchtime, they were finished. The next stage Albert explained, was that, once the paint was dry, they would mix thinners and oil together. This would then be applied to the whole vehicle, giving it a parade gloss shine effect. Richard thought to himself, that surely he was not being serious. However, he had noticed that the Troop leaders tank crew, whose paint job was already dry, had begun the process already. There was going to be a sting in the tail for Richard, as he was told by Albert that the rest of the crew were taking the afternoon off. He, however, would be returning in the afternoon to make these final touches all on his own. He was not to knock off until he had finished the whole thing from top to bottom. Richard inwardly groaned to himself, as he looked puppy dog eyed in Albert direction. This was just met with an amused grin by his commander. He obviously had not forgotten the little 'joke' that Lofty and Richard had played earlier.

After eating his lunch and wishing others from his Troop a pleasant afternoon, Richard returned to the tank park. On his way he went to the Squadron office to collect the keys, however, on checking for the key press, he could not find them. Richard made his way to the hangar and found that the door was already open. Calling out to see if anyone was there, a face appeared from around the side of the Troop Leaders tank. It was Lofty, who asked Richard what he was doing. Richard replied that the Troop Leader had given him the task of finishing off. Richard immediately understood that Albert must have had a word with him. This made him feel a little bit better, as he climbed up on to the top of the tank. For the rest of the afternoon, he applied the mixture of oil and thinners to the vehicle's exterior. On more than one occasion, he slipped on the freshly coated surface. As he gradually worked his way down to the sides of the tank, his arms were beginning to ache. He decided to have a break and called over to Lofty who was just about finished, to do likewise. The pair of them sat on the little sofa the Troop had acquired at the rear of the hangar. They chatted about the previous months since their arrival in Berlin.

They had found a lovely Yugoslavian restaurant, not far from camp, frequenting it at least once a week. They had the luxury of having the choice of so many places to eat, they didn't have to visit the same one twice. Richard also recalled the time, both he and Ken had been in a pub in the red light area of Stuttgarter Platz. It seemed like a normal Saturday afternoon. The two of them were the only ones in this small bar, and were sat chatting on the stools directly opposite the barman. After about half an hour a Middle Eastern looking guy had entered the bar, and began a heated conversation in what Richard recognised to be Turkish. French and Richard had continued their conversation, ignoring the debate going on between the two. After a short while, the newcomer departed, the pair of them did not give it a second thought. Five minutes later, Richard noticed

Ken's eyes widen. He turned to look over his left shoulder, to observe what had caught his friend's attention. Standing in the doorway was the Turkish gentleman that had been engaged in the argument with the barman. As if in slow motion, the man reached under the jacket he was wearing. This in itself was strange, thought Richard, on reflection, as the sun was cracking the paving stones outside. As his hand withdrew Richard's eyes were drawn to the sinister black shape of the semi-automatic pistol that was now held out horizontally pointing in the direction of the barman. Another heated exchange in Turkish between the two, and then in a flash of light the pistol bucked upwards. As Richard turned his attention to the barman on his right, the area behind the barman had been decorated in a deep shade of red. The mirror and optics were covered in pieces of skull and brain matter. This caused Richard to involuntarily vomit on the floor of the bar. This was accompanied by Ken's exclamation of 'I'm not having fucking that!' As quickly as it happened, the gunman had exited the bar, and the sound of screeching tyres could be heard from directly outside. An eerie silence descended on the bar, and Richard, wiping away the vomit from his chin, looked at his friend in disbelief. By the time they had regained their composure, the sounds of sirens could be heard, announcing the arrival of the Emergency Services. For the next hour or so the two young soldiers gave a brief statement of what had happened to the Police. Once the Police were happy, they were sent on their way. So, although their time thus far had been mostly happy, this incident highlighted that this was also a dangerous city.

Suitably rested, Lofty and Richard returned to their vehicles, and after another twenty minutes Lofty had finished and shouted his goodbyes, as he headed off to the block. Richard calculated that it was going to be at least another hour before he was finished. He glanced at his watch and was happy to find that would give him enough time to shower, before the evening meal.

Standing back to admire his work 40 minutes later, Richard felt a pang of pride in what he had achieved. He began to tidy up the area around the tank, removing the cans of thinner and oil and the cloth and rag that he had been using. After giving it a quick sweep, he put on his belt and beret and locked up the hangar. Heading over to the Squadron office block, he handed the keys into the duty NCO. He returned to his room where he quickly undressed, showered and put on his jeans and t-shirt and went for his evening meal.

The rest of the week was spent applying the finishing touches to the Squadron's tanks, ready for the parade the following week. On the Monday it was Third Troops turn to take over as 'Alert Troop'. This meant they came under the two can rule for the whole week and everyone, including married soldiers and NCOs (pads), were confined to camp. They needed to be ready to crash out to the gates at any time of the day or night. It was normal for them to have at least one or more of these during their week. This was down to the Troop Leaders discretion, and if he was pissed off that particular week, they could be in for some sleepless nights.

On the Monday morning the Squadron paraded, as usual, for the weekly inspection. The SSM handed over to the OC as normal, and he, at once, fell in the officers. This morning, however, before asking one of the Troops to stand fast, he announced that Argentina had invaded the Falkland Islands. There was a hushed silence throughout the assembled ranks. He then went on to ask, if any person would like to volunteer for the Task Force, that would be sent to try and retake the Islands. If they so wished, then they were to take one pace forward. After a short pause, the entire Squadron, less two men, advanced one pace forward. A broad grin spread over the Squadron Leader's face.

'That makes me so proud to see that almost to a man, you would be prepared to do your duty for Queen and Country. Unfortunately, as you might not know, our job here prevents us from being deployed. The question was just so I could gauge your reaction to the news. Sergeant Major, have a word with those two individuals, and ascertain why they haven't got the balls to serve with their comrades.' He sneered, pointing to the two soldiers, who now hung their heads, looking at their feet.

The inspection carried on as normal, and afterwards the conversation in the Troop hangars was dominated by the Falklands conflict. This was cut short by the Troop Leader who insisted that the Troop was ready to take on their duties of Alert Troop. He informed them that he had heard a rumour, that there could be an allied forces crash out. This was known as 'Nautius Maximus', and involved all the allied powers in West Berlin. The level of crash outs were as follows, he explained. The Alert Troop ones, as they already knew were called 'Pony Express'. They had a maximum of fifteen minutes, wherever they were, to be dressed, mounted and at the gates of camp. The next one up from this was a Squadron Level crash out, known as 'Trail Canter'. This involved the whole Squadron being called in, including married personnel. They had a maximum of four hours to complete this and be at the front gates, ready to roll. There was also a crash out, which involved all of the British Armoured Brigade in Berlin. This was an exercise known as 'Rocking Horse', and was the same as Trial Canter, with the exception that the Royal Military Police were instructed to patrol the streets of the city, rounding up any off duty British soldiers. They would then, return them to barracks, so that they were able to deploy with their units. The lecture over, the Troops moved back to their vehicles and ensured they were ready to take over as Alert Troop. This did not involve much work at all as they were always fully bombed up. They just needed to sign out their personal weapons from the armoury and stow them on the vehicles. They did this straight away as a Troop, taking with them also the General Purpose Machine Guns (GPMG's) for the commander's station and above the main armament.

The end of the day came and the Troop locked up the hangars, this time Troop Sergeant Hux retained the key. They did not want to waste precious seconds, having to go to the Squadron office for them. After the evening meal, they all changed into tracksuits and sweat shirts and lounged about, either in the Troop TV room or their own rooms. Around 22:00, Ken, Lofty, Sol and Richard decided they would go to the bar, for their two beer allowance. They knew to take with them, their crash out bags, containing their coveralls, boots, belts and berets. They entered the bar and Lofty ordered them a round of drinks. Sitting down at a table opposite the bar, they sipped at their drinks. They were suddenly interrupted by a siren and an announcement of 'Pony Express!' The friends placed down their beers and were off their seats and heading for the nearest exit in one fluid movement. As they left the building, and headed in the direction of the tank park, they were joined by others who had exited the building from other exits. They all converged at the hangar, and as they quickly donned their coveralls and boots from their bags, leaving the laces undone. The drivers climbed into their cabs and immediately placed the GUE's on line before starting the main engines. The gunners jumped into the turret and started up the gun kits. While this was happening the Commanders and operators were flinging open the hangar doors then mounting into their positions. It had been only five minutes since the alarm had been given and the first tank, which was Richard's, crept out of the hangar. By the time all three vehicles, had ground to a halt one behind the other at the guardroom, only seven minutes had elapsed.

The Troop leader climbed down from his vehicle and called the Troop over to him.

'Not a bad effort for your first time,' he congratulated them. 'Each time we are on, I want to see an improvement on your time. If, for any reason, you are slower than the last time, I will make sure that we practice it time and time again. There is no limit on how many times, I can crash the Troop out. So, let's screw the bobbin and get it right first time. Remember what I mentioned this morning, about the possible Allied Forces crash out.' With that, he asked them to mount back up, and return the vehicles to the hangar. Complying with his wishes, the crews climbed back onto their vehicles and, in a belch of smoke and roaring engines, the commanders guided them back to the hangars. The excitement over for the night and with the NAFFI bar about to close in ten minutes, they sprinted back inside, in time to order a drink, before turning in for the evening.

For the next couple of days, the Troop worked steadily on the vehicles, with final preparation for the Queen's Birthday parade. This was to be held the following day, so they all knew that the Troop Leader's threat of an Allied forces crash out exercise, was just bullshit. They had only been called out that first night, and, as they were leaving that afternoon, to take the tanks to the Olympic Stadium for the parade, they would not be getting called out that evening. After taking a quick lunch the Squadron lined up at the front gates, where the RMP and German Civil Police (GCP) were waiting to escort them. The journey would take them approximately 25 minutes, turning right out of camp, then onto the Heer Strasse, then into Charlottenburg and the Olympic Stadium. The call came over the air for them to set off, and the first GCP car and RMP Land Rover sped off to the first junction, while their colleagues stopped traffic outside of camp, to allow the tanks to exit. Once on the Heer Strasse, it was a clear run for about six kilometres. They paid no attention to the red lights, as the Police escort simply waved them through.

On their arrival into the stadium, they found a corrugated metal walkway had been laid by 38 Engineer Squadron, with whom they shared the barracks and the Hilton. This was done to prevent any damage to the grass by the 60 tonne monsters. They were carefully guided along the walkway, then put into their allotted positions. The whole Squadron was lined up on the far side of what would be the parade, with their barrels facing the crowd. Final checks for oil leaks and that all gun equipment were working was underway. Once the OC was happy that everything was 'squared away', he informed the SSM to fall out the Squadron. The SSM did this, leaving a skeleton crew, all from Alert Troop to guard the vehicles. The remainder, climbed aboard the buses that were waiting to take them back to Smut's barracks.

It came as no surprise to Richard that he had been chosen as one of the lucky ones to stay behind. He had expected it and, like all good soldiers, had planned accordingly. He had pressed and starched his parade coveralls. He had also bulled his boots, not that anyone was going to see them as they would all be mounted. They had also been issued bright yellow cravats to wear around their necks. He had given his room key to Ken, who was returning to camp, and asked that he brought his uniform with him the following morning.

The evening was uneventful, only broken up by the arrival of Richard's dad and the SQMS, with the evening meal. He parked his Land Rover in the centre of the lined up tanks, put down the tailgate, and placed the hay box on it. He let the guys know to go and collect their plates and KFS, he also removed a Norwegian container of tea and placed it on the ground. One of his storeman took out a six foot table and erected it. On it he placed some loaves of bread, butter, sugar and the Norwegian. The three Troopers and one Lance Corporal who formed the guard, lined up, waiting to be served. When Richard's turn came his father smiled at him in acknowledgement, and ladled a big portion of stew onto his plate. No words were exchanged, nor were any needed. Richard had visited his parents, in their married quarters, a couple of times since they arrived. This was normally to get washing done and a break from the single life. Their paths rarely crossed at work, as Tommy Hunter was normally in his stores in the Squadron Office building. The meal finished, the SQMS and his storeman packed their stuff away and left the guards to their own devices.

The Lance Corporal who was the guard commander had already drawn up a stag list and, as it grew dark, the first sentry started his patrol. The SQMS staff had also provided a tent for them to sleep in, and while one patrolled the others got their heads down. It wasn't long before the light of dawn was breaking, and they were joined once again by the SQMS, with breakfast for them. The time was 06:30 and there would not be long before the rest of the Squadron would be arriving around 09:00. He ushered them along, as he had to get back to get dressed and return with the Squadron. His Land Rover and that of the ferret of the SSM, would be carrying the Regimental flag and Standard. They, and the rest of the Units wheeled vehicles, would form a drive past the saluting dais. Within half an hour, breakfast had been served and the leftovers and equipment packed away, including the tent. The SQMS bid them farewell and left the stadium.

At 09:00 the complete Squadron arrived on their white buses. Richard could see Ken striding towards him, with a bag, and his coveralls on a coat hanger over his shoulder. Richard took them from him, and immediately stripped off and put on the clean, fresh and well ironed coveralls. He had already washed and shaved earlier, so it wasn't long before he was looking immaculate, along with the rest of the guys. The SSM fell them all in, and the Squadron Leader did an inspection of the whole Squadron. Any minor points with dress were rectified, and, after falling the Troops out, he walked along the line of tanks, inspecting them also. The final thing they tested was the blank firing charges they would be firing in a twenty one gun salute. It all went off without a hitch and the Troops waited behind the vehicles, for the time when they needed to mount up.

At 11:45 everyone was in their respective stations. The drive past was due to start at midday and the vehicles had already started their engines. The SSM and SQMS were wearing their No.1 dress uniforms or 'Blues', accompanied by boots and spurs with white cross belts. The infantry battalions, of which there were two, had already marched on, and had halted about 50 metres in front of the tanks. They had gone into open order, awaiting the time to give a Royal salute and present arms. On the stroke of midday, the Armoured Squadrons Ferret, and SQMS Land Rover led the wheeled drive past, on to the metal walkway that had been laid in front of the dais. The assembled Troops were commanded to present arms. As the vehicles came in line with the dais, the SSM saluted to his right and the vehicles behind him did likewise. Richard's father carried the Regimental Standard with pride, in his Land Rover, as it was always an honour to do this. It was normally carried by the Regimental Quartermaster Sergeant (RQMS). Richard watched the parade unfold through the eye pieces of his Tank Laser Sight (TLS). He wondered if he would ever get the chance to be given the honour of carrying that Standard. Once all the vehicles had passed by the dais, they, too, assembled in front of the infantry Battalions facing the crowd. The operators or loaders were busy preparing the blank firing rounds and charges inside the vehicles. At the appointed time, beginning from the left they fired a single round, one at a time. There were only fourteen tanks in the Squadron, so some of them would have to fire twice, to complete the 21 gun salute. The first salvo went off without a hitch, however, when it came to the second salvo, there was a slight pause. One of the tanks from First Troop had a misfire, but, as practiced, the vehicle immediately to his right fired their round. Richard wondered, as the final round was fired, if the crowd even noticed the mistake. The parade came to an end and once the wheeled vehicles and the infantry had marched off, the tanks made their way from the stadium. They were, once again, escorted by the Police, both military and civil back to Smuts Barracks.

The remaining weekend of Alert Troop passed with them only being called out once, on the Saturday afternoon. They knocked 30 seconds off their time, so the Troop Leader was happy. On the Monday morning, the crews dismounted their GPMG's and returned them to the armoury. Then, they went through the laborious task of 'de-bombing' the ammunition. This involved removing every round from 120mm High Explosive Squash Head

(HESH), Discarding Sabot, 7.62mm GPMG, and even 9mm rounds for the commanders' and drivers' pistols. Every round was counted and accounted for, then returned to their stowage positions. The process took all of the morning, however, was an evil necessity, which would come to light at the end of their posting. At the end of the day, the Troops met up in the bar, for a few celebratory beers.

Chapter 29 – Sports and Competitions

Berlin was a posting that was not all work, there was also a lot of play. Many competed in various competitions such as swimming, football, rugby, and boxing. Some of the Units even posted people into them, if they were talented in a particular sport. One of these was the Royal Signal Squadron, who were based at Brigade, near the Olympic Stadium. Nearly every year they managed to win the competition, hands down. For a small Unit, the Armoured Squadron fielded strong teams in both rugby and football. It was the former that Richard excelled in, and he had represented the Junior Army, whilst he was in training. The Squadron team had managed over the past two months to reach the final of the Berlin rugby cup. To make things even better for Richard, his father was playing alongside him. His dad told him, that as far as he knew this was the first time in Regimental history that this had happened. There were many brother partnerships in various teams within the Regiment, but very few father and son ones.

Training had gone well on the lead up to the final, and with only a day to go Richard was starting to feel a little nervous. After the training session that morning, his dad had taken him to one side and reassured him. They had never really been that close, but their time together in Berlin had rectified that. They were also playing close together as his father was the scrum half and he was playing standoff. Advising him that he should get an early night, his dad left to get showered. Richard returned to the Hilton and did the same, bumping into Ken on the way.

'Couple of beers tonight in the bar tonight, or what?' he asked, in passing.

Richard cringed inside, deliberating on what his dad had just told him. But, it was a Friday night after all, what harm could a couple of beers do?

'Aye, why not, see you there around 19:00' he replied.

It had transpired, that the team they were to meet in the final the next day, was no other than, 38 Field Squadron Royal Engineers, who they shared the Hilton and barracks with. As they entered the bar, a couple of the Engineers, knowing Richard played for the Armoured Squadron called over to him.

'Can we get you a drink, mate?'

'Aye, why not' he said, thinking that was a nice gesture. The two Squadrons genuinely got on together, they had had many parties, not only in the NAAFI bar, but in each other's respective Squadron bars. After the match the next day, the Armoured Squadron would be hosting the drinks in their bar. Richard had the firm intention of having a couple, then getting off to bed. This did not turn out as planned however, and, three hours later, he was being fed brandy and cokes by the Engineers. Early on in the evening, he saw Sol disappear with 'Jenny Mess Tin' the local German girl who was a frequent visitor to the barracks. He was starting to feel slightly drunk, and Ken realising this, persuaded him to go to bed. This caused the Engineers hurl abuse after him in an exchange in banter that only squaddies could do. It was all harmless fun and Richard took it as such, giving back as good as he got.

Stumbling out of the lift on the third floor, he staggered along the corridor. He heard noises coming from Sol's room, so he put his ear to the door. The excited gasps of a female could be heard from inside. It didn't take Richard long to work out that Sol must have taken Jenny Mess Tin to his room. In his drunken stupor, he tried the door, which, to his surprise was not locked. The sight that met him was Sol's naked back and buttocks. Sol's pelvis was moving back and forward like a jack hammer, whilst his hands clasped the firm hips of the young girl. She was crying out for him to give it her harder and faster. Being the gentleman he was, Sol obediently obliged. Richard stood there, watching the sex scene being played out in front of him. Even in his alcohol induced state, he still felt himself being aroused. Sol's arse was moving at lightning speed by this point, until, all of a sudden, he gave out an exclamation, and his body went rigid. His buttocks pumping sporadically, as he emptied himself into the now screaming girl. As quickly as he had finished, he withdrew from her and turned around. Seeing Richard standing there, he never batted an eyelid, but simply posed a question,

'Do you want two's up?' he asked, in a nonchalant manner.

Richard looked at the well-rounded, firm arse of Jenny, which had the hand print impressions on her hips. She was still rocking rhythmically, as if she was still been given a good seeing to. Her fingers were exploring her 'special place', which was now oozing with Sol's semen. 'She likes a bit of uphill gardening, if you fancy it?' Sol continued. I have some Swarfega here, if you want to lube her up,' he took some on his finger and started to massage her rectum. Feeling physically sick, which was strange for Richard, who didn't mind a bit of 'back door action', he declined saying:

'You're okay, mate, maybe next time. I'm going to get my head down. Got a big game tomorrow,' and did an about turn, exiting the room and closing the door behind him. The last thing he heard, before pottering off to bed, was Jenny asking Sol to do it again. As Richard closed his eyes and drifted off to sleep, he mused over the fact that his comrades were willing to share anything they had, even their women.

The morning sunshine broke through Richard's window blinding him and stirring him from his sleep. His mouth tasted of stale beer, and he rubbed his eyes to clear them, before swinging his legs over the bed. Sitting there for a moment, he collected his thoughts, before going to the window and looking out. The sun was full, and sat in an uninterrupted blue sky. Richard opened the window to let in some fresh air, and could feel the warmth from outside and it was only 07:30 in the morning. He stared across the Motor Transport hangars opposite into the grounds of Spandau Prison. In the garden there, the bent over figure of what was obviously an elderly man could be seen pottering about. As the prison only had one inmate, this could only be Rudolph Hess, Richard thought. This was the first time over the last year, that Richard had seen him. He was accompanied by a single guard, who Richard deduced by the uniform was American. He pondered on the justification of keeping this man locked up so long after the Second World War had ended. Putting the thoughts out of his head, he decided to have a quick shower before going to brunch.

Leaving his room, he bumped into Sol in the corridor, returning from his ablutions. They exchanged information on how the night had gone with the lovely Jenny Mess Tin. Sol gave a blow by blow account of the evening's proceedings. Richard was in fits of hysterics as Sol told the tale, knowing that, if he had been a little more sober, he would have joined in. The pair of them agreed to meet in fifteen minutes and go down to brunch together.

When the entered the cookhouse, there were already a few people tucking into massive fully cooked breakfasts including steak. They were mostly members of the rugby teams from both sides. Having placed their order and been served, Richard and Sol joined Albert at a nearby table. He was already half way through his food and greeted them as they sat down. What he told them next, knocked Richard for six. It had come apparent last night that his childhood friend Pete, and another guy from First Troop called Smudger had got pissed up in the Squadron bar last night. They had borrowed the car keys from one of their Troop Corporals and decided to go on a little sightseeing trip. Due to the state of them, it was not long before they had wrapped it round a lamp post. The German and Military Police had been called they were breathalysed and arrested. They were at that time, in the military prison of the Grenadier Guards, until they were to be charged the following week. Richard could not believe that Pete could have been so stupid, but took slight consolation that his mate had not been injured. Perhaps more to the point, nor had he injured anyone else. He knew the military had a very dim view of drink-driving, and this could have a serious effect on a soldier's career. They debated the possible outcomes of the sentence the transgressors would receive. Albert was of the firm opinion that the sentence would be a harsh one, to serve as an example. Although he did not want to believe this, Richard silently agreed.

After finishing breakfast, the three members of third Troop return to their rooms. Albert who was playing as prop for the team, asked Richard what time they were supposed to meet. Richard replied that it had been decided they would meet an hour before, to do a little training and talk tactics. The game was to kick off at midday, so they agreed to meet, at the pitch opposite the hangars, at 11:00. Richard entered his room and opened his locker to pull out his shorts, shirt, socks and boots. He had placed them in a neat pile prior to going to the bar the night before. He quickly dressed and then lay down on his bed. For the next two hours, he listened to music and thought about what Pete and Smudger would be doing at that time. Knowing the Grenadier Guards reputation for strict iron military discipline, they would be doubling everywhere they went. Their Cavalry type foot drill would be sorely put to the test. A knock on the door disturbed Richard from his thoughts.

'Come in,' he shouted, looking over his right shoulder towards the door. The door opened and in the entrance stood Lofty, a broad grin spread over his face.

'Went shopping last night to that record shop I always go to. I've got a new album,' he said, excitedly. You've got to have a listen, come on,' he gestured, with a twitch of his head.

Not wanting to burst his bubble, Richard got up from his bed and followed dutifully behind him. Lofty just lived over the corridor from Richard and his door was already open. Lofty, at once, went to his turntable where the new album had been placed, all ready to be played. Lifting the arm and placing the needle down, he looked up at Richard, saying

'You got to listen to this one,' and as the mixture of punk and heavy metal guitars crashed out, he started playing an imaginary guitar, shaking his head as he did so. He was totally immersed in the sounds, not noticing that Richard was not in the least bit interested. Looking up at Richard, he asked him what he thought. The only thing that Richard could come up with was to ask what the album was called. '*Fresh Fruit for Rotting Vegetables* by *the Dead Kennedys,*' came the excited reply. 'This track is called *Holiday in Cambodia,*' and before it had finished, he moved the arm and placed the needle down on another track. 'This one's called *Too Drunk to Fuck,*' he said, proudly. He continued to change tracks, after playing only 30 seconds or so of the ones he thought were noteworthy. At the end of it, he waited on Richard's opinion. Trying not to hurt his feelings, Richard simply offered up that it was not his cup of tea, as he was more into Reggae at that point, as Lofty well knew. This hadn't stopped Sol coming and getting Richard from his room, every time he bought a new album, though. Making his excuses that he needed to leave for the match, he left the room and knocked on Albert's door, and the pair of them walked across the tank park to the pitch.

Most of the team had already arrived and were throwing the ball among them. Richard was still not feeling a 100 percent after the evening's free drinks, kindly provided by the Engineers. His father, noticing that he looked a little pale, made his way over to him. After asking if he was okay, he immediately smelt the alcohol on his breath.

'You stupid twat. What did I tell you yesterday, after training?' he berated him.

Not knowing where to put himself, Richard gave a feeble excuse and explained what had happened. Not happy on hearing this, the SQMS went over to the team Captain and asked if he could take the warm up. This was agreed, and he immediately got the team running round the outside of the pitch. Once they had warmed up, jogging for ten minutes, he then divided them into teams and they carried out shuttle sprints, back and forth, between the lines marked out on the pitch. After twenty minutes the alcohol was streaming out of Richard in the form of sweat. From shuttle sprints, they went through sit ups, crunches and press ups, and then finished up with a five minute warm down. Richard knew why his father was doing this, but kept his mouth shut. He had been watching him perspire, with a certain amount of satisfaction on his face, only cutting the warm up short, once he was satisfied he had suffered enough. For the remaining fifteen minutes the forwards and backs went through their own separate tactics and training. They had been joined on the field by 38 Squadron, who were also going through their warm ups and tactics. With two minutes to go before kick off the referee called the two captains to him, and explained what his expectations were. The coin toss was won by the Armoured Squadron, who they chose to face the sun in the first half.

As standoff, it was Richard's responsibility to take most of the kicks, including the one to get the game started. He took a deep gulp of air, as he bounced the ball on the ground, getting the feel of it, and trying to calm down his nerves. The referee blew the whistle, indicating the start of the game. Richard raised his hand to ensure everyone was ready, and were either in line with or behind him. Taking a few short paces forward, he lofted the ball high into the air, deep into the opponents' half. One of the backs gathered the ball, and was, at once, struck by the Armoured Squadron's advancing forwards. More and more of the forwards from both sides joined the maul. The initial attack was ferocious, and no quarter was given or taken by either side. Richard's father was at the base of the maul looking for the ball. It suddenly popped out of the rear of the Engineers side and the opposing scrum half wasted no time in getting it out to his backs. Along the line it went at great speed, as the backs advanced at pace. The opposing backs had lined up, marking their opposite numbers. When the ball reached the wing they were halted in their tracks and another maul formed. This time, the Armoured Squadron had managed to steal the ball and turn over possession. Richard's dad secured the ball and looked up for options. When the time was right, he passed the ball to his left, into the path of Richard, who had anticipated it. Taking the ball cleanly in his midriff, he carried on forward, until he was about to be tackled by his opposite number. Dipping his left shoulder, he flung the ball into the path of the centre to his left. The speed of his forward movement, sent his shoulder crashing into the head of the tackler, knocking him backwards. His momentum carried him on, until he laid on top of the now poleaxed Engineer. The game went to and fro, from one side to the other, and the two evenly matched sides were still level at half time.

As they rehydrated and consumed their oranges during the ten minute rest period, both of the teams went through the good and bad points of the first half. They also went through how they could alter their tactics in the second half. They came to the conclusion that as the Armoured Squadron forwards were considerably heavier than the Engineers, they would take up most of the work. The plan was for them to drive for the line, using a rolling maul, whenever in the opponent's 22 metre area. They would then release the ball to the backs. Everyone agreed on the plan of action, the whistle sounded and they reassumed their positions for the restart. The first 30 minutes was played out much the same as the previous 40. Then, an opportunity arose, when Richard received a ball from a high kick from his opposite number in his own half. The advancing Engineers had left a gap in their 22 metre area. Richard put boot to ball, aiming for about the middle of this point. The full back spotted it, however, looking up, he saw the Armoured Squadron forwards bearing down on him. This caused him to panic and fumble the ball. Knocking it forward, the referee gave a scrum to the attacking side. Richard's dad organised the pack and shouted out a code word, once they were ready to set the scrum. Richard knew what this meant and readied himself to move to the blind side of the scrum. On the receipt of 'ball coming in ….now!' from his dad, he darted behind the scrum to their left hand side about three feet from the touchline. The pack took up the strain and began to advance forward with the rear man keeping the ball between his feet, not allowing it to leave. When they were around five metres from the try line, Richard's dad quickly grabbed the ball and in an instant had given it to Richard who charged onto it at full speed. With only one man to beat, Richard side stepped to his right and was over the line, and with no other opposition, placed the ball directly under the posts. A huge cheer went up from the side lines from the watching spectators. One of these was Richard's mum, and she smiled as she saw the father and son team embrace each other in celebration.

The Armoured Squadron converted the try and were up 7-0. For the remaining six minutes they defended doggedly until the final whistle blew and they were the 1981 Berlin Rugby Cup winners. The obligatory cheers of appreciation for both sides and the swapping of shirts was undertaken. Then, after a short pause, the teams lined up for the presentation. As they walked up to collect the cup, Richard's dad patted him on the back and whispered in his ear.

'Fucking proud of you, son.'

Richard, not an emotional person, felt himself well up but forced back the tears that he knew were building up. The presentation over with, both teams headed for the showers and were to meet in the bar in 30 minutes time.

As Richard and a few of the later arrivals entered the Squadron bar, the party was already in full swing. Some of the families from both sides had turned out, and there were young children running around everywhere. Richard just hoped that the lads would be behave themselves and keep the language down. He got to the bar and ordered a round of drinks. To his left, he recognised one of the wives of a lad in MT. He smiled at her and said hello, she returned the smile and greeting. He had heard a story about her and it went something like this.

Dell, who was her husband, had come home one evening after a hard day's work. He just felt like going for a drink. Entering his flat on the married quarter estate, where most of the pads lived, he called out his wife's name. He heard her reply from the bedroom and went to investigate. As he opened the door to the bedroom he saw his wife lying on the bed with only the smallest pairs of briefs on. She grinned at him, whilst running her finger from her neck, down her body towards her crotch, lingering there.

'Dell, tie me up, and I'll let you do anything you want to me?' she whispered.

By all accounts, she was famous throughout the Squadron for this type of behaviour. Dell pondered for a moment, then nodded his head, whilst going to a chest of drawers. From here, he removed two pairs of tights, with which he deftly tied around his wife's wrists. Then, returning again he collected two more pairs, which he proceeded to tie around her ankles, then to the bottom of the bed, so that she was spread eagled. Once this was done, Gemma, for that was her name, began to squirm on the bed gyrating her hips begging him to make love to her. She was not prepared for what happened next. Dell, once again, delved into one of the drawers and removed a pair of her panties. He approached the bed and stood over his now expectant spouse. He started to nuzzle her neck and kiss her breasts, licking the nipples as he did so. Just as he had worked her up into a sexual frenzy, he took the panties that were still clutched in his hand and placed them in her mouth. Happy that she could still breathe safely, he announced at the top of his voice.

'Right, I'm off to Smitty's for a few pints with the lads,' Dell turned about and left the flat without another word, making his way to the local pub, just on the other side of the road from the estate. There, he remained for about two hours, before returning to his flat and removing the knickers from his wife's mouth. She, of course, was raging at this point, and Dell turned up on first parade on the Monday sporting a black eye.

The rest of the afternoon was spent socializing among themselves and with the Royal Engineers. Many songs were sung, the more adventurous ones were left until the smaller children had left, later in the day. Different bar games were devised and another mini competition had begun. Richard loved the military spirit, everyone was so competitive in whatever they did. The game playing, celebrating and drinking went on into the night. It was around 02:00 before Richard fell asleep and, with the day's exertions and celebrations, he didn't wake up till dinner time on the Sunday.

The following week, the Squadron were told that Pete and Smudger had been tried, and that they had received 56 days, to be spent in the Grenadiers' nick. After this period, they would be released, but would need to leave Berlin and return to their parent Regiment in Catterick. It was a big shock for everyone, but the point had been brought home that drink-driving would not be tolerated. Putting it to bed, the Squadron Leader congratulated the Rugby team on their fine victory at the weekend. He also spoke about an up-and-coming competition that Brigade was running, which he had nicknamed 'Super Troop'. He then proceeded to read out the list of names of those who would be representing the Squadron. Five of Third Troop had been selected, Lofty, Sol, H, Hux and, finally, Richard. They looked at each other smiling, not knowing what they were letting themselves in for.

The March and Shoot competition that had been labelled 'Super Troop' consisted of a forced march in full fighting order and pack, containing various pieces of clothing and equipment. The teams were inspected prior to setting off, and teams were docked points for any item that was missing. During the twenty kilometre force march, they would go through a series of military stands. These included procedures like Armoured Fighting Vehicle Recognition (AFV Rec), First Aid, Nuclear Biological and Chemical (NBC) drills and others. The thing would culminate in race over an assault course, finishing up on the ranges. The team itself consisted of One Officer, a Sergeant and 30 guys. The Officer had been drawn from Second Troop. He was a well-grounded and respected man, standing some six feet four with dark hair, and an almost Mediterranean look about him. The Sergeant was Third Troops very own Hux and although maybe not the fittest of all the Senior Non Commissioned Officers (SNCOs), he knew how to get the most out of people. They had trained hard for the last four weeks, building up distance and how much weight they carried. Their feet had become hardened and accustomed to the long distances over different terrain. However, this would still be a very physical as well as mental challenge.

The day had arrived and at 07:00, they paraded at Brigade Headquarters, where they were lined up and inspected. After the inspection, every member of the Troop had to empty his pack and lay it out in front of him. The inspection team went along the line ticking off the equipment against a list carried on a clipboard. The inspection took around 40 minutes to be completed, and at the end of it had been deducted six points. Thankfully, Richard had not been picked up for anything, as he knew the result would have been a bollocking from Hux. They were fallen out and given a time to be at the start line, for the off, which was in 30 minutes time. They headed over to an area that had been set aside with Coffee and Tea urns, helped themselves to a brew and idly chatted. Before they knew it, Lieutenant Nickfolds, the Troop leader for the competition, was getting around them, making sure that they would be ready for the start in five minutes. Hux was ensuring everyone had all their equipment with them, and advised them to use the 'buddy buddy' system to check each other. With two minutes to go, they were called over to the start line. They lined up in three ranks with Hux as the front right hand man and the Troop Leader to the side. They had already sorted out who would be where. The slowest blokes were at the front, so that the Troop would march or run to their pace. This would ensure that they completed it together, rather than the racing snakes shooting off and losing half the Troop.

'On your marks...Get set....Go!' came the order from the starting official.

Stepping off with the left foot in unison, the Troop set off at a brisk pace, with Hux calling out the time. The first fifteen minutes were spent getting into a rhythm and getting their breathing going properly. It was 08:00 by now and the summer sun had already started its rise. The sweat was running down between Richard's shoulder blades and he was having to wipe it from his brow to prevent it running into his eyes. He was continuously adjusting the position of his helmet, it was not sitting right and was beginning to rub on the top of his head. This was only to get worse as the Troop leader announced.

'By the left, double march!' and they broke into a jog.

While this alleviated the stress on the shins, it brought new problems. Richard's helmet started to bounce up and down on his head, and it felt like a spike was being driven into the top of his skull. This came from the 'spider' which was attached inside, and was supposed to provide some level of comfort. However, in his haste, Richard had not secured it correctly. He did not want to say anything, and thought it better to wait for their first water stop. For the next 30 minutes, Richard suffered in silence, his plight was only helped when they went back from jogging to marching. In the distance, he could see a table which was manned by a couple of the SQMS staff. They had a water bowser and brews waiting. As soon as they arrived, they were told to quickly fill their water bottles, and to grab a quick brew. They were making good time, so it was decided they would have a ten minute rest. Richard quickly removed his helmet and adjusted the 'spider' inside and secured it. This done, he rushed over to the water bowser and, after drinking the remains of his water bottle, topped it up again. He then drank a quick cup of hot, sweet tea to try and replenish some energy. No sooner had they stopped, then they were falling in again, and were off at a brisk pace, once more.

They had covered almost half the distance when it was decided to drop the pace, to try and conserve energy. They were ahead of time and were being updated by the SQMS staff on route, on the other teams' times. They ran to a junction on the track that they were intended to take through the wood. The Troop leader indicated they were to turn left, which they did, although some of them, who had studied the route beforehand, were not quite sure this was the right decision. It was not until five kilometres further on that Hux fell out and approached the Troop Leader. After a quick discussion, they came to the conclusion they had taken a wrong turn. They turned about, and, at a jog, retraced their steps back to the junction. Heads were starting to hang low and moral was low. It took Hux' best efforts to keep their spirits up. There were definite mumblings in the ranks, as fatigue had started to set in. An extra ten kilometres was not what was needed and they had to dig deep to carry on. Richard looked around at his fellow team members, he felt proud to be a part of this. The way that soldiers supported each other in adverse situations never failed to impress him. The Troop Leader would never live this down, and they would have his life afterwards. The mistake had been made and there was no changing that. To make up for lost time, they jogged the next 30 minutes, until they finally reached the first stand.

Here, one of their own tanks was waiting, with one of the Corporals and crew from First Troop. The stand was Infantry tank target indication, and was something that they practiced regularly. A model had been crafted, using the terrain to the front of the tank, with models being used to simulate enemy positions. The Troop had to use the Infantry Tanks Telephone (ITT) on the rear of the tank to direct fire from the tank on to the enemy positions. As this was their bread and butter, the Troop sailed through within ten minutes and were on their way again, to the next stand. For the next two hours, they went through the NBC and AFV Recognition stands. This was a godsend, as they were able to replenish their energy levels prior to the last push towards the finish. There were only three miles to complete from their present location to the area of the assault course. As they moved from the NBC stand to the next checkpoint given by the directing staff, they entered a clearing in the wood. In front of them, were positioned a number of vehicles, some on fire, others on their sides. There were bodies everywhere and they needed to make a quick assessment of what was going on. Realising straight away that this must be a First Aid stand, they automatically began checking danger to themselves before proceeding. Once they had confirmed there was no danger, they split into small groups and began to assess the priority of the various casualties. The Medical Corps people, who had set up the incident, had been very professional, and everything looked almost real. They had used battlefield simulation makeup, to make the injuries as life like as possible. The small teams went through the casualties like a dose of salts. After treating those that they could, they were informed that one of the casualties required urgent medical attention from a field hospital. They were given a grid, which turned out to be the area of the assault course at Brigade HQ. They were shown a stretcher that had three twenty litre full, plastic water cans strapped to it. This was to simulate their casualty and they were to take it as quickly as possible to the given grid. The Troop Leader quickly appointed four men to take either side of the stretcher onto their shoulders. Their weapons were handed over to other members of the Troop. With everyone in position, they set off towards their final destination.

Pausing only to change people over on the stretcher, they covered the ground quickly. Running through rivers, along wooded tracks and then finally on to the Heer Strasse for the last mile towards Brigade HQ. They passed the Olympic stadium to their right. By this time, Richard thought that he was going to pass out, he felt physically sick. He was not the only one, some of the team had started to fall behind. Knowing they only had around 800 metres left to do, Hux and some of the fitter members, were taking bits of equipment from the weaker ones. This gave them a little reprieve, and a chance that they would all finish as a Troop. The finish line was in sight, and some of the Pipes & Drums of the Royal Irish Rangers had assembled just before the start line. These were one of the Brigades infantry Regiments and were also competing. The Armoured Squadron had its history firmly rooted in Ireland, so this was a nice touch. The drone of the pipes could be heard as the end drew ever closer. This lifted some of the Troops' spirits and gave them the strength to give one final push. The sound of the 'St Patricks Day' march continued as the last man crossed the line and the stretcher had been unceremoniously thrown down. They gathered themselves together, and fighting for breath, were herded towards the start of the assault course. As soon as they had lined up, they were given the order to go from the directing staff. They had practiced the assault course many times over the last four weeks, and everyone knew what part they were to play. The first obstacle was a twelve foot wall and the first people to reach it turned and cupped their hands on their thighs. As each person reached them they placed their feet in the open hands and were assisted up the wall. Once all but one had cleared it, one from each small team turned and hung over the wall. The person who had been doing the assisting, then ran at the wall and took hold of the out stretched hands. Grasping them, they walked themselves up the wall. Once the whole team were across, they continued over the various obstacles. These included a high cargo net and various rope swings over water. Not everyone cleared them all unscathed, some ended up in the water, and others would fall, and had to repeat that particular obstacle again. As quickly as it had begun, the last of them crossed the finished line, but there was not time to celebrate. They were immediately herded on the ranges, where they were issued twenty rounds per man. A series of targets of running men known as 'figure 11s' were presented, from 100 metres up to 300 metres away. The amount of time they were presented also varied, and the men were also asked to change fire positions for the different exposures. Due to the fatigue of the last twelve hours, their marksmanship was being put to the test. As the final shot was fired and the last person had shown that his weapon was clear to the directing staff, they were allowed to relax. Most of them just fell to the ground where they stood. Looking up at the sky, Richard knew that he just completed the hardest thing that he had attempted in his career, so far. Those that had already recovered were walking round, drinking water or cups of hot, sweet tea that had been provided. They slapped each other on the back, congratulating one another.

As the teams were set off at different times with ten minutes in between teams, it was over an hour before the last team finished on the ranges. At around 19:00 they were all called together, and the results of the competition were announced. The winner of the Major Units cup was announced as the Royal Irish Rangers and the other teams applauded sportingly, as they collected the cup. There was then a short pause, before the winner of the Minor Units were announced. It came as a shock to the Armoured Squadron as they heard that it was they who had won. All the weeks of training, and the torture they had just endured, had all been worthwhile, Richard thought. After collecting the Minor Units winners' cup, they were also presented with two crates of beer. This part of the prize lasted about fifteen minutes as the Troop went through the contents of the bottles of beer like Tasmanian Devils, before getting on the bus, for the trip back to Smuts Barracks.

After they had showered and changed, transport had been arranged to take them to the red light area in Charlottenburg. Stuckgarter Platz had become a regular haunt of the Troops over the last year. This was especially true for one of the guys who was known as Jonah. He was the Squadron Physical Training Instructor (PTI) and came from York. He lived with a girl who ran one of the bars in 'Stucki Platz', and she had laid on the venue and entertainment for the evening. It was a typical after competition party, which involved of course drinking games, singing and a novelty game of pool. This was provided by one of the friends of Renate, the girlfriend of Jonah. The bar itself was next door to where Richard had witnessed the guy have his brains plastered all over the optics. He sipped on his beer and pondered over the last twelve months.

Chapter 30 – Nautius Maximus, and all things must come to an end

The months passed and before long it was mid-winter, the temperature outside was as low as minus twenty degrees Celsius. All the sight-seeing had been done and the friends only ever went out for the odd meal during the week, and a bit of a blow out on a Friday or Saturday night. Richard normally spent the Saturday evening with Annette, after she had finished her shift in the bar. He then returned to camp on the Sunday, in time for the evening meal. It was on such a Sunday, that he had finished his meal and had returned to the accommodation on the third floor. The Super Bowl was playing that particular day, and a few of them had decided to watch it in the communal TV room. As they gathered in the room and got themselves comfortable, they handed out the beers. This was actually not allowed but was okay as long as they got rid of the evidence before any block inspection. Just as the programme was about to start the British Forces TV station was running a news item on the Falklands war which had just come to an end. They had put together a list of all those that had been killed in the conflict. As the friends sat there, drinking their beers, watching the names and units of the fallen scroll up the screen. Richard was drawn to one name in particular, 'Pte. Frederick Diner, 2nd Battalion the Parachute Regiment'. It took a moment for it to sink in until he realised who this was.

'Oh, my fucking God, I don't believe it ….' he said, in dismay, his eyes not leaving the screen. Images of the well-built powerhouse, who had joined him on leave that first time from training. After their altercation with the RMP, and subsequent arrest they had returned, not thinking anything of it. When Fred had passed off, and gone to Chichester to receive his Royal Military Police Training, he had been told that he would not be able to continue. This was due to the fact that he now had a criminal record, due to this little misunderstanding whilst staying with Richard's parents in Germany. The only thing they could do, was to offer him a transfer to another unit. After much thought, and being the action man that he was, Fred chose the Parachute Regiment. This was an obvious choice for a young man as fit as he was. He left Chichester and had gone and undergone 'P' Company and received his 'Para Wings', and was badged to the 2nd Battalion. He deployed with his Battalion on the Falklands campaign as the signaller for Lt Col 'H' Jones. He was killed with him as he led a desperate attack on an Argentine machine gun post. Richard was numb and a tear welled up in his eye. The others were staring at him, not knowing what was wrong. After asking what the problem was, Richard explained that they had gone through training together and the incident while on leave. They offered words of condolence in turn, but before they could dwell on the news were startled by the sound of an alarm. Not knowing what was going on they left the room to investigate. They were met by Albert, who was slightly out of breath after sprinting up the stairs, since the lift was currently out of order.

'They've called 'Nautius Maximus.' he managed to blurt out as he brushed passed them and made his way to his room.

They had been there fifteen months now, and thought they were going to get away with not participating in a full blown Allied Powers crash out. Richard rushed along the corridor to his room, as did the rest of the Troop. Due to the fact that they had undertaken numerous Alert Troops by this time, it came as second nature. As he entered his room, he opened his locker and threw a pair of coveralls on the bed. He also went to his drawers and removed two pairs of socks and some thermal long johns and vest. 'It was going to be a cold one,' he thought to himself, not knowing that he would be out much longer than he thought. As he completed dressing, the sound of Alert Troop passing below his window indicated that he had made good time. The average time for the Troops on standby was down to around four minutes. The record was just over three minutes which was held by First Troop, but everyone knew they had been given prior warning. As Richard left his room, he was joined by Ken, who had also made good time. They both resembled Michelin men, with the layers of clothing they had on. Leaving the Hilton by the main entrance, they were joined by bodies coming from every direction. Some of the First married personnel were being let through the camp gates. Cars sped past Ken and Richard, on their way to the Squadron block, to sign out their vehicle weapons. The Alert Troop had already left camp and would be taking up their pre-determined positions. Each Troop had been given a position they would take up in the event of a crash out. Reaching the hangar, he saw it was a hive of activity: engines had been started, gun kits online and weapons being mounted.

It had only been 30 minutes since the alarm had been given, and Third Troop were waiting on one of the married guys to turn up. The tanks had been pulled out of the hangars, a full Squadron communications check had been carried out and they were ready to roll. 20 minutes later, the Squadron was complete and the Squadron Leader gave the order for them to move to the front gate, and wait the arrival of the RMP and GCP. The engines roared in a belch of smoke and, as one, they lumbered forward. On arrival at the gates, the RMP were already waiting and had stopped the traffic. The Troops headed out, one at a time, towards their pre designated positions around Spandau and Ruhleben. It only took Richard's vehicle fifteen minutes to reach the bridge, which was their fighting position for the initial deployment. As the three tanks from Third Troop took up their defensive locations, they were joined by a platoon of infantry from the Royal Irish Rangers. Some of them had anti-tank weapons and were there to protect the armour from any close attack. The temperature was dropping rapidly, and Albert asked 'H' to put the Boling Vessel (BV) on for a brew. This, of course, had already been done, prior to them leaving and he began to pour out the brews. As Albert and H sat with their heads out of their respective hatches, they peered down at the infantry in their dug in positions. They looked up, longingly and somewhat enviously, at the tank crews. It was a well-known fact that all infantry assumed that tanks had fitted heaters. This was could not be further from the truth, the inside was like a fridge as it consisted mostly of pure metal. The only luxury they had was the BV, which was a life saver, and every good loader would have it on permanently. Feeling a little sorry for the infantry, Albert asked if they would like a brew. This was gratefully accepted and H busied himself filling up the BV, once more.

In twenty minutes, the BV had boiled again and H had already collected the mugs from the four infantry guys dug in at the side of the bridge. He returned to the tank, and added the tea bags or coffee and sugar to the mugs. With Sol's help, he dished out the brews, which were taken with thanks. It caused one of the infantrymen, who spoke with a broad Belfast accent, to point at the armoured search light, on the left hand side of the turret.

'What's inside there?' he asked, inquisitively.

Thinking for a moment before answering, H smirked to himself. 'That's where we keep our spare crewman' he replied, with a completely straight face. This caused looks of incredulity from the four young infantry soldiers.

'Feck that, I couldn't handle that I get claustrophobic,' he replied, in all seriousness.

Shaking his head and laughing, H returned to the tank, and took great delight in telling the crew. For the next five minutes, they could not do anything for laughing. However, the mirth was cut short, as the order came over the air, for them to move to another grid. On investigation, Albert saw that it was in the heart of the Grunewald, a large wooded area. Making sure everything was stowed, the Troop vacated their positions, waving goodbye to their gullible close protection as they did so. They moved a Troop at a time, along a route that had been given in the movement order. Entering the Grunewald, they immediately cut any headlights, only leaving their convoy light at the rear, for the tank behind to follow. They were about two kilometres into the wood, when they were met by the SSM. Albert jumped down from the turret and had a quick conversation with him. Once he was happy, he nodded his head and indicated to Sol that he should follow him. Guiding him forward on foot, and using a single torch, he reversed the tank into its position. As soon as it had stopped the gun kit was turned off by Richard, and Sol cut the GUE and main engine. Like a well-oiled machine, the crew jumped out and began the hide drills in silence, and in 30 minutes, tracks had been obliterated and cam nets were up. Sentries had been posted and a radio watch set up. It took only 45 minutes for the whole Squadron to arrive, complete their hide drills, and have camouflage nets up. The wood was silent, except for the odd hoot of a nearby owl. Then, suddenly, in the distance the sound of more armoured vehicles. The noise was accompanied by numerous headlights, snaking their way in the direction of the Squadron. The Squadron Leader informed them they were to have a Company of American Infantry, which would be providing their close support. The on-looking British Troops could not believe the total disregard to tactics, in the use of lights at night. They may have moved into their location unobserved, however this was all for nothing, as the position was now lit up, as though it was daylight. This was just a taster of things to come, as the Americans were to show how vastly different the Allied forces were.

On their arrival, they used their vehicles, to illuminate the area, where they would dig in their defensive positions. This would encompass the complete perimeter of the Squadron. Therefore providing a full 360 degrees of support. Unlike the British forces, everything was done non-tactically, with orders being shouted, and lights being shone in all directions. Richard wondered to himself why they had tried to disguise their presence, as all of this had been undone by the Americans unprofessionalism. It took over two hours before the Infantry Company had sorted themselves out and dug into their positions. The Armoured Squadron continued their routines as normal, with the ground sentries and radio stags changing as normal. Just before first light, the last ground sentry had gone round and woken up the entire Squadron, for them to stand to. They had climbed into their crew positions and waited on the coming dawn to break. As the low winter sun broke the horizon, the Troops stared through their sights trying to pinpoint any proposed threat. Working out that there was no risk to their position, it was decided that they would stand down. Before the order could be given, they were startled by the sound of heavy machine gun fire. Richard quickly scanning his arcs, spotted the muzzle flash coming from one of the American M113 Armoured Personnel Carriers (APC's). One of the commanders of the vehicle was manning the .50 Browning Heavy Machine Gun and shouting at the top of his voice.

'Reveille!'

The whole Squadron was astounded at this cavalier attitude to warfare, and within every tank they were either taking the piss, or shaking their heads in disbelief. The best was still to come, though. As Richard and the rest of the crews stood down, and began to prepare breakfast under the cover of the cam nets. A vehicle which looked a little similar to a removal truck, entered the wooded hide area. As it drew close to the dug in American Troops, one side opened and a bell rang out. It looked like a scene from a cowboy film, when the ranchers would beat a piece of metal against a ring, to let the cowhands know it was meal time.

'Chow time!' Came the scream, from within. From all around the hide, soldiers were emerging from their fox holes, metal plates in hand and all heading toward the sound of the bell. 'This must be their version of the SQMS,' Richard thought, as the guys lined up and ordered whatever was on offer. There was no fried egg, sausage and beans on this menu, though. They were given things like hot dogs, burgers and other different kinds of fast food. Furnished with their food, and huge cups of coke and various other sugary drinks, they returned, contended to their fox holes.

The rest of the morning was spent waiting for any further orders from Brigade, as to what would be the next move. It was not until late into the afternoon, that they were told the exercise had ended. They were to be ready to depart back to barracks, in two hours' time. The Squadron quickly took down their camouflage nets, started the engines and attempted to keep warm. To pass a little time the Squadron Leader had arranged for the Americans to have a quick look around their tanks. When they first arrived, they were given a tour around the exterior, and given a brief summary of the fighting capabilities of the vehicle. This included the amount, and various types of ammunition carried. What their velocity was, and what their effects were, on enemy armour. The Americans seemed genuinely impressed by the delivery and professionalism of Hux, who had been chosen to show them round Third Troop. As they were taken, two at a time, up onto and inside the turret they could not believe how cramped it was. This was unlike the American M60, whose turret you could stand up in, and still have two foot head clearance. Richard had witnessed this first hand when they had visited an American tank unit in the American sector.

The fighting compartment there had a fitted stereo hi-fi, and the drivers cab had fitted covers on seats. The only things he considered missing were the fluffy dice. They spent the next 30 minutes answering any questions their guests had. Then, after satisfying their curiosity, bid them a fond farewell, and intimated they hoped to work with them again. This of course was not true, but it was the British way, 'good manners and all that'. Richard was to witness, how unprofessional a fighting force these so-called allies were in the heat of battle. And, on this occasion, it would cost a number of British lives.

The experience of working with the Americans was far behind them, and they entered into the last three months of their posting in the big city. So many things had happened over the last nineteen months. They had tasted cuisine from all over the world at least twice a week. Visited Museums, Art Galleries, Bier Kellers, Nightclubs, Prostitutes and one night Richard had even taken Annette to the Opera. Any type of entertainment you could think of was on offer in this vibrant city. As Richard sat at the bar in Annette's pub, he called to mind the evening he had been invited by Danny to a show he was appearing in. They had been sitting in Annette's bar, just chatting about Danny latest play. After Richard had shown an interest in it, Danny asked if he would like to come and see it.

'I will get you a front row seat, darling' he said, in his campest voice, while extravagantly smoking his cigarette. 'It will be great fun, I can wave at you and make my boyfriend jealous,' he said in a matter-of-fact manner.

This remark intrigued Richard, but knowing the German language, he thought there must be some rational explanation for it. So, without trying to cause any offence, he formulated the question in his mind that he wanted answering, before translating it into German.

'When you say your boyfriend, you mean your friend that is a man, don't you?'

There was a pregnant pause and a look of confusion on Danny's face. 'Yes, that's right, my boyfriend,' he answered, smiling. Seeing the confusion in Richard's eyes, Annette immediately leaned forward and whispered to him.

'You do know Danny is gay?' she said, in a conspirator type tone, obviously not wanting Danny to hear.

This was like being hit with a sledge hammer for Richard. How could he have been so stupid over the past eighteen months? All the signs were there, the camp way of smoking his cigarettes, the tone of his voice and the feminine mannerisms. As it finally hit home, he stammered to speak and only managed to sound outraged when he did.

'No, I fucking didn't know he was gay,' he said, causing Danny to look in alarm, understanding that he was not happy about something. Although Danny could not understand much English, he recognised the tone of the remark, as being derogatory. He worked out that Richard had not known of his sexual preference, he moved along the bar and apologised to Richard, explaining that he thought he knew. After the initial shock had worn off, Richard simply smiled, and slapped Danny on the back. He felt stupid for reacting in such a way, and said that there was no reason to apologise. If anyone was out of order it was him, and to make things right, he ordered them a round of drinks. After a few more drinks, all was forgotten and Richard accepted the invitation to go and see the show. The night ended as usual, with him taking the tube home with Annette, and being used and abused for the rest of the evening.

Richard smiled to himself, thinking of all the other amusing and not-so-amusing things that had happened during their time there. One of the REME guys, a young Electrician, had tried to defect to East Berlin on a push bike. He was of course drunk, and fresh from the Squadron bar. He thought it would be a good idea to take the short ride to Staaken checkpoint, along with his toolbox on the back of his bike, and there ask for political asylum. The East German border guards simply laughed at him, turned him around, pointing him in the direction he had just come from. Also, the time when everyone on the tank park had observed a Hind D Soviet helicopter gunship fly over camp, and no one reported it. After the event, it came to light that terrorists had hijacked an aircraft from Aeroflot, the Russian Airline. After issuing their demands, the Soviet hierarchy had given the order for the gunship to make its way to Tegel Airport, where the drama was unfolding. Immediately when the Hind came on the scene, and hovered above the end of the runway, the terrorists gave up their hostages and the siege was ended. One of the Squadron's biggest claims to fame, and a legacy that they would pass on, was produced by one of its members. A young Trooper known simply as 'Henry' had been playing around with the idea of camouflage for an urban environment. He built a model of Chieftain Tank and tested various designs on it. Once he was happy that he had come up the right combination, he went to his Troop Leader, to see what he thought. So impressed was the Troop Leader, he immediately went to see the OC, who ordered that their Troop paint their vehicles in the new design. The design took the form of a series of brown, grey and white irregular squares. The design became known as the brick, and after testing it in various locations and taking pictures, the OC went to

Brigade to put the idea forward. Brigade thought it was so revolutionary, the whole of the Brigade were ordered to adopt the new colour scheme. What the Squadron Leader failed to mention was that it was not his idea but Henry's.

Richard also thought of 'Jenny Mess Tin' who had been a regular resident in the Hilton during their stay. However, she had not been seen for the last three weeks, and he knew there was a reason for this. She had been in the NAAFI bar on a Friday night, and had been sat drinking with a couple of the guys from the Engineer Squadron. At around 22:00 she left, arm in arm with two of them. The story went, that they had returned to their Troop accommodation, where she had taken part in sexual acts with three of the Troop. Not being satisfied with that, she asked that the others who were present on the floor join in. After another four blokes had agreed, and given her what she wanted, the fifth refused to participate. She at once began to scream 'rape'. The guard commander was called, who informed the RMP. An investigation involving the German Civil Police had been undertaken, during which time the true story came to light. Jenny had been charged for wasting police time and banned from camp.

He was disturbed from his thoughts by Albert, who asked him if everything was ready in the turret. He nodded his agreement. That morning, the whole Squadron were heading down to Ruhleben. The Ammunition Technical Officer (ATO) had condemned their vehicle ammunition on his last inspection and this was to be changed prior to handover. Each of the Troops made their way the four kilometres to the ammunition depot. Here, they had to completely remove all their old ammunition which was counted off by members of the Royal Ordnance Corps. Once they were empty, they were issued with their brand new ammunition. Each vehicle commander signed for their ammunition and were sent on their way.

For the following weeks, the Troops worked tirelessly on the vehicles, after having them minutely inspected by the Fitter Section, for any major or minor jobs. This was in preparation for their handover to the incoming unit, the Royal Hussars. It was a matter of pride for every crew, that their tank would have every piece of equipment, and all jobs complete. If anything was not complete, then they had a job number issued from the REME to say that it was either awaiting parts or was in hand.

The days flew by and before they knew it, the day had come for them to hand over. They had all eaten an early breakfast and made their way to the tank park. They began by completely unloading all the ammunition and tools on the green tank sheets, which they had put down for that purpose.

They put down each tool as the commanders called it out in accordance with the Complete Equipment Schedule (CES). By 09:00 the Troops were finished and all equipment and ammunition was lined up in neat rows easy to be identified by the Unit taking over. There seemed to be some confusion however, from the direction of Second Troop. An angry voice could be heard, berating the younger members of the Troop. Some of the blokes were climbing in and out of the turrets, legs dangled out of drivers cabs. Hux had noticed this and thought he would wander over, to investigate. When he returned, he had a broad grin on his face. Calling the Troop together, he informed them that Second Troop were missing a HESH round. The shit was really going to hit the fan over this, as they had only been issued the ammunition three months earlier. This should have come to light before now, as it was the responsibility of the Troop Sergeants to see that after every Alert Troop, the ammo was accounted for. This obviously had not been done, as the Troop had carried out three Alert Troops since then. After a couple of phone calls, it came to light that the round was still sitting on a pallet at the ammunition depot. This put a black mark against the Squadrons otherwise faultless time in Berlin and handover.

The vehicles handed over, the Troop planned one last night out in the big city. The whole of the Troop agreed to meet at the guardroom at 14:00. From there, they travelled by the usual number 194 bus along the Heerstrasse to Theodor Heuss Platz. The pub they had chosen was Pal Joes and, even at this time of day, it was teeming with people, many of them tourists. It was well known throughout the city, as one of the biggest pubs, but it also laid on live music. The Troop spent the rest of the afternoon drinking and generally celebrating their final evening together. When they departed Berlin, the Squadron would be split up, and members were posted to different Squadrons throughout the Regiment. This would not be the last time some of them served together, though, throughout their careers. The stories of their time in Berlin would be recalled every time they met, even after leaving the Army. Due to the amount of alcohol being consumed, it was thought sensible that they should get some food down them. The close friends in the Troop suggested they visited the Yugoslavian restaurant that they had used at least once every week. Everyone was in agreement and downed their drinks and they headed off for the underground.

It was only a short tube ride to the location where the restaurant stood, not far from the Kurfürstendamm. Entering the establishment, they were greeted with open arms by the management. Although the place was quite busy, and there were twelve of them, the staff joined two tables, so the friends could sit together. When Ken explained that this would be their last meal there as they were leaving, the staff were devastated. Not only had they been good and regular customers, but they had become friends also. They insisted that this last meal would be on the house and invited them to order what they wanted. So, for the next two hours, they ate and drank, then drank some more. After saying a fond farewell, the Troop poured out, once more, on to the streets. Some of them had decided to go to the red light area, but Sol and Richard said they were going to the Irish Harp. This was not the Irish pub in the Europa Centre, and was a little more authentic. They had found it after becoming friendly with one of the Irish barmaids, in the original Irish bar they had gone to on their first night out. As they neared the bar, loud Irish folk music could be heard. They opened the door and were assaulted with a cacophony of noise. The atmosphere was brilliant and although neither Richard nor Sol had ventured into a pub in Ireland, he imagined it would be just like this. The bar staff were always friendly even though they knew they were British soldiers. They had always avoided talking politics when they were there. It was a long while before they even let the cat out of the bag that they were in the British army. Rachel one of the barmaids caught their eye as they came to the bar.

'Two pints of Guinness is it, boys?' she smiled at them, fluttering her pretty blue eyes. She was a beautiful young girl but unfortunately was spoken for. Sean, who was also on the bar that evening, raised his hand in acknowledgement and welcome.

'Yes, please, Rachel' Richard replied, reciprocating the smile.

They watched every silky movement, as Rachel poured their drinks. She was something to behold, perfect in every form. Although they had fantasised about her, they would never try to seduce her. They had spent many a boozy afternoon with both Sean and Rachel, passing the time of day. They even promised that they would keep in touch after they had left. The live folk band was blaring away in the background. Some of the locals were up dancing and it always caused Richard to chuckle. At least they are enjoying themselves, even if they do look like twats. In the middle of dancing group he spied two nice looking girls. Nudging Sol, he indicated them with a nod of his head. Sol, at once, understood what he meant and, on receiving their drinks, they waited until the girls had sat down and walked over and joined them. Richard asked if they could sit down with them in his best German accent. They giggled to each other and said of course they could. The usual questions were asked, where they were from, if they worked, how long had they been there and so on. When the two girls found out that they were British soldiers, their interest heightened even more. Richard winked at Sol, knowing they were on to a good thing.

Their names were Bettina and Heidi, and Richard had taken a shine to Heidi's golden locks. Her body was not bad either, and her ample bust stood out firm under the pullover she was wearing. Before long, the girls asked if the lads would like to accompany them back to their apartment, which invitation was, of course, readily accepted. As they walked the short distance back to the nearest tub station, Richard thought back to his parting night with Annette two days ago. It was a bit of a solemn evening, as the two had enjoyed each other's company over the last two years. They knew they would probably never meet again, and as Richard left her he didn't look back.

When they arrived at the girl's apartment, which was in a quite well to do area of the city, they were quickly ushered inside. Their hosts asked if they would like a drink, which they accepted. They sat on adjoining sofas, each couple chatting between themselves. After about fifteen minutes, Sol got up and his partner led him away by the hand to what Richard assumed must be a bedroom. It was not long before Richard was also being taken to a room which led off from the corridor. Tearing off her clothes as she went, the excited young woman encouraged him to do the same. They stood in the room facing each other, Richard's manhood stood erect, twitching in excitement. It was though it was alive and had a mind of its own. Heidi began to kiss his neck, lingering only for a short while, before moving down to his chest and lingering around his nipples. Then, slowly moving down to his navel and groin. He gasped in pleasure as he was enveloped by the warm moistness of her mouth. Thrusting her head up and down, she sent waves of pleasure through Richard's entire body. He could feel his muscles tighten in his quadriceps, and knew he needed to stop her before it was too late. Gently pulling her head away from his shaft he helped her to her feet and led her over to the bed. They got comfortable and in no time at all were coiled around each other like a pair of mating snakes. For the next two hours they swapped bodily fluids both internally and externally. Although it was a cold February night, the sweat shone on both of their skins. Finally, both being satisfied, they fell into a contended sleep, only disturbed by the sound of Sol and Bettina smashing the bedpost against the adjoining wall.

Richard woke with a raging thirst. He quietly removed the quilt cover and climbed out of bed, trying not to disturb the sleeping Heidi. He crept from the room and made his way down the corridor to the kitchen, where he found a glass, which he filled with water. He drank the contents of the glass and refilled it, and once again finished it one gulp. Moving back towards the corridor he looked into the living room he noticed that Sol was in there, moving about. He did not say anything, but simply returned to the bedroom and retrieved his clothes from the floor. Heidi was still fast asleep, and he retreated backwards, out of the door. Still naked, carrying his clothes, he passed into the living room. Sol was fully dressed and was fumbling about with some objects.

'What you doing?' Richard asked inquisitively.

Surprised that he had been caught, but when he saw that it was a naked Richard he giggled and whispered.

'I'm nicking some ornaments as mementos' he grinned, as he continued to inspect the nick knacks around the living room, placing two of them in his jacket pocket. Richard thought this was a little strange but knew that it didn't matter what he said, Sol would carry on anyway.

'Well, if you are taking a reminder for yourself, I will leave a reminder for them,' and with that he began to wipe his cock on the curtains. Sol had to bite his tongue to stop himself laughing. Richard decided he had enough of his scent in the immediate area and quickly began to dress. Just as he was about ready, Bettina entered the room. Sol was still looking for items that he could fit into his pockets as souvenirs.

'What are you doing?' Came the question, in broken English.

Totally shocked at being caught in the act, and also a little embarrassed, the pair of them just looked at each other for guidance. As there was nothing forthcoming; and realising there was only one thing for it, they both bolted for the living room door. Running down the corridor, they hastily unlocked the front door, all the time they were being chased by Bettina, who by this time was cursing them in German. As they flew down the stairs of the block of flats, the sounds of her screams got ever fainter. Rushing into the cold winter air, the pair of them were in fits of hysterics, as they ran down the street, toward the underground. 'Well, it had been a great two years but all good things must come to an end,' Richard thought to himself.

Chapter 31 – North Rhine Westphalia and Hohne Ranges

The Cold War was a state of political and military tension after World War II between powers in the Western Bloc (the United States, its NATO allies and others) and powers in the Eastern Bloc (the Soviet Union and its allies in the Warsaw Pact).

Historians have not fully agreed on the dates, but 1947–1991 is common. It was termed as 'cold' because there was no large-scale fighting directly between the two sides, although there were major regional wars in Korea, Vietnam and Afghanistan that the two sides supported. The Cold War split the temporary wartime alliance against Nazi Germany, leaving the USSR and the US as two superpowers with profound economic and political differences: the former being a single-party Marxist–Leninist state, and the latter being a capitalist state with generally free elections. A self-proclaimed neutral bloc arose with the Non-Aligned Movement founded by Egypt, India, Indonesia and Yugoslavia; this faction rejected association with either the US-led West or the Soviet-led East. The two superpowers never engaged directly in full-scale armed combat but they each armed heavily in preparation for a possible all-out nuclear world war. Each side had a nuclear deterrent that deterred an attack by the other side, on the basis that such an attack would lead to total destruction of the attacker: the doctrine of mutually assured destruction (MAD). Aside from the development of the two sides' nuclear arsenals, and deployment of conventional military forces, the struggle for dominance was expressed via proxy wars around the globe, psychological warfare, propaganda and espionage, and technological competitions such as the Space Race.
(Wikipedia)

It was with this situation as a backdrop that the Regiment formed once again in West Germany. The Berlin Armoured Squadron had been split up and divided into the four sabre Squadrons, A, B, C and D, plus HQ Squadron. Richard had remained with D Squadron and they had already settled into their new camp. The new posting was a place called Detmold in North Rhine Westphalia. Ken and Sol had remained part of D Squadron also and were even in the same Troop, although Ken was on a different tank, Sol was Richard's driver. It had been almost three years since Richard had joined the Regiment. He now had moved from the gunner's seat to the loader's side of the turret. His natural bent for all things signals had been identified, while they were in Berlin. He had been asked if he wanted to attend a Control Signaller course while they were there, but had turned it down. The reason he gave was that he did not believe he was ready yet, as he had not done the job. Now was his chance to get some practical experience, as it was his responsibility to ensure all the communications equipment worked, correct battle code was in use, frequencies changed on time and all messages decoded for the commander. The commander in question was his new Troop Sergeant and was renowned throughout the Regiment. His name was Steve Marchant and was known as 'Legs'. He came from a rough area of Leeds and had played semi-professional rugby league prior to joining the Regiment. He was a fitness fanatic, and believed everyone should attain and maintain his high standards. These standards were not only in fitness, but in every facet of being a good tank soldier. He was also a Gunnery Instructor, so his dress was immaculate at all times. He put the fear of god into Richard, but this served to keep him on his toes. The words of his father, who was still in the Regiment, but due to leave later that year, rang in his ears. *'When you join the Regiment, pick a person you consider to be the perfect soldier and try to be that man'.* No man, apart from maybe Kevin from the bar in D Squadron, when he first joined had struck this chord as 'Legs' did. He was to learn to respect, even love this sometimes aggressive, sometimes very funny man. He would be his mentor, and the things he learned from him would last Richard his entire career. The Troop was a strong one with some very experienced characters in it. The Troop Leader was new, but was willing to learn and was very approachable. Normally, Cavalry Officers could be quite stuffy, often coming from aristocratic backgrounds. This one, however, was down to earth, and was immediately accepted by the rank and file. It may have had something to do with his family owning a brewery. His name was Mark, but the guys only called him that when there were no other officers, or high ranking SNCOs about. The Squadron as a whole had made a good start in their new posting and were busy preparing the vehicles to go to Hohne ranges for annual firing. In between servicing the gun equipment, aligning sights and other various jobs that are required prior to firing, the crews were put through rigorous training in the simulators. This was known as the Gunnery Training Simulator (GTS) and here, the crews could practice their drills without firing a live round. The machine itself consisted of the turret of a tank that had been engineered through the use of hydraulics, and electrical components, to resemble the fighting compartment. They could simulate different engagements from static vehicles which were identified with a flashing red light or even moving targets. They could even practice misfire drills by building into the system faults like the firing needle assembly (FNA) failing, due to an electrical failure or missing vent tube. Richard loved these sessions as it gave a chance to get rid of any pent up aggression he may have had. He was naturally aggressive, which made for a good loader. British Army tank ammunition came in three parts. The three components being projectile, bag charge and vent tube. The loader would open the breech, select his ammunition, which he would place on the breech platform and push up the barrel. He would then take a bag charge, dependant on the type of ammunition. For Armoured Piercing Discarding Sabot rounds (APDS), the charges were normally orange and cylindrical. The APDS rounds had a velocity of 1370 metres per second (m/s), so required a large charge. The High Explosive Squash Head (HESH) had a lower velocity 850 m/s, so required half the charge and were half the size. The next movement was for him to 'ram' a ventube, which inserted itself into the FNA. These were contained in a magazine at the bottom of the breech, and were fired by means of an electrical impulse. This ignited the bag charge, driving the round along the rifled barrel, causing it to spin as it did so. He would then close the breech, make the safety guard and ensure the turret switch was to 'Live' at the same time reporting 'Loaded!' A good crew could get as many as ten rounds off a minute.

They had worked hard all week and Richard was looking forward to a few beers on the weekend. When Friday came round the Squadron finished at round 12:30, but had to parade on the airfield at the top of camp in running gear. This was for the now customary Commanding Officers 'Fun Run'. It was a distance of just over three miles and for some a pleasant way to finish off the week. Running had never been a big pastime for Richard, but with one of the rules being that you had to come in before the CO, he applied himself to the task. If you failed to do this, the other downside apart from Legs kicking your arse, was that you had to do it again on Saturday morning with the duty PTI. After a light lunch Richard, French and Sol made their way to the airfield at the top of camp. Most of the Regiment were already there and were milling about, chatting, rubbing their hands and trying to keep warm. At bang on 14:00 the Quarter Master Sergeant Instructor (QMSI), who was the Chief PTI for the Regiment, gave the usual instructions before setting them off. The three friends set off at a steady jog. The really keen athletes, had reached the far end of the airfield, and were exiting the gate on the perimeter road, before the three of them they were halfway across the field. As Legs passed them, he passed on a few words of encouragement.

'You better not come in behind the CO, you lazy twats,' he sneered, blowing snot from his nose and sprinting off, passed them. The friends cringed at his words and were more fearful of what he would do to them never mind getting up first thing on a Saturday to do it again. Putting a little more effort in and looking behind for the CO, they picked up the pace. By the time they reached the perimeter road, their breathing was into a relaxed rhythm. Richard's legs ached, from the 'beasting' Legs had given them two days earlier, on a Troop five mile run. He gritted his teeth only one mile into the run, when suddenly a voice, from his left, called out.

'Get a shift on, you idle shit,' and he saw the fleeting form of his dad race past him. 'I've got twenty years on you, how can you let an old man beat you?' and with that he was gone. Richard had started to fall behind his two friends, who had picked up the pace again. He was anxiously looking over his shoulder, every couple of minutes, to see if the CO was in sight. After just over twenty minutes, he turned a corner and could see the rear camp gates 200 metres in the distance. He knew that it was just 300 metres to go to the gym from there. Taking a deep lungful of air, he stepped up his pace and passed through the gate. He covered the final 300 metres in under three minutes, and on passing the line, his time was called out as 27 minutes. Both Sol and Ken were already there, stretching their calf and quad muscles. Patting him on the back as he crossed the line, Richard bent over, in near exhaustion. After a few moments' recovery time, and glad that he had beaten the CO in, the three of them headed back in the direction of the Squadron block. It had become a custom for the Squadron to meet up in the Squadron bar after the CO's fun run for a couple of beers to end the week. This sometimes went on till the early hours of the morning, but today they had decided to have just a couple. They intended, after that, to get showered and head out to hit the town. After a few quick beers they watched a new member of the Squadron drink a 'Tankie Mind Bender'. This consisted of a pint glass full of around seven different types of spirit. The new boy would have to down it in one, without being sick and then place the empty glass on his head. The candidate was successful first time around, and knowing things were going to get messy, the three of them slipped away to get showered and changed. They had learnt by experience that things would get out of hand, and they would be caught up in a full on session.

It took them only 45 minutes to shower and change, and Sol and Richard, who shared a room passed each other's deodorant and after shave between them. Looking what they thought was smart, and smelling good, they headed off down the corridor to collect Ken and a couple of others from the Squadron. Exiting the camp, they took the road heading down into the main town. It was a steep descent for about 400 metres, before levelling out into the main part of town. They had already experienced, the slow climb up the hill after a skin full of German beer and schnapps. On the way into town, they passed a couple of bars, which were a regular haunt for the soldiers at the barracks where they were stationed. Wanting to get straight into town, they disregarded them, however, as they were feeling peckish they decided they would stop for a gyros at 'Fat Sam's'. Although they had only been there three months, this establishment was renowned throughout the Regiment. Gyros is a Greek dish of meat, roasted on a vertical spit usually served in a pitta bread with tomato, onion, and tzatziki sauce. Fat Sam's was second to none, or that was the opinion they had formed from the others they had visited. Rapidly forcing down the hot meat and salad, they bade Sam a cheery goodbye and headed off to the first pub of the evening.

Finding a pub that had a nice atmosphere, and that they were allowed in could at times be difficult. Many of the local hostelries over the years had experienced trouble with soldiers from the garrison. So to counter this, they had signs put up either on the doors, or the windows stating that British soldiers were not allowed. After a short while, they came across one that they had never used before and, as it had no obvious signs of exclusion, entered it. It seemed to be a quiet local type pub with only a few guests in at that time of the evening. The friends took stools at the bar and ordered a round of drinks. The barmaid, noticing that they were not locals and obviously squaddies, poured the beers and handed them over begrudgingly. The friends lifted them and crashed them together toasting the end of the week. As they sat and drank, they planned out how the evening would go. After a few more in town they wanted to go to a nightclub. A new face in the crowd belonged to a big guy called Steve, who Richard had not met, until the new Squadron was formed. Steve told them that he had heard of a great nightclub in the next town that allowed squaddies in. The only pre-requisite was that you had to leave your ID card (MOD 90) at the reception. After the guys had interrogated him about everything he had heard about the place, they agreed they would get a taxi later.

It was completely dark and freezing cold when they left the pub, looking for the nearest taxi rank. This was a ten minute walk from the centre of town and was located at the train station. They managed to get a taxi that would take all five of them, and Richard gave the destination in his clearest German. The driver nodded his head after repeating it back to him and set off. The journey only took fifteen minutes and they pulled up in the car park of the nightclub. Ken paid the taxi fare and they climbed out, but before climbing up the stairs to the venue, they all gave Ken their share of the fare. The sounds of 80s New Romantic music hit them like a wall, as they opened the door. Sitting on a stool behind a cash register, was a miserable looking, forty something year old woman. 'She might have been quite tasty in her day,' Richard thought to himself. Recognising straight away that they were soldiers, she asked for the entrance fee and their ID cards. This was so that, if there was any trouble, the establishment would have the names of the culprits, if they did a runner. After collecting both, she stamped each of their hands with an indelible stamp. As they walked into the main dance hall and their eyes got accustomed to the light, they observed how few people were there. Feeling downhearted, they immediately looked at Steve, as if to blame him for his suggestion. Steve looked sheepishly at the other four, and simply shrugged in resignation. Ordering the drinks the friends looked for a place where they could sit, and being spoilt for choice, they took a table in the corner. From here, they could observe the entrance from the reception area. It was also a place where no one could sneak up behind them. It was strange, but this seemed to be ingrained into most soldiers. For the next 30 minutes they fired into Steve for what a wank idea he had given them. In his defence, Steve said that he had heard, from more than one source, it was a cracking place for a night out. Regardless of his procrastinations, the friends tirelessly ripped the piss out of him, but in a way he knew was not malicious. Making good of a bad situation, they continued to party and slowly the place started to fill up. By 23:30, the bar was almost full and the ratio of men to women was about 3-1 in the men's favour. Richard was feeling a bit down, as he had just been dumped by a German girl he had been seeing for the last couple of weeks. The alcohol was not really helping either, but just as he was at his lowest ebb, two girls caught his eye. One was almost six feet in height, tall and slender with long blonde hair. She was accompanied by a shorter one, who was also blonde but a bit chunkier in shape. The tall one noticed he was looking over and turned away, seemingly uninterested. Richard looked at his drink, then looked back at the girl and thought to himself. 'Anything has got to be better than this.' Whispering to Steve, he asked if he wanted to accompany him over to the girls. Steve was a shy bloke really, not the most athletic of young men, he did not look like a conventional squaddie. Plucking up courage, the pair of them made their way, across the dance floor, towards the girls. In German, Richard asked if they would like to dance, and after looking the soldiers up and down, the girls agreed. The foursome danced and drank into the early hours, but around 03:00 the two girls, Birgit and Claudia, announced that they needed to leave. Steve and Richard walked them to the door, to say their goodbyes. They arranged to meet the following week, at the same time. Richard moved in for a goodnight kiss and was met with no resistance. The embrace lasted only seconds, but was passionate, in its exchange. Taking the lead from Richard, Steve did the same and also was not rebuffed. The pair waved off the two girls, smiled at each other, and returned to the other three.

By this time, Ken was totally out of his head and was mumbling something to Sol, who was having difficulty understanding him. They then decided it was probably time that they also made their way home. After getting Ken to understand their intentions, the friends made to leave. Ken said that he needed to take a piss and would meet them outside. They agreed and after retrieving the ID cards from the reception, descended the staircase, to the car park outside. They were joined a couple of minutes later by Ken, who was staggering all over the place. As they waited for a taxi, Ken realised he had left his ID card inside. Just as a taxi pulled up, he made his way back up the stairs. Waiting in the taxi, the friends looked anxiously for Ken, when suddenly the door at the top of the stairs flew open. Ken came down the stairs, taking them three or four at a time. Rushing over to the taxi, he pulled open the door, closed it and shouted for the taxi driver to get the hell away. Although not fluent in English, the driver understood enough to put the car in gear and speed off. Richard looked at Ken, wondering why he was so flustered. It came to light that when he had returned to collect his ID, the reception was unmanned. He had opened the till to retrieve his card, and looking inside, he had seen the large amount of banknotes, consisting the night's takings. It was too tempting an offer to refuse, so he had helped himself. He took from his pocket a number of high denomination notes, in all totalling around 400 Deutsche Marks. The four friends could not believe this and looked nervously through the rear window, to see if any police cars had taken chase. They arrived back outside camp twenty minutes later, and after paying the taxi, entered the main gate showing their ID cards to the sentry, as they did so. They made a solemn oath that they would never speak of this again, and reckoned that maybe it was a good idea they did not visit the club for the next few weeks. With this, they returned to the block and hit the sack.

For the next few weeks the Squadron completed their preparations for the annual firing camp. Richard and Steve had met up with Birgit and Claudia the following weekend, but had suggested going somewhere else rather than the nightclub. It came to light, a couple of years later, that Birgit was in two minds about meeting Richard again. She had been persuaded by Claudia and the date had gone really well. They continued to see each other, at least twice a week. The Squadron was due leave that day for

Hohne, so Richard arranged to meet up again with Birgit, in two weeks' time when they returned.

With the tanks already loaded on the train flats, the Squadron began the journey to the railhead at Bergen Hohne. The distance was not that far, but, as always, military transport was given lowest priority on the German rail network, and it was six hours before they arrived. On arrival, the usual process of unchaining and unblocking the tanks from their flats commenced. The Squadrons moved out to their designated ranges for the next couple of days. Once there, they parked up the vehicles, secured them, and then helped to set up marquees, for the administration areas. Here, the SQMS would have his staff set up a mobile shop, from which, would be sold everything from chocolate and sweets to burgers, hotdogs and soft drinks. The one difference being from normal exercises that Richard had participated on, due to the danger of working with live ammunition, no alcohol was on sale. Once everything was set up, the Troops boarded the white military buses, which had been arranged, to take them to their accommodation in Hohne camp. They left only a small complement to guard the vehicles, which consisted of three Troopers and an NCO. Luckily, this time, Richard had not been chosen. He was happy about that, as it had been a long day.

The SQMS had already taken the accommodation over and, after picking a bed and throwing their sleeping bags on it, Richard headed off, for the evening meal. As it was a Regimental Gunnery Camp, the Chefs had taken over the cookhouse and had prepared the food. As it was the first evening and they hadn't long been there, the meal was not great, but better than living on compo. The cookhouse was full, as they had not just the single soldiers to cater for, but the married personnel as well. Richard and a couple from the D Squadron managed to secure a table and quickly devoured their food. They rushed back to the accommodation, for a gunnery lecture on the type of engagements they would receive, on the following Monday. As it was Friday, no firing was allowed over a weekend. The plan for the next day was to receive the ammunition allocation for the following few days. This was delivered by the Regimental Quartermaster (RQMS) staff, but organised by the SSM. It was an activity well known throughout Armoured Regiments as 'Ammo Bashing'. So, after the lecture and the timing had been given for the next day, the SQMS opened the makeshift bar that had been setup. The Squadron enjoyed a few beers together, some played cards, and the rest returned to their rooms and got their heads down.

They had been given the luxury of a lie in the next day, and were not woken until 07:00 for breakfast at 07:30. The buses were waiting to transport them to range 7A at 08:30. It was only a 30 minute drive, by bus, to the range and they arrived just before 09:00. The SQMS had already been out and delivered breakfast to the boys that had been left to guard the vehicles. No sooner had they arrived, than their attention was drawn to a group of three 4-tonne trucks, which had arrived on the rear of the range. An 'Eager Beaver' forklift truck was already removing pallets of ammunition from the trucks, whose sides had been dropped to facilitate this. The SSM was carefully arranging the pallets along the back of the range, counting them off as he did so. Once the pallets had all been removed, he signed a sheet of paper and handed it to one of the drivers. The trucks departed back to what was known as A2 Echelon located in Hohne Camp. The SSM sent the word round that everyone was to congregate at the ammunition point in ten minutes.

All crew members tipped up where the ammunition was located armed with pliers, hammers and other implements. These were needed to snip the locking wire that secured the projectile containers, then, using the hammers to knock open the clasps. This was the first time that Richard had ammo bashed, so he watched the more experienced guys, for the first twenty minutes. After this, he was making his way through the lines of containers as though he had been doing it all his life. Although the temperature was probably around -3 degrees, perspiration had started to build on his brow. It took the complete Squadron almost three hours to complete the unboxing of the ammunition. That was just the start of it, though. They were given a short break and the Troops congregated in the SQMS marquee. They were given a small meal of pasties and chips, which had been brought in 'Hay boxes' from the cookhouse. The sweat had dried on Richard, and he was started to feel the cold now. The SQMS had set up a burner in the corner of the tent, and everyone was gathering round it, trying to keep warm. The lunch time break, over the crews were asked to return to their vehicles, to receive their quota of ammunition.

Legs motioned to Richard and the rest of the crew to mount up. Richard was to get into the loaders side of the turret. Their gunner 'Blackie', Sol and Legs stood on the back decks, waiting for the truck to pull alongside them. While they were having their break, the ammunition had been loaded on to these trucks, by a work party, organised by the SSM. Work parties were normally those not taking part in the firing, such as the Fitter section or members of SHQ Troop. When the truck finally reached their tank, Blackie, Sol and Legs formed a chain from the rear of the tank to the turret. Passing the ammunition to the turret, Legs would then begin lowering down to Richard. It was Richard's job to see that he had enough ammunition, and of the correct type, available, ready for the next day. As the turret started to fill up, it was necessary to traverse the turret, so that Richard could get access to other charge bins, which held the bag charges. The last thing was to take the vent tubes, and load them into a couple of magazines. The whole process took around two hours before they were finished. They spent the final part of the day checking electrical and sighting systems, in readiness for the final checks they would carry out on Monday. Everything had been squared away by 16:00, the guard for the evening had been detailed, and the Troops returned to camp for the evening.

The Sunday evening began with a gunnery lecture, which included the type and amount of ammunition they were to be allocated, for the next day. There were also some blackboard shoots, confirming that everyone understood the techniques for both static and moving targets. The lecture lasted around an hour, after which the bar was opened. Richard and some others from the Troop sat drinking for the next couple of hours. At around 21:00, Richard decided that it was time to turn in as they would be woken at 03:00 in the morning. He was not looking forward to this, as the trip out to the range would not be on a nice, warm bus, but in the back of a 4-tonne Bedford Truck. No sooner had he got his head down and fallen asleep, than the lights were switched on in the room. People were stirring in their sleeping bags, some complaining that it was too early to be getting up. Richard pulled himself out of bed, grabbed his wash kit and made his way to the washrooms. To his surprise, he passed a couple already returning, having finished their ablutions. Legs was one and he smiled as they passed. He was in his element, Gunnery was what he lived for and Richard just hoped that he would not let him down.

At 04:00 precisely the Squadron boarded the Trucks that were waiting on the square. The temperature was minus twelve degrees Celsius, and Richard shivered, as he took his seat. He had put on two pairs of socks and three layers of clothing. Even with his parka on, and with the hood pulled up, he could feel the cold, seeping into his bones. The journey out to the range, although short, was like torture, and by the time they arrived, Richard could not feel his feet. He had always had an aversion to the cold, and remembered when he had played for a youth football team. It had been a spring morning, and the temperature, although not as cold as it was that morning, had been enough to cause him discomfort. At one point, he thought that he was going to pass out, and every time his foot made contact with the ball, he winced. His father had been watching from the side-lines and showed no sympathy at all. His dad had been a miner before joining the Army, so the cold did not bother him. He had given Richard a tip about the cold, when on exercise. His secret was that he wore women's tights under his uniform to guard against it. Richard would one day to experience even colder conditions to this, but that would be on another continent. The truck shuddered to a halt and the tailgate was thrown down. The frozen Troops disgorged and walked briskly toward their tanks. Sol had started to unlock his driver's cab and passed the keys to Richard, so that he could do the same for the turret.

Once inside, Richard waited for the tell-tale sound of the GUE reaching maximum revs. Hearing this Blackie began to start up the gun kit, checking that the turret reacted to his operation of the duplex controller. It was still dark and the first rays of winter sunshine would not break the skyline for another two hours yet. There was enough to be getting on with in the meantime, though. As they went through their checks, they were alerted by Sol, who informed them the gun fitter had arrived, to do the 'Gauge Plug Bore Test'. This involved them placing a piece of metal, the same dimensions as a round, down the barrel. This was attached at the end to a rope. The gun was elevated and the weight dropped down the barrel. This would check there were no fouls within the barrel and that it was not warped in any way. The process was successful and took only five minutes to complete. The gun fitter satisfied, he moved on to the next vehicle, to perform the same routine. Richard then went on to check that the vent tube was aligned correctly with the breech. He did this by removing the vent tube loader and placing on a tool. This had a cylindrical piece of metal which slid in and out, on pushing it forward, he observed that it went fully home, which confirmed that the alignment was true, and the vent tube would be inserted correctly. The final thing he did, before turning on the radios, was to ensure he had the correct amount and type of rounds and bags charges, for the days shoot, to hand. Nothing would be worse, if they were in the middle of an engagement and had to traverse the gun, so he could retrieve a bag charge. A saying which would become a mantra to him throughout his life pricked his conscience; 'Prior Prep and Planning Prevents Piss Poor Performance', commonly known as the 7 Ps. Happy that everything was in order, he started up both radios, which were Vehicle Radio Clansman 353's (VRC353). After waiting for the sets to warm up, he checked that one was on the Squadron frequency while the other was on the Troop frequency. Satisfied they were, he tuned them in and placed the power switch to the minimum setting. This was because they were in close proximity therefore they required the smallest amount of power to communicate. It was also good practice to prevent 'eavesdropping' by any Soviet Direction Finding Stations (DF's). Not that it was necessary in this environment, but was good practice. He would have this drummed into him when he attended his Control Signallers course in the near future.

Looking at his watch, Richard saw that the Squadron Comms check would begin in five minutes. He put on his headsets and made himself comfortable. Blackie and Legs were still running through their gunnery checks, within the turret. While he waited, he ensured the BV was on and prepared four brews for the crew.

'Hello Charlie Charlie One this is Zero, radio check over!'

As each call sign answered in sequence, beginning with SHQ, Richard waited for his turn to come. After the Troop leader's operator answered, he paused then answered, and was followed by the Troop Corporal's tank. The last vehicles to answer were those from the fitter section and, as was nearly always the case, out of their four vehicles only one was contactable. The Range Safety tower confirmed that they had received all the Squadron, less the three fitter section vehicles. Someone was sent over to their vehicles to find why they were not on the air. Firing would not be allowed to commence until all call signs were contactable. The radio check took another ten minutes, before the tower was satisfied that everyone was on the air.

Legs and Blackie were carrying out bore sighting on the main armament. Bore sighting is a method of adjustment to an optical firearm sight or iron sights, to align the firearm barrel and sights. This method is usually used to pre-align the sights, which makes zeroing (zero drop at a given distance) much faster. A device called a boresight or collimator is used to accomplish this. It consists of an optical head and a bore-diameter, which is inserted into the muzzle of the barrel. The optical head is then attached to the protruding end of the rod. A grid pattern on the optical head is then used to align the sights with the barrel. By adjusting the sight in minute detail, this ensures that the barrel was pointing at the same point as the sight. Once this was complete, Legs returned to the turret to input the weather conditions like temperature and wind speed and direction into the tanks Improved Fire Control System (IFCS). This was given over the air, at varying times of the day, and was essential for the vehicles computer to calculate the variations of projectile flight to target.

All checks complete the Squadron spent the first part of the day carrying out 'Confirmation of Accuracy by Firing (CABF). They would fire a single DST round at a white screen with a circle on it. Depending where the first round landed, the sight would be adjusted until they were in the centre of the circle, or at least broke the line. Richard's tank took only two shots with the second round striking the centre of the target. This pleased Legs, all the preparation had been worth it, the first static shoot would confirm this. Once everyone had completed their CABF, the crews assembled in the briefing tent. After a short brief, explaining the shoot, they mounted up, one Troop at a time. SHQ were first to fire and the two crews sprinted off, to their vehicles. Once they had settled down, a series of targets at varying ranges was presented to them. On the right hand side of the range, the Squadron Leader's tank was about to engage a screen tank target that had popped up 2000 metres in front. The target had been up for around 60 seconds, when, suddenly, the loader's hatch sprung open and a body was seen jumping out and darting across to the admin tent. It was the Squadron Leader's loader and he seemed a little anxious. As he entered the tent, he looked around, searching for something. Picking up a rucksack, he delved into it, withdrawing a piece of shiny metal. It was the Firing Needle Assembly (FNA) which initiated the vent tube. These were always removed in the evening but were inserted first thing, when carrying out the gun checks. This showed that the checks had not been done properly and someone was going to be in the shit. The loader somewhat sheepishly made his way back at rapid speed to his tank. This was much to the delight on the on looking crews, whose laughter rang in his ears. 'Not a good start,' Richard thought to himself, but how the hell had they carried out the CABF without it. The only explanation was that the loader had been over zealous and removed it after CABF had been completed, and forgot to return it afterwards.

It wasn't long before it was Richard's Troop's turn to mount up. As they raced across the firing point, Richard could feel his heart beat raise noticeably. They clambered into their crew positions and awaited the order to go to action, from the tower. Looking around the turret, Richard did a last minute check of his ammunition stowage. Then, all of a sudden, Legs broke the uneasy silence.

'DST ....tank ....on!' Came the excited but professional order.

Richard instinctively picked up a DST projectile and throw it into the open breech. Opening a charge bin he removed an orange bag charge, forcing it up the barrel until it stopped. Depressing the plunger on the vent tube loader, it inserted a vent tube into the breach. Pulling the breech lever, he closed the breach, made the safety guard and ensure the turret safety switch was at live.

'Loaded!' he screamed at the top of his voice.

Blackie had already identified the target, and was waiting for this shout from Richard. Once he was happy that he was aimed directly onto the centre of the target, he pressed the laser with his left thumb. He had already selected the type of ammunition to tell the computer the type of flight for its computations. He ported to Legs that he was lasing, and after checking in his range finder display, Legs reported.

'Two thousand fire!'

'Two thousand…..Firing now!' came the reply from Blackie, at the same time pressing the fire button.

The whole tank shook and rocked, as the vent tube ignited the bag charge, propelling the projectile along the barrel. In just over a second, Blackie reported that they had hit the target. Legs confirmed that the target was destroyed and gave the order to stop the engagement. Richard had already began loading the next round into the chamber, and, within ten seconds, was once again making the safety guard and informing them that they were loaded. Another target popped up closer this time and Legs laid the barrel near the target releasing his grip switch to allow Blackie to take over.

'DST tank on!' he screamed, at the top of his voice, and waited for Blackie to confirm he had identified the target.

'On lasing!' came the slick reply, as he depressed the lasing toggle switch, once more. Legs read out the range from his range readout, immediately this was repeated by Blackie. Two seconds later a second round was on its way, and a further hit was claimed. The firing continued, using both AP and HE rounds. The crew was having a fantastic shoot, unlike the Troop Leader's tank. On their first engagement, which had been at 1200 metres, the round had gone over the top. Another round landed in exactly the same place. It wasn't until the commander had checked his computer, he noticed that he had a manual range of two thousand set in it, and had failed to cancel it prior to firing. This was a schoolboy error, and one that would create a lot of derision later on, in the debrief. The shoot came to an end, the crews dismounted and went to the admin tent to see how they had done. As expected the Gunnery instructors had picked up on the mistake by the Troop Leader and it was highlighted. Looking embarrassed he nodded his agreement, but the Troop on the whole had done well and destroyed ninety percent of the targets presented. The Troop leader had the piss taken out of him for the rest of the day though, but he would learn by the mistake, which was all that mattered.

For the next week, the shoots got increasingly more difficult, with more targets presented, and individual tanks having to cover each other's arcs, either when they were checking their muzzle reference system (MRS), or had a stoppage or misfire. The Squadron as a whole, were performing well and had moved onto Troop battle runs, which consisted of the Troop moving as one, a bound at a time, down the range. It took the same form as if they were on exercise, except that this time they would be engaging targets with live ammunition. The Troop moved with two up, being the Troop Corporal and Troop Sergeant. Once they were firm and reported back to the Troop Leader, he would move to join them. During this time, targets would pop up, and were engaged by the two tanks that were firm. They would cover the complete frontage, denoted by inverted Day-Glo chevrons, on each side of the range. As before, if they had any problems such as misfires or the need to check sight alignment, they would inform the other vehicles, who would then cover their arcs, while they were out of commission. They would continue down the range, a bound at a time, taking on all static moving and infantry targets presented to them. Richard loved the infantry engagements, as the sound of the GPMG mounted on top of the gun gave a sense of realism. However, along with the build-up of gases from both the main armament and machine gun, it had an adverse effect on a night. It was what became commonly known as cordite farts. This strange phenomena, was caused by the inhalation of the fumes from the cordite, that was released into the turret. After a day's firing the accommodation area was unbearable, especially during the evening briefings.

The range period was drawing to a close and the Squadron had moved to the last battle run range of the week. This was known as battle run twenty, and it would be their most difficult scenario of the last nine days. On their arrival, the SSM was waiting for them, with a new batch of ammunition already been broken down, which was waiting to be loaded on to the tanks, from the trucks. As they pulled on to the firing point, they were told to make ready to receive it. For the next hour or so, the crews frantically bombed up their vehicles. After the ammunition had been dished out, the SSM put the word round for everyone to check that they had their complete compliment of vent tubes. The reason for this was he had one left over, and needed to account that everyone had the correct number for the number of projectiles they had. Legs shouted down to Richard to check his vent tube magazines. Richard went to the container that held his vent tube magazines, pulled one out and began to unload it. After emptying the container, he counted them back in again, replaced the magazine and picked up his next one. Following the same procedure, he unloaded and loaded again. Legs was getting impatient now, asking if he had counted them, as he wanted to let the SSM know they were okay. Richard was on his last magazine, and was about half way unloading it and decided that he would tell Legs that they were all accounted for. He heard his commander shout down to the SSM that they had all theirs, while he continued to count. His heart sank, as he got to the bottom of the magazine and realized that they were one missing. Not believing it, he counted again but came up with the same, horrible result. He could feel the sweat build on his forehead, despite the cold outside. How was he going to tell Legs that he had made a mistake? Racking his brains, he came up with what he thought was a viable solution. It just so happened that he had been chosen to provide the range guard that evening, and would rectify the situation then.

The tanks were all fully bombed up now, and the transport had arrived to take the Squadron back to camp for the evening. Locking the vehicle down, Richard made his way to the guard tent. The SQMS had brought out a hay box full of range stew for the sentries. This was quickly devoured along with copious amounts of bread. Even though they had eaten this many times already, Richard never got tired of it. The SQMS left them and the NCO in charge of the guard complied a stag list for the evening. Things were a little more relaxed on the range, and the sentries were only expected to patrol for a short while. They could return to the tent to get warm every twenty minutes or so. Richard had been thinking about the vent tube since the Squadron had departed. He knew he would have been found out, when the gun failed to fire the next day, when they were down to their last round. There was only one thing for it, he thought and waited for it to get dark.

On his last stag of the evening at around 02:20 he made his way towards the tank. Climbing up on to the turret, he unlocked the operator's hatches and climbed inside. He took a bag charge and a projectile from their stowage positions and placed them on top of the turret. He transported them to the floor, and opened one of the side bins. Taking a shovel from the bin, he looked around to make sure he wasn't being observed. Picking up the bag charge he walked to the rear of the firing point, well away from where the vehicles were parked. Here, he began to dig a hole, and after placing the bag charge in it, returned for the projectile. After putting that in the hole too, he covered them up and patted down the ground. His work finished, he made his way back to the tank, returned the shovel to the bin and locked up the turret. The evening passed and at 05:00 the Squadron returned for its last day of firing.

There was a buzz of excitement, s the crews prepared their vehicles for what would be the most challenging day of the last two weeks. Richard had counted all his projectiles, bag charges and vent tubes, for about the fourth time. He knew he had the correct amount but what had happened on the day before had put him on edge. He couldn't help himself from peering over at the area where he had buried the projectile and bag charge. The ground did not look as though it had been disturbed, as some wheeled vehicles had driven over it that morning. He just hoped that he had buried the ammunition deep enough, and that it would not be discovered before their departure, later that day. After all checks were complete and communications check done, the crews assembled for the last time, in the briefing tent. The Gunnery Instructor, who had been monitoring their progress and would write a report at the end of it, congratulated them on their drills over the last nine days. He then proceeded to explain the shoot for that day. It would take the form of a Troop advance to contact, during which time they would be presented with multiple targets. They would be static, moving, transport and infantry, and the length of the run would be four bounds. He then went on to explain the range layout, including arc markers, lanes and 1safety points. Once he was happy that everyone was fully in the picture and any questions answered, he dismissed them.

The first Troop headed off to their vehicles, while the rest of the Squadron grabbed themselves a brew from the SQMS tent. Gathering round outside the tent, they found a spot where they could observe the action. Hopefully, they would get some idea of where the targets were, and how complex the shoot was. The flags on the tower turned to red, as did those on the tanks, indicating they had gone to action. The sound of the engines rose and they leapt forward, line abreast. They had only reached halfway to the first bound, when three targets were popped up at different ranges. The tanks engaged them while still moving and by the time they reached the first bound markers, they had been 'gone down'. The sound of main armament and GPMG fire filled the air for the next 30 minutes. It wasn't long before Legs grabbed his crew in readiness to mount up. He wished them good luck for the day and encouraged them to do what they had done for the last couple of weeks and, if they did, everything would be fine.

They waited in their crew positions waiting for the order to advance. They had already gone to action and Richard had loaded a DST round into the breech and made sure there was a belt of two hundred rounds on the GPMG. The command to advance came and Sol kicked the vehicle into gear. It lurched forward, driving up though the gears, he kept it at a steady pace. This was to ensure he gave a stable enough platform for Blackey to engage any targets, whilst they were mobile. It was not just about the gunner hitting the target, this was a team effort, with everyone bringing something to the party. All of a sudden, Blackey spotted a tank target, which had popped up in the distance. As it was in their arc, Legs gave a quick contact report, whilst Blackey engaged the target. The target was struck dead centre and dropped immediately. Other targets were presented out of their arc and were taken on by the other two call signs. At the first bound, they halted and immediately reported they were firm. From their left, a tank target was crossing their path from left to right.

'DST tank on mover!' came the cry from Legs. Blackey immediately took over, after Legs had laid him on in the area and released his grip switch.

'On lasing!' he replied and waited for the range to be called back. Once this call was received, he hit the autolay button and the gun drove up and centred itself on the target. Tracking the mover, he waited for 'loaded' from Richard. As soon as he heard it, he hit the fire button. Another first round hit, and the sounds of 'Fuckin' well done!' from Legs, rose above the sound of the other two tanks which were also firing. The battle run continued in the same vein, until they reached the final bound. The Troop Leader was calling for ammunition states from his other two call signs. Legs looked at Richard to confirm he had the same amount of rounds as he thought they should have. Richard took a quick count and confirmed, before Legs reported back to the Troop Leader. The last bound was frantic, with multiple tank, transport and infantry targets being presented. Each tank took on the ones in its arc, unless a call sign had a problem. Richard's vehicle fired its last main armament round, then began engaging the infantry targets to its front. Richard was leaning over the gun, feeding the belt and rounds, ensuring they were not going to get caught and cause a jam. As soon as they had started, the order came to check fire and to go green in the turret. The past 30 minutes had flown in a flash, but all Richard could think was, 'thank fuck he had enough event tubes,' and he had not been caught out.

The Troop made its way on the return lane, back to the firing point, for the debrief. There, they were met by the Squadron Leader, who congratulated them, along with the visiting Gunnery Instructor, on an excellent shoot. Richard was filled with pride, as Legs looked at him, nodded his head and smiled. It had been a good two weeks and his first baptism of fire.

They had been back in camp for three weeks now and Richard had been told that he had been loaded on to a Control Signaller course in a month's time. The course would take place at the Royal Armoured Corps Signals School in Bovington. This was a step on the ladder for Richard, and if he passed, he would be eligible for promotion. For the next four weeks, he spent most of his time in the classroom, brushing up on voice procedure and familiarising himself, once again, with the range of equipment used on armoured vehicles. He was also introduced to 'Skywave', which was a method used for HF communications. This was adopted in areas where it was required to transmit over long distances, and involved some calculations. On a vehicle, the Tuning Unit Automatic Antennae Matching (TUAAM), as its name suggested, matched the frequency to the length of the antenna. However, when using HF equipment the user had to work out the length of the antennae required to fit the frequency being used. *In radio communication, skywave or skip refers to the propagation of radio waves reflected or refracted back toward Earth from the ionosphere, an electrically charged layer of the upper atmosphere. Since it is not limited by the curvature of the Earth, skywave propagation can be used to communicate beyond the horizon, at intercontinental distances. It is mostly used in the shortwave frequency bands* (Wikipedia)

Among other new equipment that he was introduced to, Richard was learning how to run a Command vehicle (CV) and also mobile generating engines, to produce power. Alongside this, he was taught how the enemy can use transmissions against you, and defences against this. Richard found this subject of Electronic Warfare fascinating. The preparation training for the course was really well set up. The Instructors from the Regiment were highly professional, and Richard knew from that moment, this was the path he wished to take. They ran through all the equipment and lessons that they would come across on the Control Signaller Course. At the end of it, the candidates, of which there was two, had to sit a test to confirm they were proficient and ready to go on the course. By the end of the training period, both of them passed with flying colours and were given the 'green light' to attend the course.

Richard's free time recently had been mostly spent with Birgit, and they were growing closer together. He would finish work, shower and change and make his way to the train station. He had not yet acquired a car, so was dependent on public transport. Sometimes, as Brigit had a car, she would pick him up, but this was usually on a weekend. As he entered the station, he checked the clock and found that he had half an hour before the next train. He decided to grab a bite to eat, as he did most nights. He had found that it was usual, in German households, to have bread and butter, with a selection of cold meats or jam for their evening meal. Richard learned quickly that this was not enough to sustain a growing, young man and had been cheating by having a pizza or kebab before arriving at Brigit's parents' house.

The first time he had been introduced to them he felt slightly ill at ease. After the Second World War, the house which had belonged to Brigit's grandmother had been taken over by the British Army. So as soon as he entered the house, he felt as welcome as a fart in an astronaut suit. This was all in his head, and although her parents could not speak much English he was made most welcome. Over the years, he would grow very fond of them and there even came a time, prior to getting married, that he moved into the ground floor of the house, along with Birgit. Every evening, when Richard visited, her father would invite him into the living room, where he would offer him a beer and a schnapps. They would sit chatting and drinking while Birgit and her mother prepared tea. After a beer or three, they would get the call to join the ladies in the kitchen. The table had been set, with the various different meats, spreads and cheeses, along with different types of bread laid out in neat lines. Nearly all German families sat together for meals; there was no sitting, eating, in front of the TV Everything seemed very formal and it took a while for Richard to get used to it. He often wondered if her parents ever wondered why he ate so little. He kept this secret for many years, before it came out in a conversation.

After the evening meal, Richard and Birgit spent time listening to music or watching videos. Brigit's room was on the ground floor, which was only accessible by way of a staircase from the dining room. This was handy for the couple, as they were always alerted if someone was coming down the stairs. It had happened on more than one occasion when they were in a state of undress and were panicked by the sound of footsteps descending. They had just enough time to dress before they would have been discovered.

It was the day before Richard was due to leave and the pair of them were lying on her bed, watching TV. She turned to him and admitted that she would miss him for the eight weeks that would be the duration of his course. They spent the rest of the evening in each other's arms, slowly caressing. At around 21:00, Richard decided it was time he was leaving, as he had to finish off his final bit of packing, before catching the plane the next day. Birgit agreed to drive him back to camp and, after saying goodbye to her parents, they set off on the 35 minute drive. As she dropped him off, they kissed passionately and Richard thought he saw a small tear in her eye, as he turned to walk through the gates.

Richard woke shortly before dawn and rose silently from his bed, trying not wake Sol, with whom he shared the room. He quietly opened the door and made his way along the corridor to the shower room. He climbed into the cubicle and turned on the water, causing him to take a sharp intake of breath, as the cold water hit his body. In no time at all the water warmed up, and after the initial shock he enjoyed the next ten minutes, cleansing his body. Fully invigorated, he stepped from the shower and began to towel himself down. As he did so, he called to mind a strange occurrence that used to happen while they were in Berlin. One of the Troop called Reg had a peculiar habit of coming into Richard's room, just after he had returned from the shower. Reg's door was always open and he could observe anyone who passed it. He would come into Richard's room and make small talk, Richard never paid it any attention at first. That was until one time as he was drying himself, and Reg asked if he could borrow his hair brush. It seemed like a strange request but Richard agreed and pointed to the wash basin, where it was located. Brushing his hair, Reg continued to chat, looking at Richard in the mirror. It was not until this had happened more than one time that Richard began to think. He mentioned it to Ken, who admitted that Reg did the same thing to him too. Richard chuckled to himself as he applied the shaving foam to his face. He knew Reg was not gay, as he had seen him with girls, in the time they spent in Berlin. But nonetheless, this seemed like very strange behaviour. He completed his morning routine and returned to the room.

Sol was still fast asleep; Richard dressed quickly in civilian clothes and picked up the bags he had placed near the door the previous night. He made his way to the guard room to meet the transport which had been arranged for him and the other guy on the course, who was from A Squadron. They had got to know each other while they were doing their course training. Richard had taken an immediate shine to him, he was a very humorous bloke and easy to get along with. As he approached the guard room, he noticed that Spike was already there and chatting to what must have been their driver. Greeting them both, Richard asked where he should put his suitcase and rucksack. The driver indicated the white mini bus parked at the side of the guardroom. Placing his luggage on the rear seat of the transport, he was joined by Spike. The driver finished the cigarette he was smoking, climbed in and started up the engine. The journey to Hannover Airport was only an hour and a half and at that time of the morning, the Autobahn was quiet. They arrived in good time and after thanking the driver, they took their cases and headed for Departures.

The British Army chartered flights from the airport, so everyone on their flight was either military or families. It was a well-oiled machine and they were processed very efficiently. Within an hour, were boarding the Tri-Star aircraft to Luton airport. They touched down in the UK mid-morning and were through customs and baggage collection without any difficulties. The next stage was for them to catch a train into London, for their onward journey to Wool Station in Dorset. There was a direct line from the airport into the city and the two of them enquired about the train times. They were informed that they ran every twenty minutes by the girl on the Information Desk. Following the directions they had been given, they found the escalator, which took them down to the railway platform.

The Bedfordshire countryside sped past, as Richard stared out of the window. Spike was dozing opposite, as he had spent the night before in his Squadron bar. Before they knew it, the train guard announced that they were pulling into Kings Cross Station. Waking Spike, Richard and his new mate collected their bags and departed the train. They took the short journey by tube, across to Waterloo Station, for their connection to the South West. Checking the departure times at Waterloo, they concluded that it would be an hour before the next train to Wool. Seeking out the nearest bar, they did what all squaddies did in this situation and went for a drink. As they sat chatting about the course and what they expected of it, Richard's mind started to wander. Had it really been four years since he sat in this very same bar, prior to boarding the train for his journey to the Junior Leaders Training Regiment? A lot of water had flown under the bridge since then. He could actually state he was a fully-fledged tank crewman now, he was no long the NIG of the Squadron and now younger members even asked his advice. The time was nearing for them to board the train, so they finished their pints and headed off for the platform.

As the train pulled into Wool Station, Richard felt a shiver run down his spine. He was looking for the reception party, dressed in their uniforms and highly polished boots, instinctively. This time, when they stepped off the train, there was no one to meet them nor transport arranged. They were big boys now and were expected to be able to function for themselves. A lone taxi waited in the station car park. They headed over to it, and asked the driver if he was free. The driver nodded his answer and stepped out of the vehicle. Miserable twat, Richard thought to himself, as the driver went to the rear and opened the boot. He looked at them, waiting for them to load the luggage into the open space. Not offering to help them, he slammed the boot shut, and climbed back in to the driver's seat. The guys looked at each other, obviously thinking the same thing, they simply smirked at one another. Both climbed into the rear of the taxi, neither of them wanting to sit next to the obnoxious pond life, which would convey them to the camp. It would take them less than ten minutes, Richard knew from experience, and, on the way, they passed some young recruits in lightweight trousers and boots, running with a log.

'Thank fuck I don't have to do that anymore,' he commented to Spike.

Spike agreed and said they had gone through similar experiences at Catterick, where he had joined as an adult soldier. The only difference being was that their training only consisted of twelve weeks of basic training, they then moved on to their trade training. After less than six months, they were passing out and joining their Regiments. Richard knew that the Junior Leader system was much tougher and, in his opinion, made for better soldiers. He kept this to himself though, as they passed Stanley Barracks on their left hand side. As the taxi pulled up outside the gates of the resident Regiment at Catterick, they begrudgingly paid the driver. He took the offered money, without a thank you and drove off. They showed their ID cards to the barrier sentry, who allowed them to enter. Noticing that the guard commander or 2ic sitting at the reception window, they called out, asking if he could point them in the direction of the Signal School accommodation. He beckoned them over and asked for their names and Regiment. Having been supplied the information, the NCO looked down at an A4 sheet of paper in front of him, which listed the courses that were starting that week. Having found their names, he told them that they needed to report to the Training Squadron SQMS, who would issue them bedding and allocate a room. They thanked the NCO, and headed off in the direction he had given them. The camp was well signposted, and it didn't take them long to find the sign pointing to a building labelled 'Training Sqn SQMS Stores'. As this posting was a mixture of Regiments the signage was red and yellow, which were the colours of the Royal Armoured Corps. Placing their luggage down, the pair opened the door to the store and went in. They were greeted by a stern looking Scottish 'full screw' (Corporal), bizarrely from an Irish Cavalry Regiment. He took their names, and in typical storeman fashion, issued them their bedding and keys to their room. He warned them that there was a block and room inspection every week, and the SQMS would jump on anyone who did not keep their accommodation spotless. Richard took an instant dislike to this bloke and stared him out, not breaking his gaze, showing that he was not intimidated by him. As they left the stores, he turned to Spike and simply remarked,

'What a prick' but little did he know their paths would cross again, in the not too distant future.

They made the five minute walk through the maze of corridor, eventually finding there room after getting lost twice. Spike turned the key in the door to find it was already unlocked, and as they opened it, a tall blond haired guy looked up from unpacking his suitcase. Putting down the clothes, he moved towards them with his hand outstretched in a form of greeting.

'All right guys, I'm Chic, Scots Dragoon Guards,' he said in his deep East coast accent. Richard recognised the difference in dialect from spending the year with Gus in training. He was also Scots DG, and as Richard shook Chic's hand and introduced himself, he asked if he knew Gus. Chic laughed out loud and said of course he did. Since joining the Regiment Gus had made a bit of a name for himself. He, like most of the Regiment, enjoyed a few pints now and again. However Gus' few pints normally ended in a fight and a night in jail. Richard laughed out loud:

'I guess he hasn't changed then?'

The introductions over, Spike and Richard each chose a bed, put down their luggage and began to unpack. When they were just about finished, the door opened once more, and in strolled a rather beefy looking guy. Richard's first thought was, "how the fuck did he manage to pass a Basic Fitness Test (BFT)". As usual, the mandatory introductions were made and accepted and Dave took the remaining bed by the window. Dave was from the 17th/21st Lancers, who were nicknamed the 'Boneheads'. The reason for this was that their cap badge, which they preferred to call their motto, was the skull and crossbones. Under the skull on a scroll were the words 'Or Glory', meaning 'death or glory'. They were famous for their part in the Charge of the Light Brigade during the Crimean War. They recruited mainly from the Nottingham and midlands area, and this was where Dave was from. Once everyone was unpacked and had showered, they decided to hit the NAAFI bar for a few quiet pints.

The NAAFI bar was just like any other bar in any camp. The only difference in this one being that most of its inhabitants were from different Regiments, on various courses. The four roommates found themselves a table, Spike got the order for what they were drinking and wandered over to the bar. Looking over in his direction, Richard realised why he had so quickly volunteered to get the first ones in. The barmaid was around five feet ten inches with a huge rack, and long blonde hair. Richard was to find out that Spike was a bit of a ladies' man, as it took him a good ten minutes before he returned with their drinks. Setting them down, Spike winked at

Richard, knowing he had been observing his flirtations with the barmaid. They raised their glasses and wished each other good health and an enjoyable course. Over the course of the evening they were joined by more candidates, who were there to attend the Control Signallers course. By the end of the night, they had taken over three tables and numbered around fifteen in total. Everyone had spent time introducing themselves and getting to know one another. As a whole, the majority of them seemed like decent lads, Richard thought. There were, as there are in every walk of life, a few characters who did not quite fit the group dynamic. The evening soon drew to a close and the camp Night Orderly Sergeant was making his rounds, ensuring the bars were all closed. They were asked to leave, but had to prise Spike away from the embrace of the barmaid, who had closed the shutters and had made her way to the other side of the bar. 'First night here, and the jammy bastard's scored already,' Richard thought, as they meandered their way back to the accommodation and bed.

Morning came, heralded by bright sunshine streaming through the open window. Richard was first to get up, but was soon joined by the rest, each grabbing his wash bag and heading off for the showers. They all returned around the same time and got dressed into their barrack dress and No2 dress shirts. After breakfast, the roommates headed over in the direction of the Signal School, which Richard and Spike had spotted the previous day; it was just over the road from the SQMS stores. They had all received joining instructions, which stated that students were to arrive by 09:00. It was only 08:10 so they had plenty of time, as they entered the building. On the notice board directly ahead of them was a series of sheets of A4 paper, pinned to the wall. On one was the list of names of those attending the course, this had been broken down into two parts. Half of the course would be taught by one Instructor, while the other half received different lesson with another Instructor. This was down, they found out later, to the limited amount of equipment and classrooms available. Theirs was not the only course running at that time. There was also a crew Commanders course, which was in its last two weeks. There was the list for a Morse operator's course, which would begin the following week. Richard looked down the list of names and found that he and Spike were in different groups, Dave was in the same as Spike and Chic was with Richard. It was normal for the Instructors to split up people from the same Regiment, a bit like a school teacher not letting the naughty boys sit together. This analogy tickled Richard, as it seemed like he was walking back into school. A voice called out to them from an open doorway:

'You the Con Sig course starting today?' it was more of a statement than a question. The person who had posed it was small in stature, but powerfully built. On his right arm, he wore the 'scrambled egg' of a Regimental Sergeant Major (RSM). Chic piped up, immediately straightening up as he did so, with his fists clenched, and thumbs down the seams of his trousers.

'Yes Sir!' he bellowed.

The RSM smiled warmly and said there was no need to be so formal, this was a learning establishment, not the drill square. He directed them to an area where there was a vending machine with coffee and soup. Also, if they needed it, the only area they could smoke was outside, on the veranda. With that, he said that he would see them in twenty minutes, in the main lecture room, for the course introduction. The lads thanked him and made their way for a brew and a smoke. They were the first ones there and were joined by others in the next five to ten minutes. It was now 08:25 and they all made their way to the lecture theatre. Taking a seat, they settled down and awaited the arrival of the RSM. The RSM entered the room, followed by a rather tall man, and with well-groomed hair; behind him followed four others wearing the rank of Sergeants. They assembled at the front of the Lecture theatre, with two Sergeants on either side of the lectern and the RSM behind it. The tall gentleman took a seat directly behind the RSM, who cleared his throat and addressed the waiting students.

'Good morning, gentlemen, I am WO1 Kennedy and I am the Regimental Signal Instructor (RSMI) of the Signals School. I would like to introduce you, first of all, to the Officer Commanding the School, Major Crane.' With that, the tall gentleman rose to his feet and bowed curtly to the audience. 'Next, we have the instructors, who will be taking your course. From my right, Sergeant. Bowman, Sergeant. Campbell, Sergeant. Judge and Sergeant Walton. You will find, on your seats, a course programme; please ensure you study it and make sure you are on time for each lesson.'

He went on to run through the drills in the event of a fire, then asked Major Crane to say a few introductory words about the school. The introductions and rules set out and explained, the students were dismissed for a quick coffee and cigarette break. They were told to be in the main lecture theatre for their 'in test' at 09:30. This 'In Test' was confirmation that the students were adequately prepared to undertake the course. If anyone scored less than 80% they would be immediately 'Returned to Unit' (RTU). This was the worst thing that could happen to any student in the military, the bollocking they would receive when they got back did not bear thinking about. With this he, the OC and the Instructors left the room.

There was a buzz of excitement and apprehension, as the students left their seats and headed for the veranda, for a cigarette and brew. The conversation centred on the previous evening, in the NAAFI bar. One of the blokes Richard was speaking to was Mark Simpson, a member of the 'Blues and Royals'. He had spent a couple of years on ceremonial duty, as part of the mounted contingent at Knightsbridge. He was now 'Operational' as the Regiment performed both duties; both ceremonial and on Scimitar and Scorpion reconnaissance vehicles. He had taken part in the Falklands War eighteen months previously. Simpson was a very confident, charismatic character and Richard enjoyed his company from their first meeting. Before very long, it was time for the students to head for their first lesson. Richard was pleased to find that Mark was in his half of the course for the duration. They checked their timetables, and the first lesson was on the Vehicle Radio Clansman (VRC) 353. They found the - and filed in taking a seat around the room. The seats were laid out in a semi-circle, in front of a VRC, which had been mounted on a trolley. At exactly 09:30, one of the instructors who had been introduced as Sergeant Bowman, entered the room. He began by introducing himself once again, and went through the fire drill. After this, he explained how the lessons would be run, with the timing of its various elements. Then, moving to the equipment on the trolley, he turned to face the students.

'This, guys, is the VRC 353,' he indicated with a silver extended pointer, which he held in his right hand. He then gave a brief introduction to the system. 'It is a vehicle-mounted VHF FM transceiver, built by Marconi Space and Defence Systems. The frequency range 30-75.975 MHz range, with possible 1840 channels, spaced 25 kHz apart; it has a power setting up to 50W. Antenna systems are provided to give improved performance in semi-static situations, such as an elevated broadband vertical dipole, mounted on an 8 metre mast. The VRC is also capable of data transmission and when used in conjunction with an add-on unit (Digital Master Unit), provides a medium level secure speech network. We will be covering that in a much later lesson.'

He then went on to explain the switches and features on the front of the unit. After full descriptions, including the 'Operational limitations', he then demonstrated how to tune, open up, and close down the set correctly. He then got one of the students to come up and had the class talk him through the opening up and tuning drill, including closing down. Asking if there were any questions, he split the class into pairs, and instructed them to go to the equipment that was set up around the room. Richard had been paired with Mark, as they were seated next to each other. The students practised the drills that they had just been shown, first one, then the other, from the pair. During this time Sergeant Bowman paced around the room, checking that everyone had understood his demonstration. Making sure that each one of every pair had participated, he called the class back to their seats. He asked once more if there were any questions. Observing that there were only shakes of heads, he took it that everyone had understood the lesson.

He then went on to confirm that he had put the lesson over as he had laid in his objectives. He first went round the room and asked questions on the Operational limitations. He would pose a question, pause, then choose someone at random. This was too keep the students' interest and make sure they were all concentrating. After finishing with the questions, he picked out a couple, to point out various switches and features. The final thing was for one of them to go through the complete opening up and closing down procedure, to include a frequency tune.

As Richard had not been chosen to answer a question, it was no surprise when his name was called. He got up from his chair and systematically went through the drill, as he had been shown, starting with the antennae and moving in a methodical manner. On his completion, he was asked to sit down, and Bowman asked the class if they had seen any mistakes. All the students shook their heads and Bowman agreed that it was a good drill, carried out well. Richard beamed inwardly to himself. This method of instruction, known as 'Explanation, Demonstration, Imitation, Practice and Confirmation (EDIPC), would become very familiar to Richard, when he returned later to attend his Signals Instructors Course.

The morning continued in the same way, with introductions to equipment such as the PRC 351/2. This was an infantry platoon level backpack VHF FM transceiver.

Built by Racal BCC, the PRC 351 has 4 watt RF power output, and operates in 30-75.975 MHz range with possible 1840 channels spaced 25 kHz apart. This Richard noted was identical to the VRC 353. The radio was also capable of being mounted on a vehicle in conjunction with the TUAAM. The PRC 352 is identical, with the addition of a 20 watt RF amplifier and can be used as a ground station. (Wikipedia)

This lesson, like most of the lessons, took the same form. The only difference would be if it was a factual lesson; in that case, it would be Explanation, Demonstration and Confirmation (EDC). The course broke for lunch, and the men were reminded to return on time for the first lesson of the afternoon at 13:30.

The course met again in their respective classrooms at 13:30, and at the first lesson of the afternoon, the students were all feeling tired after a large lunch. The subject they were to cover for the rest of the day was 'Voice

Procedure' (VP). This was to include Infantry Tank Target Indication and Artillery target 'Fire Missions'. For this lesson, they had Sergeant Walton, who was a tall, somewhat hairy, aggressive Yorkshireman from Leeds. He sported a bushy, blond moustache, with hair sprouting from his shirt opening. After going through the usual preliminaries to the lesson, like introducing himself, he then went on to explain his aims and objectives for the afternoon. Next, he highlighted the process the infantry used to bring fire from a tank on to an enemy position. This was accomplished, generally, by using the Infantry Tank Telephone (ITT) located on the rear of the vehicle. They would lift the armour lid, and attract the commander's attention by pressing a button. This then gave them direct access to instruct the commander, where they wished the fire to be directed. It normally used the barrel as a starting point and would go something along the lines of:

'Reference gun barrel. Go two o'clock small wood. 200 metres plus, telegraph pole. Small mound with infantry and BMP's dug in. Neutralise in two minutes. Over!'

The commander would follow the instructions, until he had identified the target, and would then report, 'Seen!' He would then bring fire to bear on the position. This was not the only way it could be done, the infantry could also indicate the position by firing a series of tracer rounds. They would instruct the commander to 'Watch My Trace' and give directions from there. Once again, the commander would confirm he had identified the target and engage it. Walton went through some examples on the board, before choosing someone to raise a call, using the example he had drawn on the board. After practicing this for around 40 minutes, the class broke for a short smoke break. When they returned, they went into Artillery Target fire, known as calling for a 'Fire Mission'. The procedure was similar to that of Infantry Target indication, except it began with the pro word from the vehicle to the guns of 'Fire Mission'. This, then, followed the following format, the observer would give a grid to the target. Then a direction in mils from his vehicle to the target. This was known as the 'Observer Target Line' (OT). He would then give a brief description of the target, for example 'Three tanks, with dug in infantry, on edge of wood line'. The final part was to relay what was to be done to it, when and for how long. For example 'Neutralise with High Explosive (HE) in 2 minutes for five minutes'. This was repeated back from the Artillery guns to the observer, to ensure that they had received the information correctly. If there were no mistakes, then they would tell the observer to 'Wait Out'. After the two minutes had passed, they would inform the originator that a round was in the air and its time of flight. This was done by the phrase 'Shot, two zero'. Indicating that the round had been fired and would be in the air for approximately twenty seconds. This let the observer know that he should be looking for the fall of shot, and getting ready to adjust it from where it landed if necessary. Using either the commander's sight or a pair of binoculars, the commander would adjust the fire, left or right, up or down, until they had brought the fire on to the target area. This achieved, he would then inform the guns, 'On target, fire for effect.' This would complete the fire mission, and, if he thought it may be useful to use the same one in the future, he would instruct the guns to 'record as target'. The class went through the same procedure as before, Walton would do some demonstration examples on the board, and then they would do one of their own. The lessons continued for the rest of the afternoon until 16:30, where the students returned to their rooms, and prior to the evening meal being served.

Mark had suggested that, after tea, they went out to a pub he had heard of, in between Wareham and Poole. Spike, Richard and a few others from the course agreed, but Dave decided he was going to do a bit of revision. Richard found this strange, he had always found learning new things enjoyable and never a problem. Everything they had been taught that day was firmly lodged in his brain, he spent half an hour after the evening meal going over some of the operational limitations of the equipment they had covered that day. Happy that he had retained the information, he showered and dressed and waited on his other two roommates to do the same. Once they were ready, they called a taxi from the guardroom and set off for the pub by 18:30.

The pub itself was set in a quiet little village, with one private housing estate built next to it. As they walked into the bar, they commented on how busy it was, for that time of evening. Mark confidently strolled up to the bar and greeted the barmaid as if he was a local and had known her all his life. He was quite a good looking lad, and the girl behind the bar was obviously attracted to him. He had all manner of chat up lines, which he used throughout the evening. They had only been there fifteen minutes, when Spike sloped off and started chatting up one of the local girls.

'He's like a dog with two dicks.' Richard commented to Mark.

'Fucking good drills, is all I can say, mate' came the reply from Mark, in his deep Cockney accent. Quite a number of the 'Household Cavalry' were from the Home Counties, particularly London. This was because the Ceremonial branch of the Regiment was always based in Knightsbridge. Mark went on to explain some of his experiences while serving in the Capital on the 'gee gees'. One evening in one of the local pubs, he had picked up this girl and, after a few drinks, she agreed to return with him to his room, in camp. He had to sweet talk the guard commander, to allow her to come in, and he agreed to turn a blind eye. Taking her to his room, it wasn't long before they were undressed and at it like rabbits. Half way through the love making, the girl had frozen, her eyes opened wide and she exclaimed:

'You're him, aren't you?' she questioned. Mark, not having a clue what she was talking about, asked her who she meant. 'You're the devil, aren't you?' Came the somewhat crazy question. Realising quickly, that this girl was deranged, he immediately jumped off her, got dressed and escorted her from camp. The Army, however, is a very close knit community and the story soon got round. For the next couple of weeks, every time someone bumped into Mark, they would greet him by asking, 'Hi, Mark, how the devil are you?' This became a regular joke and, being a cracker, took a while to wear thin.

Near where the barracks in Knightsbridge were situated, were a couple of pubs frequented by a gay clientele. When the lads were skint, some would go to these pubs and be picked up by a gay man. The older gays had a penchant for men in uniform, and when they leaned these young soldiers were members of the Household Cavalry, they thought all their Christmases had come at once.

One story revealed how a fresh faced lad in Mark's Squadron, had been approached by one of the regulars in the pub. When the older gay learned that the young squaddie was a member of the Blues and Royals, he invited him back to his apartment, on condition he brought his uniform. Mark's mate agreed, after first of all making clear he would not get involved in any sexual behaviour. The gay man opened his heart to the young soldier, and said that he would not physically touch him, it was just that he got excited looking at men in uniform. Once they had cleared this up, he handed over a piece of paper with his address. The young Trooper dashed back to camp, stashed his uniform in a large rucksack and headed off in a taxi to the address given.

Opening the apartment door to the lad, the older man asked if he would like a drink which was declined. Shown an area in the lounge, and told this was the only area available, the Trooper took off his casual clothes and donned his ceremonial gear, complete with breast plate, helmet and plume. While he was doing this, the older man, with no embarrassment, was playing with himself. By the time the Trooper was fully dressed, the excited gay host could not hold back any longer and ejaculated all over the floor. He went across to his wallet, lying on the nearby table, and thrust five twenty pound notes into the Trooper's hand. Thanking him, the

Trooper got dressed back into civvies, packed away his uniform and left. This was the easiest £100 he had made in a long time. This practice as well as the more brutal 'gay bashing' became popular pastimes for the Troops stationed at Knightsbridge. Richard could not believe his ears, and decided to keep his platonic friendship with Danny in Berlin a secret.

For the next hour, Richard marvelled at the unparalleled bullshit that came out of Mark's mouth, as Mark chatted up a number of girls, in the bar. The women hung on Mark's every word, staring at him, longingly. By the end of the night, thanks to the silver tongued devil, Richard, Spike and Mark managed to wangle themselves invites to a private party being held by one of the girls. Leaving the pub, they walked, with the girls, to the estate, not 500 metres from the pub. It seemed strange, as they were the only three males in the house for the first fifteen minutes. After a short while, a few more people turned up and the party was in full swing. The music was blaring and Richard thought to himself he was glad he was not the neighbours. He found himself chatting to a pretty young girl, but his mind returned to thoughts of Birgit, back in Germany. Spike had no such qualms, he had already disappeared with the girl he had been chatting to in the pub. Richard suspected one of the bedrooms was probably getting put to good use, at that moment in time. Mark was surrounded by three of the girls that had been hanging round him, since they had left the bar. It wasn't long before he, too, disappeared, with all three of them! The party continued, with people coming and going all the time. At around two o'clock in the morning, Mark and Spike had re-appeared and they reckoned it was about time they sorted out a taxi. One of the girls said she would call them one, from the house phone, and it arrived in ten minutes. They were back in camp and tucked up in bed by 02:30, after what was to be the first of many nights out on the lash. Although Richard had come to gain a qualification and step on the promotion ladder, he was enjoying the social side of things even more. It was to be a recurring theme throughout his career, and one that was not looked upon favourably, by some.

The next week concentrated on how to run a Command Vehicle CV, in order to support a Battlegroup. A battlegroup is formed around an infantry battalion or armoured Regiment, which is usually commanded by a Lieutenant Colonel. The Battalion or Regiment also provides the command and staff element of a battlegroup, which is complemented with an appropriate mix of armour, infantry, support personnel and weaponry, relevant to the task it is expected to perform. The first lesson they learned, was how to erect the tent that extended the vehicles' ability to house O Groups. The tent was built into the rear of the 'Sultan' CV and had an extendible frame, which slid away into the rear of the vehicle; and was secured by straps. The lesson itself took only 30 minutes to complete, using a team of four, simulating a working CV crew. Also, when working as Battlegroup complex, the vehicles backed on to each other, normally with three of them forming a 'Crucifix'. In periods of long habitation, where the complex would not move for a considerable time, the use of generators was necessary. So, another lesson taught was how to set up and maintain the 500 Watt generators which were carried on top of the vehicles. These were used to power any additional lights and all the equipment within the CV. They also charged the vehicle batteries, so the students were taught the rules for battery maintenance, and how to set them up in series and series parallel. Another skill that needed to be mastered was what was known as 'map marking'. This was a NATO standard method of manually marking maps, by using a set of common symbols. The history of it, actually, goes back to just after the end of the Napoleonic War, when it was adopted by most western armies. It was when the colour red for 'enemy forces' and blue for 'friendly forces' was introduced.

They were also shown the use of BATCO and Secure Orders Cards (SOCS), a method of encrypting and standardizing operating procedures.

Once they were proficient in all these skills, they were taken through how to erect an 8 metre and 12 metre mast. This was known as an Elevated VHF Antennae (EVHF) and was an elevated end fed dipole for use with the VHF Radio to extend the range when mounted on an 8 or 12 meter mast.

Great care and attention was taken that they were perfectly erect, which was confirmed by a spirit level bubble, mounted to the telescopic sections, secured by a series of guide ropes in a triangular formation. Once fully erect, the coaxial cable was fed back from the Automatic Tuning Unit (ATU), which had a nickname of 'the pineapple' because of the shape, to a coaxial connector on top of the vehicle. These masts were also used by the Morse course, who were into their second week of training, by now. The 'Con Sig' students had seen them walking around the masts, with a sloping wire antennae attached to the top of the masts. They would have a Morse key strapped to their thighs and would traverse round the pole, trying to get the best signal. They looked like Morris Dancers twirling around the May Pole, except that they were dressed in 'Disruptive Pattern Material (DPM) combats and boots, and didn't wear bells.

Another form of communication they were required to learn, was that of telephony. For this purpose, they were taught the Unit Level Switchboard (ULS) 16 Line, a piece of equipment that could connect up to sixteen telephone handsets extensions, used in Battlegroup Command Complexes.

The sub units would lay line from their positions into Battlegroup HQ, and could communicate when on radio silence. This would keep their interception by enemy Directional Finding (DF) Units to a minimum. The downside to this was that it took time to setup and, therefore, they were not secure. The line could be easily tapped into and conversations intercepted, by simply attaching a handset with some cable and a safety pin into the line. This line and how it was laid was explained in a separate lesson, which covered the type of equipment used, and crossings and obstacles they may come across. The equipment they carried was remembered by a mnemonic, as were most lists in the army. It was known as PCSTILLS, and they were told to remember this, as it would be useful, at the end of the course test. The acronym stood for Pliers, Clasp knife, Tool Compression, Insulating Tape, Linesman's Belt, Labels and Spun yarn (String).

Each night, the course members would go out on the town, Poole had become a popular destination and a certain disco had become popular on a Wednesday night. It had become known as the 'Cattle Market' and Wednesday night was 'grab a granny' night. This didn't mean that every female in the disco bar was a wrinkled old woman, but neither were they teenagers or girls in their early twenties, as was the case, on a weekend. The guys would have bets on, as to who could pull the least attractive girl, nicknamed the 'pig', and, perversely, this was a title of great prestige to be won.

They would normally meet up with Spike. who had been living with a girl from Bournemouth, since the end of week one. She would pick him up after the course had finished for the day, and they would go back to her place for the evening. She was about six years older than him and her reputation of being a real 'dirty bitch' was well deserved.

The friends would meet in a pub called Colonnades, which was just below the 'Cattle Market'. There, they would have a few drinks, prior to the club opening around 22:00. They would also eye up any possible talent, which might be going to the club, later. If they saw anyone they liked, they either chatted them up and invited them to join them, or waited until they were all inside. Mark had been with a different girl each night, which meant, on many occasions, him not returning to camp until just before the course was due to start. It hadn't affected his studies, as he had passed all the tests given, during the end of each week. This particular evening had been a quiet one and the group, as a whole, struck out and ended up, returning to camp by 01:00.

It had reached the final week and the first few days were taken up with learning the Army new encrypted radio and telephone systems. This was known as Clansman Secure Speech Harness (CSSH) and the Ptarmigan, which was a terrestrial trunk communications system.

Ptarmigan is a mobile, cryptographic digital and modular battlefield wide area network communications system based on the Plessey System 250 architecture. It was initially designed to meet the needs of the British Army of the Rhine in West Germany and replaced the BRUIN system. The system consists of a network of electronic exchanges known as trunk nodes. These nodes are connected by multichannel UHF and SHF radio relay links that carry voice, data, telegraph and facsimile communications. The Single Channel Radio Access subsystem is effectively a VHF secure mobile telephone system that gives isolated or mobile users an entry point into the PTARMIGAN network. Ptarmigan has undergone a number of upgrades since it came into service in 1982. (First delivery of Ptarmigan equipment was to 1 Armoured Division HQ and Signal Regiment in December 1984, and did not enter service until February/March of 1985)(Wikipedia)

During the last two days, the students were taught how to test vehicle equipment, cables, and audio accessories. This teaching was not quite at the level of an electronics technician, but was a Unit first level repair option. The equipment used were the Test Set Condition (TKC), Test Set Audio Accessories (TSAA) and the Test Kit Handset (TKH). Although Richard had been introduced to them on his pre course training, it was an area in which he was weak. He could recite all the facts and figures about them, as he had an almost photographic memory, but, when it came to practical use, he found that he was a little clumsy. This showed in his level of skill in repairing equipment that needed soldering. Nonetheless he got through it, and before long, it was the night before the end of course.

The course was complete and the Instructors had arranged an 'end of course piss up' at a pub in Wareham. Wareham was a small town, only a few miles from the camp. Food had been laid on and the drinks flowed. Some people, who had not seen eye to eye during the course, took it on themselves to sort it out. This, invariably, ended up in the protagonists stepping outside, for a short while. They would then return, the best of friends, be it covered in blood or cuts and bruises. The night had gone well, everyone returned together and were tucked up by midnight.

On the final day, the course met in their separate rooms, where they sat the final exam. It incorporated everything they had covered over the eight weeks they had been there. Practical tests had already been undertaken, the previous day. They had moved round a series of stands, taking in Generator use, erecting of masts, setting up a CV, Line Laying and Equipment fault diagnosis. Richard had passed all the practical tests and was looking forward to the final written test. No one had ever got 100% on it, but he had made it his mission to do so. It came to the time for them to start and the students turned over their papers. Richard smiled, as he quickly leafed through the questions. He didn't think there was anything that was going to give him problems.

After the allotted one hour, the students were asked to put down their pens, and hand their papers to the front. This was done, they were dismissed and told to return an hour later, when hopefully their papers would have been marked. With a scrape of their chairs they got up and returned to the rooms, for a last minute tidy up, to make sure the rooms were ready for handover, as soon as they were released from the course. Richard felt good, and expected that he was close to getting the perfect score. On their return, they settled down in the lecture theatre, and awaited the OC, RSM and Instructors. They turned up not five minutes later the RSM smiling and making way for the OC to address the course. He thanked them for all their efforts and hard work, and the feedback he had received from his Instructors had been mostly positive. He also informed them that something had happened for the first time that he knew of in the Signal School, and that was that someone had scored 100% on the written paper. A murmur went round the room and they all looked at each other wondering who it was. Waiting for the room to calm down, the OC announced at the top of his voice.

'That student is,' he paused for effect, 'Trooper Hunter, well done!'

A round of applause rang out, not only from the students but from the Instructors as well. Richard had been a popular member of the course and he felt a pang of pride, as he was beckoned up to the lectern, to be congratulated, personally, by the OC. As he shook his hand, Richard thought about how far he had come, since joining the army, in that very same Garrison town three years earlier.

Chapter 33 – Command Troop

On Richard's return to Regimental duty, he was informed that he was due to transfer to 'Command Troop'. This Troop was part of Headquarter Squadron, and provided the communications for the Commanding Officer and the Battlegroup. Although this would add another string to his bow, Richard felt a deep sadness. He would be leaving a great bunch of guys, especially Legs, who had had learned to love and respect in equal measures. He would also be leaving behind Sol, with whom he had served, for the last three years. So, it was with feelings of apprehension and melancholy, that he began the task of packing away all his belongings.

The following morning, he said his goodbyes to Sol, it was not as though he would not see him again. They were to remain close friends up until the last time he would see him in sunnier climes. He left the room and walked the short distance to HQ Squadron offices, where he reported to the SSM. He was a large, rather jovial character and, unlike most of the Regiment, he originated from down south somewhere. He welcomed Richard to the Squadron and after a short introduction brief, took him to the SQMS stores, where he introduced him to the SQMS. Richard immediately recognized this man, as he had been Troop Sergeant of Fourth Troop in Berlin. He smiled as he welcomed Richard and they went through the task of issuing Richard his equipment and bedding for his room. The whole process took only 40 minutes and before long he was dragging his heavy suitcase and bedding across the square to the accommodation block. As he walked along the corridor, he checked the names on the doors of the rooms. He was just about to give up finding his name, when he came to the last door on the right. There, he saw his name in bold letters, and he chuckled to himself when he saw that Ken was to be his new roommate. He turned the key in the door and entered the room, to be pleasantly surprised, by the size of it. There were only two beds in the room and a huge sofa took centre stage. In front of this, was a massive TV, situated between the two windows at the far end of the room. As it was around 10:00 by this time, the room was empty, as the Troops were on the tank park. Richard set about the task of making up his bed and packing away his clothing, into the empty wardrobe.

Just over two hours later, as Richard was making the finishing touches to his personal effects, including straightening his 'Action Man' quilt cover, the door opened. Framed in the doorway was Ken, with the largest shit eating grin Richard had ever seen.

'How ya doing, ya wanker?' Ken said, in the usual squaddie greeting.

'Not bad, mate,' Richard countered, as the pair hugged each other.

In the Army, the act of embracing a colleague, was not seen as a sign of homosexuality, it was more a sign of respect and recognition of good and bad times shared. In times of conflict, a soldier was always there for his comrades. He was an agony aunt, listener, shoulder to cry on, and piss taker all rolled into one. The action of ribbing, or making fun out of a friend or situation, was a coping mechanism that all soldiers used, to defuse times of conflict or hardship. An example of this was if someone had received a 'Dear John' from a girlfriend, saying the relationship was finished. Rather than receive compassion from his colleagues, it was used as a stick to beat him with. It was almost reverse psychology and was meant to take the persons mind off his troubles. It was not malicious, however, squaddies did seem to take a perverse pleasure doing it. Yet, it was this 'bond' that kept them going when things got tough, soldiers always knew their friends were there for them. The two friends talked for the next half hour about the Troop Richard was joining. Ken had joined three months earlier, as the Commanding Officer's gunner. It was a position of great prestige, and marked him out as a potential gunnery instructor. Ken was being sent on his 'gunner mech', the equivalent of the Cong Sig that Richard had recently completed. Ken had been in the Regiment for a year longer than Richard, but their career paths seemed to be running side by side. It was normal for Troopers to complete their class one courses at around the three to four year point. They were normally then put on the list for promotion to Lance Corporal, soon after this. Although that was the usual way things worked, it would prove a little different for Richard, due to events in the next three years.

After lunch, the friends strolled from the accommodation to the tank park. Headquarter Squadrons' hangars backed onto the airfield where the CO's fun run started. Richard prepared himself for the inevitable introductions on entering the hangar. As they opened the door and went in, all eyes turned towards them. Richard recognised a few faces, but the one that caught his gaze immediately was Spike. He, on his return, had also been given the news that he was joining Command Troop. He raised his hand in recognition and Richard went over and shook his hand. A large bloke wearing the wrist band of a Warrant Officer came across to them. Richard knew his face from somewhere but could not bring to mind exactly where.

'I'm Staff Sergeant Galloway, and I'm the Regimental Signals Warrant Officer,' he said in a deep, gravelly Cumbrian accent.

Then it hit Richard where he knew him from They had met one night, before Richard had joined up, in the Warrant Officers and Sergeants' Mess. His father would take him there, occasionally, and Galloway was a close friend of his father's. Or, that was what Richard assumed, secretly his dad thought Galloway was a little mad. He then took Richard and Spike around the Troop and introduced them to the blokes. Firstly the Troop Sergeant, who was a guy called Stuart Crane, who, funnily enough, was also known as Spike. He was a slight figure but immaculately turned out. He eyed the two newcomers with what Richard took to be disdain. Richard was to find out later that that was Crane's normal manner with everyone. The next personality introduced was their Troop Corporal who was called Kevin Mason. He was from an area in Leeds but had Scottish parentage. He also was very well turned out and his coveralls looked like they had never seen a sport of oil. Working with the most senior Officers in the Regiment, they were told that their appearance was to be of the highest order at all times. This was to prove hard for Richard as he was used to getting stuck in with the driver in the engine decks on a tank. The Troop Sergeant Paul led Spike away with him and introduced him to his new crew; while Kevin did the same with Richard. Command Troop was comprised of three CV's, 0B, 0C and 0D. They were bolstered by two tanks which belonged to the CO and Second in Command of the Regiment. Also, a tracked ambulance which acted as the Regimental First aid post, and was manned by the Medical Centres Chief Medic and the Regimental Medical Officer (RMO). Richard was to be on 0C, which was commanded by the Regimental Signals Officer. It had a crew of five, three operators, including the Troop Corporal and a driver. The driver's name was Alan Berryman, but was simply known as Al. Although he was deep in the engine decks, when he was called by Kevin to meet his new crew member, his appearance, like the majority, was spotless. They were to become good friends over the years and would gain promotion around the same time. This would be hard earned on their Leadership cadre, which they would have to pass to get their promotion. The other crew member and operator was another Cumbrian named Trev. He was busy testing the radio equipment, as Richard climbed inside the Sultan with Kevin. He looked like he had been out on the town the previous night as his eyes were bloodshot, and Richard could smell the pungent whiff of alcohol on his breath.

The introductions over, Richard was shown round the CV by Kevin. He pointed out where all the equipment was stowed, and explained that it was the same for all CV's. This was due to the fact that they were required at times to move around the vehicles, so everything was in the same position, no matter which vehicle you were on. 0B was the main Battlegroup CV and its commander was Paul, it carried the CO, when he was not on his tank or Land Rover. The RSWO also travelled on this vehicle and co-ordinated the setting up of the whole complex. The remaining CV was 0D and was manned by the Regimental Intelligence Officer and his assistant, who was a Staff Sergeant. They were responsible of briefing the CO on any intelligence information gathered by forward reconnaissance forces or any other Intelligence matters passed down from Brigade command. The only vehicle which had not been show to Richard was a Spartan. After asking Kevin what its function was, it was pointed out that it was used as a rebroadcast station, to extend the range of the complex if communications were proving to be difficult. It would situate itself in a position that would enable it to 'pass through' or rebroadcast radio traffic from Battlegroup HQ to the 'Sabre Squadrons'. Or, in fact, back to Brigade as the Regiment or Battlegroup advanced. Richard was told that the Troop were preparing for a radio exercise, using simulated battle scenarios, on and around the river Weser. The main thing that Richard had noticed was that there were very few Troopers in the Troop. He was to find out that the Lance Corporals and Troopers did most of the work. It would take some getting used to, after operating within a tight knit crew, where everyone mucked in.

The next week was spent preparing the vehicles and kitting them out with all the maps, stationary and everything that was required to run an effective Command Complex. They had spent a full day using Fablon, a sticky clear material, to cover the maps. This meant the maps could be marked with soluble pens, then wiped clean. A map of the whole exercise area had been covered and placed on the map board, in the back of every vehicle. Once they had arrived in their position on the first evening and the CO had received his orders, the maps would be marked up. All the stationary and other equipment were placed in 'battle boxes', which were containers with a hasp on them. These were secured using 'Ingersoll' padlocks, since they contained cryptographic material.

On the morning of the start of the exercise, the Troop gathered in the hangar at 06:30. They started the vehicles and did their first parades, to make sure all were in good, working order. Unlike when the tanks went on exercise, for this particular one the CV's and other tracked and wheeled vehicles would 'motor', under their own steam, to the exercise area. During the briefing the previous day, the RSO had gone through the route they were going to take, to an area just west of the river Weser. It had been arranged with a local farmer that they could have the use of his barns, which was received with grateful thanks by the Troops. It meant that when they got there, they would not need to cam up. Also, as it was the middle of winter and the temperature was currently minus fifteen, it would provide them with a level of protection from the elements. The journey itself would take around three hours to complete. They would drive in convoy, taking particular attention to timings and spacing's between the vehicles. The RMP and local German Civil Police had been informed which areas they would be travelling through. They would man any junctions where they thought the Troop movement may cause an issue.

At 07:30 precisely, the vehicles departed from the side gate, onto the main road. The RMP had stopped traffic, until all military vehicles were out and had set off, along the given route. Richard made himself as comfortable as he could, it was nice and snug with Kevin, Trev and himself on the comfortable seat, in front of the map board. As the vehicle sped along the German roads, at an average 30 miles an hour, it provided an almost soporific effect. The rhythmic movement on the even roads made for a comfortable journey. This was mainly down to the skill of Al, and his smooth gear control of the Sultan. The three of them gently nodded in the back, and Richard thought to himself that he was glad that he was not in the RSO's shoes, with his head out of the hatch and the cold winter wind blasting in his face. He was disturbed from his dozing by Kevin, who asked him to get a brew on for the RSO, who after 30 minutes must have been frozen through. Richard did as he was told and filled the mugs with coffee and tea to order. Even Al received one, which he placed in a holder he had fashioned for himself, for that purpose. He would wait until there was a stretch of road where he would not be required to change gear or to steer. That would then allow him to take a swig of the welcoming beverage and feel it warm him, from the inside. The brews all finished, Richard topped up the BV, from the internal water tank. Before closing the lid once more, he placed in a couple of tins of compo, which would save them some time, when they reached their final destination. These would be heated several times on the journey, as the BV was boiled at least another three times, for the teas and coffees.

A little over three hours since receiving in their movement orders, they were pulling off the main road and on to a farm track. The vehicle started to bounce around, due to the uneven terrain. This was made much more noticeable than inside a tank, as the vehicles were much lighter and suspension was not of the highest quality. Al tried his best to give them a smooth a ride as possible. Within five minutes they had reached the farmhouse, and were reversing into the barn, whose doors stood wide open to receive them. With small movements of the sticks, the Sultan backed its way into the barn. The Close Vehicle Reconnaissance Tracked (CVRT) were very manoeuvrable in tight spaces and could turn on a hairpin. It only took a matter of minutes for all the vehicles to be reversed in and positioned, so that they backed on to each other. This formed the recognisable 'Crucifix' form, Richard had learned on his course. As soon as the vehicles had stopped and their engines had been shut down, the crews emerged from the rear of the vehicles, stretching and shaking their legs to try and get the circulation back into them. They may have been more comfortable to ride in, but their cramped space, and the amount of equipment and people they carried, counteracted this. The drivers jumped from their cabs and began to run through their vehicle checks, ensuring that the oil levels were okay, and if not, they were topped up. They also checked under the vehicles for any leaks, as they did not want to upset the farmer, by leaving oil stains in his barn, when they left. The operators and rest of the crews began to unclip the 'Penthouses', that would be joined together to form the complex. The majority, other than Richard and Spike, had done this many times before, and, in a flash, the structure was complete. The next task was for two of the crews to take their EVHF equipment and eight metre masts outside. Here, one crew erected their mast and connected it up to the VHF frequency; while the other set up a dipole antennae, that would be used for the HF 'Guard Net', which was for the administration frequency. Both of the coaxial leads were fed back to 0B, which was, at that time, being used as the primary CV.

As soon as Communications had been setup and proved, the crews set about connecting up three 500 watt generators, to provide power to the whole complex. They were placed outside of the bar, because of the fumes emitted in an enclosed space. This was also the reason why the vehicles would only be run once a day, to top up the main driver's batteries, for a 30 minute period. As the barn was used as a storage area for the farmers hay, they were under strict instructions that there was to be no smoking in the barn. As soon as the complex was complete, the crews set about making the evening meal, in their individual areas. The Commanding Officer had left for Brigade in his Land Rover, with his driver. It would be there, he would receive his orders for the next 48 hours or so. In the meantime, his sleeping area would be set up by other members of the Troop, under the direction of the RSWO. The evening meal prepared, the Troops dug in and, once finished, cleared everything away. This would be the normal practice, Richard found, as they never knew when one or all the vehicles would be required to move.

The CO returned around two and a half hours later, and he called the RSO, RSWO and Intelligence Officer together, to give them a brief. Once this was complete, the RSO briefed the Troop, he had marked up his map from the one the CO had given him. This showed all the boundaries of the battlegroup and their defensive positions. Richard recognised the symbols being used, as they were still fresh in his mind, from his course. Handing over the map to the crew of 0B, he instructed them to mark up the map in their CV. The RSWO and Intelligence Officer gave theirs to 0C and 0D, and told them to do the same. So, for the next hour or more, the operators painstakingly copied the symbols from one map to the large ones, which were attached to the map boards, in the back of the vehicles. This was a great learning experience for Richard and he was now gaining knowledge of the full battle picture. He had been used to only dealing with things at a Squadron level, but this showed how other Support Arms linked into the battle plan. All this new acquired knowledge would stand him in good stead for the future. With the CV's all set up, and the radio list and ground sentry list posted, the Troop began the normal hide routine. A watch-keeper, who was normally an officer or Senior Non Commissioned Officer, accompanied an operator on radio watch. A ground sentry patrolled the area of the farm complex, but, because of the risk of fire, one of his secondary roles was that of fire watch. The Troops had scattered themselves throughout the barn, a couple of them drinking bottles of beer, which they had brought with them. It was not as it was on tanks, where everyone was quite open about having a few beers. Here, it was done in more low key fashion, and was not surprising, bearing in mind the personalities that worked within the Troop. It would not set a good impression to a visiting high ranking officer, to see the battlegroup Headquarters staff, four sheets to the wind. Richard joined a couple of them and took the beer that was offered to him. After one or two he felt a little sleepy, so, unrolling his sleeping bag on some bales of hay, he climbed in and was soon fast asleep.

At 02:00 in the morning, he was woken by the sentry, gently shaking him and letting him know it was his turn for radio watch. He unzipped the bag, wiped the sleep from his eyes and shivered as the cold immediately seeped into his bones. He dressed quickly and walked across, swiftly, to the crucifix area. As soon as he lifted the flap on the rear penthouse, he felt the warmth wash over him. This came from a petrol heater, that had been set up behind 0B, which warmed up the complex.

'Close that fucking flap!' Came the agitated voice of Paul, the Troop Sergeant.

Richard did as he was ordered, then climbed inside the CV and took his place, next to Paul, facing the map board. He was relieving one of the guys from 0D, who, before he left, gave Richard a quick brief of what had happened during his shift. He confirmed that the frequencies had been changed and that they were on radio silence. With that, he disappeared to his bed. There was an uneasy silence between Paul and Richard. At least he hadn't got one of the Officers as watch-keeper, thought Richard to himself. The silence was finally broken by Paul, who asked how Richard's Con Sig course had gone. Richard told him that he had thoroughly enjoyed it, especially the exercise and theory behind Skywave Propagation. This seemed to break the ice with Paul and the pair of them chatted away, about different aspects of communications. Their conversation was interrupted by smoke drifting into the penthouse area. Before they could react, a voice was heard shouting an alarm.

'Fire! Fire! Fire!'

The penthouse flap was thrown back and the sentries face peered in.

'There's a fire in the barn, guys!'

The pair of them leapt from the CV and out of the penthouse. Some of the Troop were already tackling the fire, beating it with shovels, others pouring water on it from Jerrycans, from the vehicles. To the left, they saw one of the crew from the Rebroadcast vehicle, who Richard only knew as 'Smiler', being tended to, by one of the medics. He had something stuck to his neck and was writhing around in agony. The Troop continued to fight the fire until it was completely extinguished. As things settled down, the RSWO was trying to ascertain exactly how the fire had been started. A little later, he called the Troop together and explained that 'Smiler' had been smoking, in his sleeping bag. It wasn't made clear if it was due to alcohol or simply tiredness, but he had fallen asleep. The cigarette must have fallen from his fingers, onto the hay bales he was lying on. Unfortunately, when he realised that the place was on fire, he panicked and the zip on his sleeping bag had stuck. The plastic hood covering had melted due to the heat on to his neck, causing severe burns. The RSWO reiterated the fact that there was to be no smoking in the barn. Things could have been a lot worse, if the sentry had not been so alert. The unfortunate 'Smiler' had been whisked away to the nearest hospital for treatment. His nickname would change from that moment on from 'Smiler' to 'Toasty', which everyone thought was hilarious.

For the next week, the Troop were tested on command and control of an imaginary battlegroup. This was purely a radio exercise and no vehicles were deployed, except Brigade and battlegroup command elements. They were given certain scenario and battle plans, on which they were required to act. The Brigade signals attachments would try and intercept and disrupt communications. On more than one occasion, sometimes twice a day, 0C was given the order to prepare to 'Step Up'. This was the drill carried out to simulate the Battlegroup HQ moving forward with the battle. 0C would detach its penthouse from the crucifix and pack away all their equipment. They would move to an agreed location, and once there, would set up communications and inform 0B that they were 'firm'. On receipt of this, 0B and the rest of the Troop would drop their masts, pack away their generators and all other equipment. Once this was complete, they would move to join 0B, they would set up the complex once more and the exercise would continue. By the end of the week, Richard had fallen into the routine of the Troop, without a problem. It had helped that he was fresh off the course, as everything was still lodged firmly in his brain. He had forgotten the amount of times he had remarked the maps that were located on the map boards. The battle picture was forever changing, but in this short time he had acquired insight into how everything fitted together. The day consisted of either radio watch, servicing the generators, cooking or sleeping. It was on one of the many radio watches, that he had been drawn with the RSWO. During their stag, they had talked about his father, and it came to light that the RSWO was bit of a practical joker. He recited the story of a certain exercise, where he had decided to play a prank on Richard's father. His father had been SSM of A Squadron at this time and was doing a recce of a hide for the Squadron's night time location. He put out a call to the A Squadron SSM, asking for assistance. He informed him that the CO's Land Rover driver had broken down with a puncture and didn't have a jack to change the tyre. Richard's dad was travelling in a 'Ferret Scout Car', which was also wheel based. After asking where the Land Rover was located, the RSWO gave him a bogus grid. Tommy acknowledge the grid and set off to give assistance. On his arrival, he found there was no vehicle there, so got on the air to confirm the grid. The RSWO gave his apologies and said he would get back in touch with the driver and find out. After a minute or so, he came back on the air, informed Tommy that the original grid was wrong, and gave him a new one. Richard's dad set off again to the new location, but again could not locate the broken down vehicle. This went on for a good two hours, until Tommy realised that he had been had. Biting his lip he congratulated the RSWO on his jape, but Tommy was never one to let things lie.

The old maxim of 'revenge is a dish best served cold' was firmly lodged in his mind. Two days later at 02:00 the RSO was on watch-keeper and a call came over the air from SSM Tommy Hunter. He asked to speak to 'Pronto', which was the appointment title for signals personnel. When the RSO answered he said, 'No, not you, the fat one!' The RSO sent a runner to go and get the RSWO, and, once he had been woken and had dragged his tired arse to the CV, he picked up the handset offered him by the RSO, and gave A Squadron SSM call sign and asked the caller to send his message. The reply was simple and to the point.

'I've found my jack. Out!' And, with that the air went dead. The RSWO had chuckled to himself, admitting that he had been well and truly stitched up. The remaining days of the exercise flew past, and it wasn't long before they were packing up for the final time, and heading back to camp.

For the next year Richard spent most of his time either on exercise in the field or doing map board exercises. These were held at the Brigade and Battlegroup Trainer in the nearby town of Sennelager. The idea was to hone the skills of commanders, and could be set up for any terrain in the world, without having to leave camp. They also tested, if that was the right word, how logistical support could be stretched, during conflicts. These scenarios could run 24 hours a day, and provided a valuable training tool. There was no pass or fail, just a report on lessons to learn, at the end of it. As the vehicles were nearly always ready to be deployed for their next exercise, a lot of free time was awarded to the Troop. Richard took advantage of this and had managed to make the Regimental rugby first team. On his first training session, he was delighted to see that he would be partnering Legs, who was the Regimental Stand Off, at that particular time. Richard's dad had left the Regiment just two months earlier, after his 22 years' service. It was customary for a CO, or sometimes a Squadron Leader to be pulled out of camp on a vehicle. Tommy had heard a rumour that this was lined up for him. Being a shy person and not one to be in the limelight, he had made his escape from camp, without having to endure this. Richard was sad for him, as he was a respected member of the Regiment and people wanted to show their appreciation. Richard also regretted the fact that he had not made the rugby first team prior to Tommy's departure. He would make sure that he would do his utmost to play for the shirt, which his dad had also worn. The first game he played in, was against a Welsh Infantry Regiment, stationed in the next town. It was a hard fought game and a severe baptism of fire for the young Richard. The Welsh team had a couple of players who had played for the Army. One of these was a dark haired Captain, who would go on to achieve greatness for his country. It would be Richard's claim to fame in the coming years to say that he had played against Will Carling, the future England Captain.

Richard's relationship with Birgit had gone from strength to strength, he spent most of his time at her parents' house now. He had been with the Regiment for four years, and although he had gained in experience, this was not reflected in his use of common sense. He had spent a number of times in the Regimental 'Hotel', a euphemism for the jail. He had committed various crimes that had seen him incarcerated there for different periods of time. Mostly they were all down to the amount of alcohol he consumed while out on the town. It was probably the reason why his promotion to Lance Corporal eluded him. His work within Command Troop was not questioned, he was a respected operator, but at times lacked self-discipline, which let him down. One example being, when he had been given the responsibility of commanding the CO's Land Rover. The CO had chosen to travel on his tank, and wanted someone to take his Land Rover to the next location, where he would meet up with it, later in the day. Richard was given this responsibility by the RSWO. As he collected his webbing and weapon, Paul the Troop Sergeant took him to one side. He stressed the point that Richard needed to be at the RV, where the Troop would join them, in a few hours' time. This was because the CO would need to go to Brigade, for his orders group, that evening. Richard said that he understood, turned away and climbed into the Land Rover, next to John, the CO's driver. John had been in training at JLR the same time as John, but he had been in a different Troop, so they had only really known each other in passing. He had been in Berlin, too, but had, again, been in a different Troop. He was a giant of a man and the deepness of his voice belied his age. With this booming voice, he posed the question in his deep York accent.

'Where we off, then?'

'Oh, only about twenty kilometres away, should only take about 40 minutes,' Richard said, with a mischievous grin on his face. He showed John on the map the place they were heading for, and, once he was happy with the route they were to take, he put the vehicle in gear and they set off along the track, which joined the main road. After only ten minutes driving, Richard asked if John fancied a bit of breakfast. John nodded his head and Richard asked him to pull over, in the next village. Entering the village, Richard spotted a bakers and asked John to park outside it. He got out of the vehicle and went into the bakers, returning five minutes later, laden with fresh bread rolls, cold meats and cheese. It was a feast fit for a King. 'Only one thing missing,' Richard remarked to John. Climbing out of the Land Rover, he headed over the road to a supermarket and, to John's dismay, came back with a bottle of wine. Obviously, John would not be able to partake, and he knew Richard's reputation for liking a drink or two. John knew that this would, probably, end up messy. They ate and drank, while listening to the battle going on, over the air. Richard had finished half the wine, when he decided that it was probably best that they head for the final RV. He guided John along the route, having to concentrate on the map, as the alcohol dulled his senses. As John had been on a number of recces of the area with the CO, he knew the area quite well. They were just two kilometres away from the grid they had been given, when Richard asked John to pull over, once more, in the village they were transiting. John did so, thinking that Richard probably needed to get out and relieve himself. However, Richard walked straight into another supermarket and purchased another bottle of wine. John tried to remonstrate with him, but when Richard was in this mood, there was no stopping him. They sat in a car park finishing off the rest of the rolls, cold meats and cheese. Richard had almost finished the second bottle, when John turned to him and said.

'Do you not think you should get your head down for an hour? I will listen out on the net and give you a shout when they are on the move.'

Richard agreed, clambered into the back and tried to make himself comfortable. Within minutes, the vehicle was filled with the sound of his snoring. The next thing that Richard knew was the rear door of the Land Rover being opened and he felt himself toppling out. He had been lying with his face against the petrol cooker and it was covered in black soot. The Troop had already arrived and had set up the complex. Al, their driver, spotted Richard's condition, and hastily grabbed him, whisking him away before anyone could see him. It hadn't gone unnoticed though, and an hour later he was summoned to see the RSWO, to receive the biggest bollocking of his life, so far. This was one of many little episodes he would go through, before reaching the dizzy heights of Lance Corporal.

Two months had passed since the drunken Land Rover incident, and the Regiment were told that two Squadrons, A and B, would be providing the manpower for the security of the Maze Prison. Her Majesty's Prison Maze was in Northern Ireland and was used to house paramilitary prisoners during the Troubles from mid-1971 to mid-2000. It was situated at the former Royal Air Force station of Long Kesh, on the outskirts of Lisburn. This would not be their only responsibility, they would also provide bodies for the Crumlin road jail in Belfast and patrols of local areas around the Maze including Craigavon, Portadown and Banbridge. To increase the numbers of the 'Sabre Squadrons', elements from HQ Squadron were assigned to the two Squadrons. Richard had been chosen to go with B Squadron, and on a warm, autumn evening, he transported his bedding and clothing to B Squadron accommodation, where rooms had been found for the newcomers. He was not the only new one, as members of Recce Troop and Guided Weapons (GW) had also been assigned to either A or B Squadron, for the duration of the tour.

On the first morning of training the two Squadrons joined together and paraded as one. The Squadron for the duration of the tour, would be known as the Prison Guard Force (PGF). The Squadron Leader for the tour was someone that Richard had never come across before. His name was Major Lovett and, on first appearances, he seemed an amiable kind, for an officer. Not stuck up in any way, shape or form, Lovett was very articulate, and Richard could tell he was respected by those who knew him. The initial thing the Major did, was to give them all a brief history on HM Prison Maze. Then, an explanation of the duties and roles they would be carrying out in the four months that they would be over, in the 'Province'. Finishing with the formalities, he then handed over to the SSM, who, Richard knew, had a wealth of experience, when it came to Northern Ireland. Richard had met him just before he had joined up. He had been with his dad in the local German pub when this bloke had walked in. Tommy immediately raised his hand in recognition and the newcomer sat down with them. His name was William Watson and he had spent a couple of years working undercover in Northern Ireland. The Unit was called 14 Intelligence Company, or more commonly known as the 'Det' for short. It was a Unit formed from the Intelligence Corps, and operated in the Province from 1970 onwards. Its prime task was to gather intelligence on suspected, or known Republican and Loyalist terrorists. Although he couldn't say too much about things he had been involved in, Richard had found him intriguing and fascinating. The SSM now stood before them and went through the nominal roll to check that everyone was present. As he called out each name, he assigned them to a Troop. They had tried to keep A Squadron and B Squadron people together in the same Troops, with the addition of the extra people from HQ, split between the two. The Troops were along the lines of an infantry platoon and were 32 in number. This gave them eight teams or 'Bricks' as they were known, with four to a brick. More than one 'Brick' was called a multiple. There were four Troops, which were classed as rifle Troops, and a SHQ Troop which provided the logistics, communications and administration.

Richard's name was called. He had been assigned to Second Troop. Once the SSM had finished the roll call, he instructed the respective Troop Leaders to carry on. The Troop Leaders asked that all members of their Troops to gather around them. The Troops did as they were asked and the Troop Sergeants of the individual Troops took another roll call, to ensure they had everybody. After the usual introductions, the Troops were given time slots of when they were to draw their kit from the Regimental Quartermaster. The rest of the morning was taken up with administration, training was to start in earnest the following day.

Lacing up his newly issued brand new Northern Ireland Patrol boots the following morning, Richard admired how light they felt, compared to his old DMS. He tucked his lightweight trousers under the elastic 'twisters' he had placed at the top of the boots. Zipping up the Combat jacket he reached down for the 'flak jacket' that lay on his bed. It was one of the new types and had a holder in the front and rear for a ballistic plate to slide in. This added even more weight and he strained as he picked it up. Placing his arm through one side, he put his other arm through the remaining hole and, using the Velcro strip, fastened it snuggly, around his torso. It was uncomfortable at first and he felt like he was inside a pressure cooker. He would spend many hours in this thing over the coming months, and would learn to love and hate it. They were to parade at 08:00, for their first introduction to the Northern Ireland Training and Advisory Team (NITAT). These were normally members of the Infantry, who were seasoned veterans of the Troubles in the Province. They would be taken for their in barracks training, prior to completing their range packages. The culmination of this would be a stay, at the purposely built training facility, known as 'Tin City', on the Sennelager ranges.

The Squadron paraded on the car park outside the accommodation block, and the NITAT Team made their introductions. There were four members of the team, two from the Royal Green Jackets and two from the Parachute Regiment. Between them, they had completed over sixteen tours of Northern Ireland, from Londonderry to South Armagh. So, they had a wealth of experience of both urban and rural patrolling. Once they had introduced themselves, the Troops were designated an Instructor, who would go through various aspects of patrolling, vehicle drills, rules of engagement and enhanced first aid skills. Second Troop were assigned one of the Para Regiment guys as their Instructor. He took them inside the block and into a makeshift classroom, he had organised. In the corner a black board, had been set up with a diagram of a street map. Once everyone was seated, the Para, who had introduced himself as 'Wacker', began the lesson. He went through various formations that could be adopted, in urban and rural areas. The use of hand signals to indicate direction and formation and the method of giving a contact report. The classroom work lasted most of the morning, each phase ending in a question and answer session. They were sent away for their lunch break and told to assemble outside the block in full patrol order, including weapons. The Troop filed out of the room in a buzz of excitement, coming from those like Richard, who had never been involved in this type of training before. He had taken part in infantry type exercises on Dartmoor whilst in training, but this had a more serious feel to it. This time, lives could really be on the line and any mistakes they made could end in someone being killed.

An hour later, the Troops withdrew their weapons from the armoury, and made their way to the car park, outside the accommodation. Wacker was already waiting for them and, on their arrival, he pulled the Troop Leader to one side. After a brief conversation the Troop Leader handed over a piece of paper to the Para Corporal. Wacker asked for Richard's team or 'Brick' to fall in on the road. The brick consisted of a Corporal called Martin, who was the team commander, and was assisted by his 2ic, a tall, thin man called Hesh. Richard and a bloke from Recce Troop called Ron completed the team. The NITAT Instructor reminded them to think back to the lessons they had covered that morning, in relation to patrolling in built up areas. Once the team had arranged themselves, he asked them to advance up the road, dealing with any obstacles like junctions, as they had been taught. The team had situated itself on either side of the road in a staggered formation. Richard had been assigned the point or lead position, behind him was the team 2ic, followed by the Brick commander. Ron brought up the rear, or tail end Charlie, position. Under direction from Martin, Richard stepped off slowly, observing any buildings to his left, any open windows could conceal a gunman, so he scanned them carefully. After every few paces Richard would turn round and take a quick look at the guys behind him, also checking the two on the other side of the road. The spacing looked good and his pace seemed to be okay, so he faced back, to the front. Spacing was important, they had been told, this was in case they were caught in an Improvised Explosive Device (IED). If one of these home-made bombs were detonated, the spacing would, at least, minimise the number of casualties. As Richard approached the first road junction, he slowed, not quite sure what to do next. The Brick commander sensing this, told him to go firm and cover down the street to his left. He then ordered the 2ic on the opposite side of the road to go forward, and join Richard on the right hand side of the junction. Once he was in position, he was to cover down the road to the right. As soon as they were in position, he and Ron jogged across the road on their respective sides and went firm on the other side of the junction. They faced outwards, down the road, covering the same areas as Richard and the 2ic. Martin gave the nod for Richard and Hesh to cross the road, which they did, at a jog. On the far side of the junction and passing the two kneeling figures of Ron and Martin, Hesh and Richard continued the patrol. As they moved up the road, they were followed behind, closely, by Wacker and the rest of the Troop. The Troop had been asked to observe and note any mistakes, or find any way the patrolling could be better. Finally, the team reached the far end of the road, when it came to a T-Junction, Wacker called an end to it and gathered the Troop together. He asked them how they thought it had gone. The consensus of opinion was that it had gone pretty well, in the main. Wacker agreed with them, although he criticised them for too much chat, advising they could have used hand signals. This, however, would come with practice, in the many hours ahead of them, before they got to 'Tin City.' Although the patrol had only walked the distance of approximately 500 metres, Richard thought how tiring it must be to be to concentrate, for a full length patrol. These could last a couple of hours at least, in all weather conditions, and with the addition of carrying a lot of equipment, could prove taxing. The Troop practiced a Brick at a time, for the rest of the day, and were critiqued, at the end, by the remainder. It had gone quite well, for the first time and, by the end of the day, they were sent away feeling positive.

The whole week was dedicated to patrol skills, both on foot and mobile in Land Rovers. The drills were getting much slicker, and the need for voice commands or even hand signals was at a minimum now. Most mornings started either with a PT session in the gym or a run. The intensity of the gym sessions, and length of the runs was increased over time. The building up of stamina was essential, to enable them to function properly, when patrolling for a number of hours. Not only that but, if they were unlucky enough to be 'contacted' by a terrorist gunman, their fitness would be tested. These situations required dynamic and robust responses, and, at times, over great distances. This was to become apparent in the next week, when they would move on to contact drills. But, on this day they were going to learn about IED's, a major threat in the Province. Their Instructor for this lesson was a bloke from the Royal Army Ordnance Corps, called 'Dusty'. He was an Ammunition Technical Officer (ATO), his call sign 'Felix' was one that was well known throughout Northern Ireland. He had completed six tours of the Province, in all the major hotspots. He had dealt with almost every type of IED in rural and urban settings. He began the lesson which was attended by the whole Squadron, by defining what an IED was.

An improvised explosive device (IED) is a bomb constructed and deployed in ways other than in conventional military action. It may be constructed of conventional military explosives, such as an artillery round, attached to a detonating mechanism. IEDs are commonly used as roadside bombs. (Wikipedia)

They came in many guises and could take the shape of a car bomb, culvert, beer barrel, milk churn, rocket propelled or mortar. They were initiated or triggered by means of command wire, radio or phone signal, or victim operated. The Provisional IRA used these methods from 1969 to the present day and were very proficient. They had become highly sophisticated, featuring anti-handling devices such as a mercury tilt switch or microswitches. These devices would detonate the bomb, if it was moved in any way. Typically, the safety-arming device used was a clockwork timer, which armed the bomb up to 60 minutes after it was placed, by completing an electrical circuit supplying power to the anti-handling device. Depending on the particular design (e.g., booby-trapped briefcase or car bomb), an independent electrical circuit supplied power to a conventional timer, set for the intended time delay. However, some electronic delays developed by IRA technicians could be set to accurately detonate a bomb weeks after it was hidden, which what is what happened, in the Brighton hotel bomb attack just the year before. As Dusty went through the various type of detonation or initiation devices the terrorist used, he picked up a radio transmitter and depressed the button. To Richard's right one of the Squadron leapt out of his seat with a loud yelp. His chair had been rigged with a battery and receiver, and when it received the signal from the initiator, it sent an electric impulse through the chair, much to the amusement of the rest of the Squadron. That part of the lesson complete, Dusty dismissed the Troops for a ten minute smoke break.

As soon as the Squadron had finished its smoke break, it returned to the classroom, the men filed in to receive the rest of the IED package from Dusty. Taking their seats once again, they settled down, waiting for Dusty to begin. The ATO waited patiently for the last few remaining stragglers to get to their seats and, just as he was about to start an enormous bang reverberated round the room. One of the NCOs from SHQ Troop leapt from his chair, looking around the room, in disbelief, as smoke drifted from his chair across the room.

'That, gents, is why we always check the immediate vicinity where we are, for any suspicious wires or disturbances to the ground.' Dusty smiled, as he indicated the small pad protruding wires, which had been placed on the seat. In the dimness of the room, it was difficult to see it but, once pressure was applied to the pad, it completed a circuit and initiated the small charge that had been put under the seat. This was a sobering lesson, and led nicely into the topic for the afternoon, which was searches, both personal area and vehicle. Going through the basic drills on the blackboard, Dusty confirmed, with a few questions, that the Troops had grasped what he was saying. They then made their way outside, where a couple of vehicles had been positioned. Each Troop were assigned a vehicle and given the task of searching it for any suspect packages, weapons and the like. Following the drills they had been taught, the Troops swarmed over the vehicles, eager to find any devices or contraband. Each of the teams in the Troop, took a turn and found at least one or more items, ranging from suspect packages, detonators, weapons and suspect cables or wires. Feeling rather pleased with themselves, they beamed at Dusty, but their confidence was about to be shattered, as he retrieved at least three items that none of the teams' members had found. They were located in the most obscure places, and in places no one would have looked. It hammered home the point, that the people they were up against were not stupid, but rather cunning and inventive. The introduction to search techniques concluded, some of the Squadron would be picked to attend specialist search courses. This would enable them to have a fully functional 'Search Team' within the Squadron.

To end the day, they were taken through measures to counteract Remote Command Improvised Explosive Devices (RCIED). Unlike IED's, which were initiated by command wire, these devices were more difficult to locate. To provide the Troops on the ground with some level of protection, they were issued with various types of equipment. These were Electronic Warfare (EW) counter measures against RCIED's. The equipment that a team would carry included the Antler, and White and Brown Snifter. These pieces of equipment transmitted a jamming frequency, and provided a safety umbrella around the team. There are many unknown, uncontrolled variables such as enemy transmitter power, distance between transmitter and receiver, and distance between jammer and RCIED. Therefore, it was impossible to calculate an actual 'Protection Distance'. The only way to effectively defend against this threat was with a barrage type jammer with brute force to jam the receiver from receiving the enemy signal to detonate. The whole subject fascinated Richard, as it had done on his course. The equipment was basically communications equipment which emitted an RF signal. Where the white and brown sifter were quite small an easily portable, the Antler was a different beast. It came on a carrying frame and was a considerable weight. This was normally carried by the junior man in the team. The lessons over for the day, and with no lectures or briefing that evening, Richard decided he would visit Birgit. Since the training had begun, he had only seen her on a couple of occasions. He decided he would buy her a present, so he headed into town before catching his train. There was a shop he knew that sold novelty items, so he popped in for a browse. Immediately he saw the item he would buy. It was a large, yet cute looking gorilla. When he looked at the price, he gulped. It was priced at 100 Deutsch Marks, at that time it was a huge amount of money. Throwing caution to the wind, he handed over the cash, and walked to the station.

Arriving at Birgit's house, he rang the bell and waited. A pair of legs could be seen descending the stairs towards him. Smiling through the glass pane in the middle of the door, Birgit opened it and greeted him with a kiss. Richard then produced the gorilla, from behind his back and it was obvious Birgit instantly loved it. After having the evening meal, Richard and Birgit retired to her room, where they spent the rest of the evening watching taped videos of the comedy show 'The Young Ones'. They talked about the Troubles in Ireland and why the British Army were there. She had become used to Richard being away on exercise, but this would be the first time he would be in harm's way. He tried to dispel any misgivings she had, but knew she did not believe his rhetoric. At the end of the evening, she drove him back to camp. They would not see each other again, until after he had finished the training in Tin City.

The training had started to get more intense, and that morning they were being briefed for a Troop multiple patrol. The Troop Leader went through every detail, with a fine tooth comb, assigning routes to each of the teams. There would be two mobile patrols and four on foot, the scenario given was that there had been tensions overnight, in a particular part of their area. The Squadron had made the accommodation block into a sort of Security Force Base. This was to replicate how they would work in the Province. There were sand pits with sandbags for loading and unloading. A simulated gate had also been erected, where they would exit and return through. Just as the Troop Leader was about to finish, they were interrupted by the sound of a siren. This indicated to everyone that they were under a mortar attack. Members of NITAT were strolling around the block monitoring the Squadron's reactions. The Troops immediate action drill was to take cover, and this they did, instinctively. The Troop providing security for the 'Fort' for that day, would be scanning the area with binoculars for the Mortar Baseplate firing point. Once this had been identified, the Quick Reaction Force (QRF) were crashed out to secure the area. As soon as the QRF had reached the firing point and cordoned it off, the Directing Staff called an end to the scenario, and the QRF withdrew back into the fort.

The excitement over with for the moment, the Troop Leader called the Troop together to ensure they all understood the orders. Everyone nodded their heads in agreement. The team leaders took away their Bricks and did a quick equipment check. All pouches were checked to ensure they were secure, all ECM equipment was turned on and checked they were working. The final thing was they dressed to the loading bays and the team leaders, with a command of.

'With a magazine of twenty rounds…load!' The men were supervised loading their weapons. Once they had completed the loading drill, they dressed away for the next team to do the same. Once everyone was ready, the mobile patrol mounted up and departed the gates. One by one, each of the teams 'hard targeted' out of the base. This was a method of sprinting the first fifty yards or so, in a zig zag motion, to try and make as difficult a target as possible for any waiting gunman. Richard's heartbeat increased as he bomb-burst out of the gates, until he was clear of the so called danger area, when he slowed down into a brisk walk. The adrenalin rush he got from being point man and first out of the gates was massive. In only three weeks' time he would be doing it for real, and could only imagine it would create a more heightened rush of adrenalin. The patrols were soon all under way, and everything seemed quiet. They moved now in a very professional manner, no words of command spoken, minimal hand signals, everyone now knew what their responsibilities were. In the air, they could hear the sound of a Gazelle helicopter. Then, without warning, Richard's team leader Martin put up his hand, for them to stop. He was listening intently to the earpiece in his right ear. After a few moments, he shouted out.

'The chopper has spotted a command wire leading to some barrels, possible IED. It's by the side of the road in a hedge. We have been tasked to move in to investigate!' With that, he pointed, to Richard, the direction they were going to take. The team knew exactly from the description Martin had given where the possible IED was located. They stepped off with a sense of urgency, but still ensuring they checked for any threats from around them. It took only ten minutes before they arrived in the area where the command wire and suspect IED had been spotted. Checking the map, they began to draw a 200 metre cordon round the area. Taping off any entry into the area with white mine tape, Martin looked for a suitable location for the Incident Control Point (ICP). On the map, was a building just outside the cordon area, he knew this was unused and would be perfect for the purpose. Letting the Troop know of his intentions, they moved towards it. The team 2ic moved into the building, to begin setting up communications, as he disappeared through the door frame, a loud explosion rang out. Smoke drifted across the street and Richard knew at once what had happened. This was a common tactic of the terrorist to draw Troops into an area, and focus their attention in one spot. Once they were where they wanted them, they would initiate another device in a location the soldiers would possibly use. This had been the case, unfortunately, and Richard's team had fallen for it. It didn't matter how much they practiced, complacency was their biggest enemy. Richard went to rush into the building, but was stopped by Martin, warning him to check, for any other devices. In the meantime, he got on to the radio and gave a contact report. The teams that were acting as satellites were beginning to converge on their position. The Directing Staff (DS) had told Martin that Hesh had initiated an IED by stepping on a pressure pad as he entered the building. He was 'Very Seriously Injured (VSI), and would require 'Casualty Evacuation (CASEVAC). Martin relayed this back to SHQ in the fort, who dispatched an armoured ambulance, to extract him from the scene. Checking the door frame for any further booby traps, Richard dragged Hesh from the building. Once he was clear, he began to assess his injuries, and was told by the DS that he had sustained severe damage to his upper right femur and was bleeding badly. Richard ripped the field dressing from Hesh's webbing, and applied direct pressure to the wound. Once he had stemmed the flow, he wound it round his thigh, talking all the time to reassure him. One of the teams nearest to them arrived and the Team leader was briefed by Martin. The ambulance had arrived and Richard and Ron carried Hesh to it. Once he was made comfortable, the rest of the team were invited to climb inside. With only three men, they were not effective on the ground. Martin handed over to the other team, and the ambulance started to make its way back to the base. They were only two minutes away, when they heard the unmistakeable sound of automatic machine gun fire. The traffic on the air erupted, as the team who was making its way to the cordon area came under machine gun fire from a building. SHQ sent the mobile patrols to cut off any routes of escape, the team in contact returned fire in the direction of the firing position. By the time the ambulance had reached the base and unloaded the casualty, and Richard's team had unloaded, the situation was well under control. After an hour or so, the other patrols returned to base for a debrief. During this, the NITAT instructors went through exactly what had happened. It was a common mistake made by Troops in Northern Ireland to get sucked into an area, where the IRA would detonate an IED, or set up a shooting. Their enemy had an active program of observing. They deliberately staged hoaxes, in order to analyse the behaviour of the police and the security forces, timing them, filming them, and discovering the security forces' methods. Secondly, after an incident or an attack, the IRA would carefully analyse it. They conducted a rather careful and detailed post attack analysis and investigation. 'What worked? What failed? That is what they would be doing now, so that they could tailor their next attack, to make it even more successful. The morning had taught the Squadron valuable lessons, and mistakes made hopefully would not be repeated.

To ensure that if, or when they came under attack they could return fire as effectively as possible in all situations, the training was underpinned by many hours spent on the ranges. Their initial visit was for the purpose of zeroing their weapons. The definition of zeroing is finding a target's true centre of mass. To aim at dead centre, they had to ensure their round would go there. Some rifles are off to the left or right, or can shoot high or low when aimed at the centre of mass Zeroing was done at a range of 100 metres. They would slide their rear sight to the 300m setting, and were given the order to assume the prone supported position, where the support forearm was resting on a sandbag (no sling). The Range conducting officer (RO) would give the order:

'With a magazine of twenty rounds… load!' Checking that everyone had carried out his instruction, he would continue. 'Five rounds grouping, in your own time, go on!' The guys would fire single control shots at the top edge of a white square positioned in the centre of a figure eleven target. This was a full size target, with a picture of a man running forward, complete with helmet and weapon. After everyone had fired their five rounds, the RO would check that everyone had finished, then give the order to 'stop', which meant they applied the safety catch and laid down the rifle. RO would then say `stand up and dress back.' They would then stand and step back from the rifle. The Range Officer would then say `take your weapons', which was the cue to adopt the prone supported position once again. They were to do this, firing five rounds, groups prone supported and getting up between each string, until the twenty round magazine was emptied the. "Getting up between five round strings" means adopting the same position again, despite having moved.

The RO would then unload everyone, go forward and examine the targets. When they went forward to examine the targets, it was obvious whether they could shoot straight - or not. A four inch (extreme spread) group, at 100 yards, was considered adequate to achieve an acceptable 'zero'. Richard had done this and only required a slight adjustment to his weapon, to bring him on centre. They then dressed back and fired a further five rounds as confirmation.

Richard dressed forward after they had been unloaded once again and was pleased to see that he had achieved a three inch group, all except one round, which he had 'snatched', but the instructors disregarded this one. He was told he could dress to the rear of the firing point, chill out and have a brew. It took some of the Squaddies the whole day to zero their weapons and the instructors were pulling their hair out by the end of it.

The zeroing had been the easy bit; they then moved on to targets, presented at 100, 200 and 300 metres. Here, they had to fire shots from the standing, kneeling and prone positions. Richard found this a little more challenging; he had to repeat the shoot twice, before he reached the required amount of hits to pass. He was not the only one. A number of the Squadron were not natural riflemen. One of the instructors took them away, a couple at a time, and went through the marksmanship principles. These were that the Position and Hold must be firm enough to support the weapon. The weapon must point naturally at the target, without any undue physical effort. Sight alignment and the sight picture must be correct. The shot must be released and followed through, without undue disturbance to the position. Richard felt better after this period of instruction and applied the principles on his next attempt. To his surprise, it paid dividends, and he sailed through, only missing five of the sixty rounds fired.

The final week of ranges, before deploying to Tin City, was a mixture of Electronic Target Ranges (ETR), moving targets and night shoots. These were not the only other subjects covered, they were also taught such skills as face recognition and body searching. When it came to body searching, the main obstacle was teaching the guys to search another 'man' properly. The DS made them 'pat him down' properly - he would hide guns or grenades down his pants. If they didn't 'find' the weapons, he would show them how easy it was to disguise the whereabouts of 'large' items. This would not be done in a manner that belittled, but the exercise would be repeated until the DS was confident they could, and would, search properly. Lessons on face recognition ran late into the night. Catch phrases like 'absence of the normal and presence of the abnormal' were repeated over and over again. Mug shots of known terrorists and major players were shown and had to be memorised. Each person was also given a smaller list of people they were, when deployed, to keep an 'extra' lookout for and to report immediately the time, date and location where the person was seen.

However, the Ranges were the main focus of training. The first test they were given was on the ETR range; from a console, targets were controlled, as the name suggested, electronically. There were ten lanes, with a man in each lane. The targets started at 100 metres and moved out to 300. As all the Troops had already passed their weapons test, they could adopt any stance they were comfortable with. Once they had engaged the target up to 300 metres, they would then move back to 100. The guys were told to count their ammunition, so they knew when they would need to change magazines. No extra time would be given for stoppages or mag changes. The targets were exposed for varying amounts of time. After the engagements of up to 300 metres and back again, the targets were popped up at different ranges. It was the guys' job to engage the targets they felt more comfortable with and utilise the ammunition left to them.

Richard really enjoyed the buzz this type of shooting gave him. He had started the range package a little apprehensive and not at all confident, but with the help of the Skill at Arms Instructors, had found it most satisfying. This range finished, they moved on to moving targets. This was done as single person shoots, with the range given up to just one shooter. At the far end of the range was a series of hardboard Hut facings, set at two 100 metres. A running figure eleven target would appear from one side of the range and move in between two huts. The shooter was required to fire at least one round at each exposure between the huts. This was done from left to right and repeated from right to left. The trick was to aim slightly in front of the target, before gently squeezing the trigger and not snatching. Richard's first shot missed as he misjudged the speed of the target. Adjusting his second, he hit dead centre. By the time the target had completed its two runs, he had missed with only two rounds. The end of the week culminated in a single man patrol, across a range set up with a series of obstacles; these could be used to provide cover. As each man in turn traversed across the range from either left to right, or the other way round, he kept his attention down range. Here, various targets would be popped up and the men were expected to react immediately. This could be by firing from the standing, kneeling or adopting the prone position. However, due to the fact that they had been provided with things like small walls, burnt out cars and mounds of earth, it made more sense to use them. Simulated gunfire was also used as an extra bit of realism, and to give a sense of urgency. The Troops trickled through the urban range test throughout the day, and, to a man, everyone agreed it was the best thing they had done on the whole range package.

They spent the last hour of the day cleaning their weapons and picking up brass from the range. The darkness was drawing in as they made the final journey back to camp. On their return, they would have 48 hours' rest before departing for Tin City.

Chapter 35 – Tin City

The Sennelager Training Centre in North Rhine-Westphalia was requisitioned by the British Army at the end of the Second World War. By the mid-1980s, the camp, nicknamed Tin City, was used to recreate a modern, urban, combat situation, establishing the look, sound, feel and tension of various war zones, such as Northern Ireland. It would later be used for training Troops in other conflict areas, such as Kosovo, Iraq, the Falklands and Afghanistan. Makeshift streets of Belfast and Derry were filled with models of supposedly ordinary people, so that each soldier could train to make the instantaneous decision as to whether a target was a gunman or a member of the public. In the recreated streets, cul-de-sacs, houses, pubs, banks and chippies, the soldiers would play split-second guessing games with the flip-up targets, deciding quickly who is innocent and who is a gunman. This was in order to prepare them for the deadly Northern Ireland patrols to come.

The Squadron arrived at Tin City in the middle of winter. There were no leaves on the trees and it was bitterly cold. Surrounding the area were open fields and hedgerows, as far as the eye could see. Richard pondered for a moment, how much this looked like the UK and not at all like Germany. Perhaps this was the reason it was chosen, or maybe just a coincidence? The Troops left the bus and gathered their rucksacks from the hold underneath. They formed up in three ranks, under the direction of the SSM. An NCO stepped forward and introduced himself. Richard saw that he was a member of NITAT and his Regiment was the 'Black Watch'.

'Good morning and welcome,' he said, 'it's going to be a slow start to the day. We just need to settle you into your accommodation and get through a bit of admin'. Then off to their left, a massive explosion broke the winter silence. A plume of smoke rose high into the air and debris rained down. The NCO smiled at their shock, then asked them to follow him into the Security Forces (SF) Compound, which was called 'For Knight'.

After dropping their rucksacks, the men returned, as he had instructed, outside the perimeter, and were taken through an explosives demonstration. The first type of bomb shown was a letter bomb. It was of normal size and the NITAT Instructor explained that these were normally detonated by a photo-sensitive device. A table had been setup outside, which was made of wood. The NCO placed the envelope on the top of the table, ensured they were all at a safe distance and detonated it remotely, simulating it being opened. A massive explosion rang out and the desk was converted into small splinters of wood. The Troops stood, open-eyed at the devastation such as mall device wreaked. They were then shown an even smaller device, in the form of a cigarette packet. The guy from the Black Watch explained to them that they were generally used in department stores or shops. The terrorist would drop them on the ground in a crowded area and they were normally detonated by a timer. This gave the bomber time to make his escape. The fireball produced by the small device was of a considerable size and the onlookers gasped when it was initiated.

The show stopper was a car bomb, which had only four pounds of plastic explosive placed in the boot. When it exploded, the whole vehicle was tipped 180 degrees and ended up on its roof. This was brilliant stuff, thought Richard, although it was also sobering and thought provoking. The demonstrations complete, the men were led back inside the SF base. They were given a ten minute break so that they could have a quick cigarette and a brew. They were shown where the lecture room was and told to be there after the break.

As they entered the darkened room, the eerie sound of 'Clannad' filled the air with the theme from 'Harrys Game', and images of riots, bombings and soldiers on the streets of Northern Ireland were being projected on to the screen at the front of the hall. As the music died down and everyone took their seats, the lights were turned on. The Officer Commanding the NITAT team at Tin City gave his opening address. After he had introduced his team, he went on to say 'We have nothing much planned for today, except to show you a few videos.' The term 'nothing much planned' was to become a well-known phrase during their time there, and one that did not reflect reality. As they would find out, things that happened at Tin City were not always planned. The civilian population or 'Civ Pop' as they were known, was made up of soldiers from Units all over Germany. They had volunteered for the task and put all their efforts into making it as realistic an experience as possible. They worked from a 'Pink', which was a sheet of arranged incidents. This, however, was not always the case, as things happened, depending on the reactions of the Troops.

They were then shown a film on patrolling techniques, and were told that, after lunch, they would go on to the streets and see what 'bad habits' they had picked up. This caused a ripple of laughter around the room. With this, they started a series of films, some taken from in-barracks training of various units, and others were footage from the Province. The pieces had been filmed from different perspectives, one of the Troops on the ground the other from the terrorist's angle. Everything that happened in Tin City was filmed, and this caused a great deal of conversation, people knowing that their fuck ups would be laid bare for all to ridicule. Better to make the mistakes here in a 'safe' training environment, than to make them out on the streets for real, they were told.

After a hurried lunch, the Troops put on their patrol kit and assembled in the car park of the SF base. They were met by a couple of the NITAT staff, who beckoned the Troops to follow them out of the corrugated gate, which was the main exit and way into the base. This was overlooked by a sangar, which faced directly down one street to the front, and a second street, which joined it at angle of 90 degrees, from the right. There was a loading and unloading bay to the right of the gate, but as this was just a walk through/ talk through, they would not be required to load up. Once they had entered the streets, the NITAT staff asked them to gather round. Waiting until everyone had formed a semi-circle round them, they then asked if one of the teams would like to volunteer to show off their patrolling skills. There was a hushed silence, as team leaders tried to avoid the gaze of the DS. As there were no volunteers, which was always the Army way, a team leader was chosen at random. To no-one's surprise it was a young Troop Leader, who was fresh out of Sandhurst. He blushed, visibly, when he was chosen, knowing full well that if he fucked up, he would be having an 'interview without coffee' with the OC. As they did not yet know the layout of the town of Killymurphy, they were first of all given a guided tour by NITAT. It consisted of three main streets, running parallel to each other. These were intersected by three more in a grid type system, typical of the rabbit warrens of the estates in Northern Ireland. The town had its own laundrette, Community Centre, petrol station, church, pub and chippy. Each of these locations would become very familiar to the Troops, over the next week or so. The perambulation around the streets, pointing out the various buildings and street names took only 40 minutes at a slow, leisurely pace. Completing the tour, they returned to the SF base gates, and the team that had been chosen took up their positions, ready to begin the patrol. Under direction of NITAT, they set off down the street, adopting fire positions, as they encountered street junctions. The rest of the Squadron and DS followed, a short distance behind them. As they progressed down the main street, they passed the pub called Murphy's, towards the fort. Reaching the base, one of the NITAT staff walked up to one of the patrol and asked him a question.

'If you were engaged from that window, there,' he said, pointing to a window, which was ajar, the curtains blowing, in the breeze. 'Would you fire back?' The surprised Trooper looked at the instructor, inquisitively, wondering if this a trick question. He was racking his brains on the rules for opening fire. After coming to the decision that, if he was fired upon and it was a serious threat to life, he was allowed to open fire, he answered that, of course he would return fire. Then, the Instructor said, in a sarcastic tone.

'Then, you better put up your rear sight, you fucking muppet,' and with that, he retuned back to the crowd following behind. He had said it loud enough for everyone to hear. This was not to embarrass the lad, although that is what it did. It was to push home an important lesson. The patrol continued until they reached the far end of the town, where they were told to head back and head towards the fort. Once they had reached there, they were fallen out and everyone was invited back inside the lecture room. As soon as everyone had settled down, the screen was filled with a video of the patrol. This had been taken from various angles, from static cameras stationed round the town. Also, one of the NITAT members had been following the patrol, with a mobile video camera, taking close up shots of any mistakes made, the rear sight being one example. The staff then went on to debrief the whole of the Squadron on the good and bad points of the patrol. They pointed out that, at times, the patrol was a little too close together, and more attention to windows was also needed. When taking up fire positions, they also needed to remember to check the immediate area around them, such as doorways. The checking for booby traps and possible fire positions would, in time, become second nature. These videos, although they highlighted many 'fuck ups', proved invaluable as a training aid. The stars of the video were asked to stand up and take a bow, which they did, much to the approval of the rest of the Squadron. They were all dismissed and given the rest of the day and evening to sort out all their administration. They were to be fallen in, outside the base at 08:00 the following morning, for a trip out to the ranges for another demonstration.

The evening had been spent sorting out webbing, being issued the various bits of kit that they would require whilst in Killymurphy. Each man was given twenty rounds of blank ammunition, which would be checked after every patrol, to ensure none had been lost, out on the street. This would be the case for all weapons and equipment. The Squadron relaxed for the evening and paraded the following morning, then boarded the bus, out to the range, which was just ten minutes away. The demonstration this morning was one on firepower. The Troops left the bus on their arrival, and lined up under direction of the NITAT staff. They were taken through a series of stands, which showed the effects of different weapons on different materials. Weapons like the M16, AK47, and M60 American General Purpose Machine Gun (GPMG) capabilities would be demonstrated. These were the type of weapons that they may come up against. It was not just the effect but the different sounds they made that would be useful, when on operations. A member of the Small Arms Training School (SASC), who were stationed in the main camp in Sennelager, would be providing the demonstration. The Squadron gathered round the firing point, where the instructor had a series of weapons laid at his feet. Explaining each one in turn, its magazine capability, range and rate of fire, he asked if there were any questions before continuing. As there were none, he picked up the first weapon, an American M16, a favourite weapon of the IRA. Adopting the prone position, he got himself comfortable. Down range at approximately 100 metres there were arranged various targets. Some were dummies filled with sand, others were brick walls, plates of steel and there was even a pig carcass. He fired a series of aimed shots at each of the different materials and, once his magazine was empty, promptly unloaded, and encouraged the crowd to follow him and observe the effects that the weapon system had produced on the different materials. Walking down the range behind the SASC Instructor, the Squadron were taken to each target or piece of material in turn. The effects to each were, of course, quite different. It was just to show what the weapons could do to a body or, indeed, a wall if a soldier was trying to take cover behind it. This process was repeated for each of the weapons in turn. The American M60 GPMG was a devastating piece of equipment and just about destroyed the wall that had been setup. The pig carcass jiggled about, rapidly, as the rounds slammed into it. Not only were the terrorist weapons demonstrated but also their own. They were shown the results of a Self-Loading Rifle (SLR), which was the British Army standard issue rifle for the Infantry and Troops in Northern Ireland. The high velocity 7.62mm rounds were highly effective, and in the words of the SASC Instructor 'Could take the arm or leg off a man'. He had also brought with him a Barret .50 sniper rifle, taking careful aim at a steel plate that was positioned directly in front of him, he fired one round. The Troops were amazed to see that the round actually carried through the plate and kicked up dirt, behind the target.

'I hope the fuckers over there haven't got one of them,' came the remark from one of the lads from Third Troop. The crowd laughed, but the demonstration had left a lasting impression on them all. The next weapon they were shown, was the M79 Grenade launcher. The Instructor raised the weapon, to an angle of approximately 45 degrees and squeezed the trigger. The weapon recoiled, visibly, and the round left the barrel. It arced towards a target that resembled a house, and entered through an open space, which had been cut out, to replicate a window. An explosion just behind the target, confirmed that, if it had been for real, anything within that building would have been neutralised. The last weapon system they were shown, was one that they would become familiar with during their time in Tin City and across the water. It was the Federal Riot Gun or FRG, also known as a baton gun as it fired baton rounds. These were intended to be bounced off the ground to dissipate its inertia, and were used for riot control. They could also be used to fire tear gas canisters, as another form of riot control.

After the demonstration of all weapons was complete, they were invited to try them out for themselves. There was a mass scramble for the .50 Barrett sniper rifle, as there would not be many times to grab a chance to fire one of these 'bad boys'. In the time allocated, Richard managed to get to fire all the weapons, except the sniper rifle, which he was most pissed off about. The last thing they did was a little bit of fun. A set of targets representing a riot crowd had been setup, about twenty metres away. The winner would be the one who could knock the most heads off, using the FRG. There was a limited number of baton rounds, so two people from each Troop were chosen to take part. Ron from Richard's team was one picked, to represent them. They were given five rounds each and were asked to fire in pairs. At the end of the competition, the targets had been decimated, but it was agreed that Ron, with three decapitations, would be declared the winner. His keen marksman skills would serve the team well, especially during the next few days.

The Squadron returned to Tin City on the buses and were ushered into the lecture room, once more, where they were told they were now 'live'. The civilian population had arrived and started to occupy the houses within the town. They had already been briefed by the NITAT staff and 'players' had been assigned their identities and given their 'pinks' to follow. The OC of NITAT gave the Squadron a full intelligence brief, of what had been happening in the town of Killymurphy and the surrounding areas. Montages of known Active Service Unit (ASU) members and known associates were distributed. The 'montages' were an A4 set of photographs, which everyone was advised to memorise, along with their names and addresses. He, then, handed over to the Squadron OC to give his orders, while he and the NITAT members left the room. The responsibilities of patrolling, both in the town and the surrounding countryside were divided up, among the Troops. The manning of the sangar and base security, was another task, which had to be undertaken. These were all rotated on a daily basis, so that everyone got a fair share of the training. Richard's Troop had pulled the short straw and were first to provide security for the fort. Straight after the brief the Troop Sergeant drew up a stag list for the sangar and the gate sentry. There was only one sangar which overlooked the town that was manned. The other two were covered by security cameras run from the Operations Room (Ops Room).

After the evening meal, Richard gathered his webbing, flak jacket and weapon and walked out of the room, to the area around the loading bay. Here, he was met by Hesh, who would be carrying out the duties of posting NCO, for the first eight hours. He waited until they had been joined by John, another member of the Troop, who would be on gate sentry for the first hour. They had decided to do just one hour, instead of the normal two hour stag, because of the biting cold temperatures. Once a man became cold, it was difficult to maintain focus and concentration. Hesh loaded both the guys up and Richard made his way to the staircase, which led up to the sangar. Once inside, Hesh went through all the equipment that was there. This ranged from binoculars, night sight, log books, GPMG and 200 rounds of ammunition, torches and communications, both radio and landline telephone. Panoramic photographs of the area outside, and possible mortar base plate positions were distributed throughout the sangar. Hesh read through Richard's orders, and confirmed his arcs of fire and observation. After making sure he was happy, Hesh left, to return to the warmth of the Ops room. Richard settled into his stag. Picking up the night sight, he turned it on and confirmed it was working properly. Looking through it produced an eerie green picture of the streets outside the fort. There were only a couple of people moving around, as it was still early evening. Over the next hour, he noted down anything he saw, that he deemed may be of a suspicious nature, in the log book provided. Every 30 minutes the Ops Room would come up on the air, confirming they were still in contact. Before long, Richard was alerted to the sound of footsteps, coming up the stairwell. It was Hesh, with his relief. He had been so engrossed with looking outwards, that he hadn't noticed the next two guys being loaded up, in the loading bay. He did a quick hand over, reporting that nothing out of the ordinary was going on and left with Hesh. After being unloaded with the gate sentry, the pair of them headed off to the accommodation, to get their heads down.

Richard was asleep as soon as his head hit the pillow. All the fresh air had taken its toll on him. He was rudely wakened by the sound of a burst of automatic fire, from the rear wall of the base, outside the town. An alarm sounded and everyone was hurriedly putting on their webbing and grabbing their weapons. Crashing out through the door, people were assembling in the vehicle park.   Two snatch Land Rovers were screeching out of the gates. They were the QRF and had been launched literally two minutes after the firing had stopped. Richard could hear the panic going on, over the air, the Ops room were screaming out for situation reports (sitreps). From the moment the firing had started, until the QRF returned, was only 40 minutes. The next morning, they were shown a video of the incident and learned exactly what had happened. A brown Ford Cortina had driven past the outside of the fort, on the road that came from the next town. A masked gunman had leaned out of the car and fired a burst of around eight rounds into the unmanned sangar on the outside wall. They had sped off down the road and turned left, into the town. This had all been observed by the Ops room, whose reaction was instantaneous. The

QRF had been crashed out, with a description of the car and the direction it was taking. The Cortina had been intercepted, just by the BP petrol station, where it had been searched and the occupants questioned. Although they were known players, no weapons or anything suspicious were found in the vehicle, or on them. They were released and the QRF had returned to the base. The Squadron was then shown a series of footage, filmed by NITAT, of the gunmen. After firing at the sangar, they had picked up the empty cases and hidden them, inside the vehicle. Entering Killymurphy, they had dumped the weapon, in a dustbin, in a garden. They had then gone to the petrol station to fill up, where they were caught. However, after being stopped and searched, they were released. The video zoomed in and showed the 7.62mm empty cases under the driver's seat. The look of recrimination from the Troop Leader, who had provided the QRF, was evident. The DS pointed out slackness like this was why they were here to learn. No-one got it right first time. With this ringing in their ears, the Troops left the lecture theatre, for an early breakfast.

The food finished, the Troop Leader and team leaders went to the Ops room, for their patrol brief. They were given the details of the suspected shooters from that morning, and asked to keep an eye out for them, and others on their watch list. It was to be a routine patrol, just familiarisation of the area. After leaving the Ops room, the Troop leader called the rest of the Troop together, and gave his orders. Three teams would deploy as a multiple with two teams providing QRF. The Troop Leader's team would take the centre road, so that he could control the movement better, while the other two teams would take the roads on either side of this. He answered any questions that were forthcoming and ordered them to be ready to move in five minutes. The guys began checking each other over, to ensure they had all equipment and that everything was secure and all communications were working correctly. They then, one team at a time, loaded up in the loading bay. When they were ready, they gave the nod to the gate sentry, who opened the gate and, a team at a time, they hard targeted out of the base. As soon as they were far enough away, they moved into their patrol formations, and began the slow movement down the routes given. The team leaders checking in with the Troop Leader every couple of minutes or so, giving him updates of their location and progress.

Richard had taken up a position on the corner of a street, looking down it, for any suspicious activity. Deciding it was clear, he looked back at Martin and nodded that it was okay to move on. The team carried on, in staggered formation, on both sides of the road. Something did not feel right. Richard noticed the suspicious looks of some of the people on the street. They appeared to be waiting for something to happen. Out of his peripheral vision, Richard noticed a movement of a curtain, in one swift movement, he swung round and dropped to the kneeling position. Just as he did so a bright, orange muzzle flash erupted from behind the curtain. Richard immediately returned two rounds into the open window. As he did so, he cringed. Had he done the right thing? All hell broke loose and Martin was straight on his presell.

'Contact wait out!' he screamed. He then shouted at Richard, asking what he had seen. Richard took a deep breath and indicated with his barrel, that shots had been fired from the open window. He could not confirm that he had seen the gunman. While the team covered the house, the remaining two Bricks were racing, to try and cut off any escape for the gunman. Once they were in place, a message came over the air, for the men to check out the house. From what they understood, it was supposed to be empty. Martin sent Richard forward. As soon as he was in position, by the door, he ran across the road to join him, hammering on the door as he arrived. Hesh and Ron covered the houses on the opposite side of the street, in case of a secondary attack. After two minutes, the door opened and there stood an individual, trying to look as nonchalant as he could.

'Could I ask what you are doing here?' Martin asked in a matter of fact way. 'We were led to believe that this property was unoccupied.' The guy didn't flinch, he merely pointed over his shoulder to another bloke, who stated that he was an estate agent, showing the first man round. Checking his identity over the radio, it came to light that he was a known member of a local Active Service Unit ASU. Martin called the Troop Leader forward and said that he would require a search team, to go over the house. He also got on the air, for a Police patrol to attend and arrest the pair of possible gunmen. The drama was played out over the next hour or so, until they were ordered to return to the base.

On their return, and after going through the mandatory unloading drills and checking of equipment, they filed into the lecture room, for the debrief. Richard was running the exercise and patrol brief through his head, and the rules of engagement. The wait was agonising, as the NITAT staff entered the room, Richard just stared at the ground, not wanting to make eye contact. The video of the incident was played back, on the screen, at the front of the room. They were all shocked how quickly the team had reacted to the contact, all moving in unison, like a well-oiled machine. The gunman had only appeared for a split second, but the video evidence proved that Richard had been correct to open fire. Martin and the rest of the team nodded their approval at Richard, and the DS praised him on his alertness, aggressive and robust actions. They were informed that the search team had turned the house upside down, and had retrieved an M16 rifle. The pair had been arrested and taken away for questioning. Capturing them, they were told, was not supposed to have happened, as the ASU had been told to make their escape, through the back of the property. However, due to the quick reactions of the teams on the ground, their escape had been cut off. The whole Troop, feeling pleased with themselves, left the lecture room and made their way back to the accommodation, to get their heads down.

Over the next few days, the incidents and scenarios got more complex, as the DS started to ramp up the pressure on the Squadron. Lack of sleep was a big factor, and small mistakes were starting to creep in. One patrol had over reacted, when a yob had pushed one of them, on a routine patrol. Their aggression towards him, had caused unrest in the town, and things were getting ugly. It was under these circumstances, that the Squadron were briefed that there was to be a pub visit that night, to lift one of the ASU commanders. The room was full of tension, as everyone started to put on their webbing and body armour. They had been briefed that it would be multiple patrol, with two mobile elements and four foot patrols. One of the foot patrols would enter Murphy's pub, and, if the ASU commander was there, they would extract him. The arrest was to be in support of the local police, who would make the actual arrest. Richard's team would be providing cover, outside the pub, and had instructions that they would enter, only if things got out of hand. The mobile patrol left the base, with a screech of tyres. They would do a circuit of the town, and report back the situation before the foot patrols left. In the meantime, the foot patrols loaded up and received their last minute orders. All radio communications were checked and Electronic Counter Measures were turned on. Finally, after a ten minute wait, they were given the all clear, to leave the fort. One by one, each Brick sprinted out from the base, and along their designated patrol routes. Richard's team followed on, behind the team that were going to be entering the pub. There was a strange atmosphere on the streets, they seemed unusually busy. This was not the norm, and that started alarm bells ringing. As they turned right, onto the main high street, the sound of Republican songs could be heard, coming from Murphy's bar. The local Police had arrived and were awaiting the arrival of the team that would escort them into the pub. Martin put up his hand, to indicate that the Brick was to go firm and cover the entry of the team, into the pub. This they did, ensuring they covered both ends of the street and all windows on both sides. Once the entry team were in position, they escorted the Police into the bar. Although he could not see what was happening, Richard heard the music stop, instantly. An eerie silence spread along the streets, darkness had fallen and it was all very tense.

Suddenly, the lights in the pub were extinguished. A split second later, the sound of an FRG riot gun was heard. The lights, miraculously, came back on. Within two minutes, a commotion was heard in the pub and a body was being dragged out by the uniformed police. Their withdrawal was being covered by the team that had gone in. As soon as the Police and extraction team had exited the bar, the whole Troop started its tactical withdrawal, towards the base. They were followed by a large, angry crowd that had spilled out of the bar. Their anger was evident and they pursued the patrols all the way back to the base, throwing anything they could find as missiles at them. The Troop used the mobile patrol vehicles as a barrier between them and the crowd. The unrest was to last for the next few hours, but this was just the prelude to what was to come their following, and last day, in Tin City.

It had been a restless night for the Troops, as disturbances in the town went on into the early hours. At breakfast, the talk was about a possible large scale riot, after the arrest of the ASU commander, the evening before. It was only 07:30 and some of the patrols had reported people milling about on the street already. Cars had been hijacked and set on fire, on the street that lead up to the fort.

Youths had been seen, gathering anything they could lay their hands on that may be used as a projectile. At 08:30, the Squadron was called in to the main lecture hall, for an intelligence briefing, by NITAT. It was revealed that the rumours they had heard were correct. It looked like they were in for a major riot that day. This came as no surprise to the guys who had been deployed to Northern Ireland before. The training in Tin City almost always culminated in them being tested on their crowd control techniques. Richard was starting to feel a little apprehensive. Although, they had practiced riot control in the barracks, he had the feeling this would be more intense. As soon as the briefing had finished, and tasks assigned to the various Troops, they exited the lecture room. The Troop who had been assigned the role of base security, were not well pleased. After all the training, they would be relegated to manning the sangar and gate, only providing backup, if required. The remaining teams went to the SQMS stores and withdrew their riot kit. This included six feet Macrolon shields, helmets and visors, batons and smaller shields. One man from every team was issued with five rounds of baton gun (FRG) ammunition. This was given to Ron in Richard's team, as he had proven himself to be the best shot. Martin gathered his team together, to give them a last few words of wisdom. They would be forming part of the 'snatch squad', which would make any arrests if required to do so.

The adrenalin started to pump through Richard's body, as the Troops started to take up their positions, behind the 'Pig' armoured vehicle, which would be their cover, on deploying from the base. The gate sentry threw open the gate. The vehicle moved forward, with the Troops tagging on behind it. As soon as it was clear of the fort, the guys carrying the six feet shields, took up the positions on the left and right of it, forming a baseline. Behind them, the snatch teams, with their small, circular shields, inched forward. Along the baseline, two, armed with FRG's, stood ready to open up, if required. Bringing up the rear was a Land Rover, with the SSM and some of SHQ, who would act as the arresting cell, and would 'plasti cuff' and detain anyone brought back, by the snatch teams. One of the blokes from SHQ also stood by with a fire extinguisher in his hand. He was known as the 'fireman' and he was to assist, in the unfortunate event that someone should catch fire, and make sure the flames were put out, as soon as possible. They had only moved twenty yards down the street, when the missiles rained down on them, relentlessly. Some of the Troops, who were providing sniper cover, and were not as well protected as the rest, and were receiving casualties. These were limping back or being helped by other members of the Squadron to receive medical treatment. The baseline and snatch squads slowly advanced forward, like an unstoppable machine. It resembled a scene from the film *300 Spartans*, as they stepped over the debris of broken bottles and masonry, which littered the road. The baseline was, at this point, receiving a severe battering, as some of the crowd charged them, trying to disrupt their rhythm and advance. The baseline commander, situated at the rear of the Pig co-ordinating the move, gave instructions, that on the next charge, they would part the shields. The crowd rushed at them again, and, on his order, the shields opened and some of the attackers were dragged through. The snatch squads wasted no time in subduing them, by the use of 'minimum force'. They were then pulled to the rear, to be dealt with the SSM and his team. Once they had been processed, they were handed over to the Police, to be deal with.

As they continued down the street, a ball off flame engulfed a car, blocking the road. The black smoke drifted across the road, in front of the baseline, obscuring the crowd. Suddenly, there was heard sound of glass breaking. Flames engulfed the front shields of the baseline. The baseline commander ordered them to keep their shields touching the ground. Just as he said this, another petrol bomb exploded, on Richard's side of the line. He watched in horror, as one of the guys holding the shield, was engulfed in flames. He called the attention of the fireman, who had already started to make his way to the victim, rolling on the floor, in agony. Within seconds, he had been enveloped in a cloud of vapour, from the extinguisher. With the flames out, he was dragged back to the rear and given medical attention. The unfortunate soldier, known for his bright, red hair, had the obvious nickname Ginge. He was awarded another, after that day. From then on, he was forever known as 'Singe'. His story would be told for many years. There was no time to reflect on what just happened. Richard was alerted by Martin, shouting in his ear.

'Standby, lads, the FRG's are going to let rip. They have been given possible ring leaders as targets. Once they have fired, I want you to follow me. We grab any fucker, who has gone down. Are you ready?'

He paused, waiting for the team to acknowledge him, with a nod of their heads. Richard's heart beat faster, as he waited for the sound of the FRG's opening up, from the baseline. The shields parted, to allow the snatch teams to move forward. Martin led them, with Ron to his right, carrying the FRG. They carried on, till they came to someone rolling about, on the ground. Going three paces past him, they adopted a protective stance, while Hesh and Richard grabbed him under the arms, dragging him, unceremoniously, backward, towards the baseline. Ron and Martin stepped back, not taking their eyes off the crowd, until the shields opened and they were back behind the relative safety of the shields. The carnage went on for the next hour, before a loudhailer sounded, with those immortal words 'Endex, Endex, Endex'.

When they returned to the fort, Richard was still pumping with adrenalin, he had never been so scared in all his life. He did not have time to dwell on this, as they were all ushered into the lecture hall, for the final debrief. The wash up lasted a good 45 minutes, but they were told at the end of it that they had achieved the standard required for those who deployed to the Province. It was not until they had handed back all equipment, cleaned the accommodation, handed it back and were settling into their seats on the bus, that Richard fell fast asleep, exhausted.

Chapter 36 First tour of Northern Ireland and The Troubles

The Troubles refers to a violent thirty-year conflict framed by a civil rights march in Londonderry on 5 October 1968 and the Good Friday Agreement on 10 April 1998. At the heart of the conflict lay the constitutional status of Northern Ireland.

The goal of the unionist and overwhelmingly Protestant majority was to remain part of the United Kingdom. The goal of the nationalist and republican, almost exclusively Catholic, minority was to become part of the Republic of Ireland.

This was a territorial conflict, not a religious one. At its heart lay two mutually exclusive visions of national identity and national belonging. The principal difference between 1968 and 1998 is that the people and organisations pursuing these rival futures eventually resolved to do so through peaceful and democratic means. This ascendancy of politics over violence was not easily achieved.

During the Troubles, the scale of the killings perpetrated by all sides - republican and loyalist paramilitaries and the security forces - eventually exceeded 3,600. As many as 50,000 people were physically maimed or injured, with countless others psychologically damaged by the conflict, a legacy that continues to shape the post-1998 period

In 1968, the Northern Ireland parliament had been dominated by unionists for over fifty years. Its attempts to solve social and political ills, such as institutional discrimination against Catholics, were too slow for nationalists and republicans and too quick for many unionists. This gave rise to growing tension and violence between the two communities.

The mounting scale of the disorder led successive UK governments to intervene. In 1969, the situation was so grave that British Troops were sent to help restore order. By 1972, things had deteriorated so badly that the British government suspended the Northern Ireland parliament and imposed direct rule from London.

At this time, the Provisional Irish Republican Army (PIRA) - the main republican paramilitary organisation in Northern Ireland - was uninterested in any solution short of British withdrawal and Irish unification. The 'Provisionals' had split from the 'Official IRA' in 1969 and are subsequently referred to here as the IRA.

For them, the 'long war' was the only option. This strategy had been gaining traction since the introduction of internment (imprisonment without trial) in 1971 and the killing of 13 people by the Parachute Regiment on Bloody Sunday the following year.

When secret talks with the UK government in 1972 collapsed, the IRA leadership resolved to erode the British presence in Northern Ireland through a war of attrition.

For their part, the major loyalist paramilitary organisations of the Ulster Defence Association (UDA) and the Ulster Volunteer Force (UVF) had resolved to use violence to resist republican paramilitaries and to oppose Irish unification.

It was against this backdrop of soaring violence and increasingly entrenched positions that moves to find a lasting solution began.

(BBC History Archives)

The training over, the only thing left to do, was to pack up their personal belongings. Any items of equipment, or personal belongings that were not going to be taken, were put into wooden boxes and stored in the Squadron cellar. Everyone had been advised to take out Army Life Insurance, which was a sobering thought. The fact that one, or more, of them might not return, was enough to get even the most experienced of them, to consider their own mortality. Richard had spent as much time as possible with Birgit, since returning from Tin City. He had, once again, tried to dispel any concerns she may have had, about the problems he would encounter over the water. They had said their goodbyes, and would not see each other, until he returned on rest and recuperation (R&R). This would only be for a few days, but he was sure it would be a welcome break. The length of the tour was only to be four months, this was shorter than the six month tours that were normal for Northern Ireland and other operational tours. As he packed the last of his belongings into the box, and screwed down the lid, he thought about his father, and the many times he had talked about his tours in Northern Ireland. Tommy had made it sound so exciting, yet Richard did not feel that excitement, only apprehension. Maybe, when he had got an operational tour under his belt, he would feel more relaxed. Birgit's father had given him a copper figure of a naked lady, just like the statue of the mermaid in Copenhagen harbour. It was meant as a talisman, and Richard made sure he placed it in the left hand breast pocket of his combat smock. His packing complete, he helped Ron screw down the lid to his box. Taking hold of each end, the two roommates carried their boxes, down to the cellar, where they would be stored, until their return in four months' time. The final thing they needed to do, was to ensure that they packed their Bergen's and hand luggage. They were to gather at the Movement Control Checkpoint (MCCP) at 08:00. They were the main body of the Squadron, as the Pre-Advance and Advance parties had already departed, some days ago. They would have taken over the accommodation and equipment, and it should be just a simple case of moving in.

The two friends waddled their way, under the weight of their burdens, into the hangar that was being used for the MCCP. It was being run, as always, by a couple of Royal Corps of Transport (RCT) men, supervised by a Warrant Officer. As they entered the hangar, they were told to put down their luggage, in the area indicated. Their weapons were to be handed over to an NCO, who had been assigned to transport them, to the airport, and to ensure they were loaded safely on to the plane. Before the luggage was loaded, they were asked to fill out a mountain of what seemed like meaningless paperwork, including Next of Kin (NOK) forms and certificates to say that their luggage was free from explosives. A number of the Squadron were selected to have a random bag search, to ensure they had complied with the statement they had just signed. Within an hour, they were climbing aboard the bus for the two hour journey to the airport. This process had become old hat to Richard, although it was the first time he was flying into a conflict zone. As the bus made its way to the airport, and their onward journey to Belfast, Richard cast his mind back to four years ago. He remembered the words he had spoken to himself, when the four friends had said their goodbyes, outside his house in Germany. 'Would I ever feel this same bond to others, as I do now, with these three?' As he looked around at his comrades on the bus, heading off into the unknown, he felt that same bond of friendship, knowing that each one of them would risk their lives to protect his, if the situation arose. The hardships and adversity they had shared, not only during the training for the tour, but the experiences they had endured in their short careers, cemented a special relationship that would last a lifetime.

The sound of the wheels screeching, as they struck the tarmac at Aldergrove airport, north of Belfast, woke Richard from his slumber. His stomach was turning, as the 'fasten seat belt' signs were extinguished. When they were given the order, the Troops collected their hand luggage, from the overhead racks and exited the plane, under the direction of the cabin staff, from the RAF. 'That must be a fucking, boring, repetitive job,' Richard contemplated, as he smiled at the girl pointing to the exit and the stairs off the VC10 aircraft. The brisk walk across the apron, towards the arrivals and baggage door, with the wind cutting into him, heightened Richard's senses. He looked around at the high ground to the south and west of the airport. It seemed such a peaceful, tranquil scene, which seemed to belie the hate and anguish, harboured among its inhabitants. The Troops were ushered straight through the arrivals lounge, and out a private door, where four Bedford trucks were waiting with their tailgates down. There was no need for the new arrivals to wait for their baggage, which would be unloaded and transported after them. They climbed aboard the waiting trucks, the last to mount up were two of the advance party guys, who were armed with SLRs and fully loaded magazines. They would be riding shotgun and took up their positions at the rear of the vehicle, looking outwards. The trucks set off in convoy, with a good distance between them. They headed east along the A57 in the direction of Templepatrick. It took only fifteen minutes, before they had reached the M2, which was the main artery into Belfast. As they entered the outskirts of Belfast from the north, the mood within the truck grew more sombre. The two guys providing protection at the rear, became visibly more alert, scanning the area for possible threats. It took them at least twenty minutes to transit through Belfast on the M2, which then turned into the A12 and M1, with the notorious Falls Road and Milltown Cemetery to their right. Leaving Belfast, the mood lightened slightly, as they continued south, then leaving the M1 and heading towards Lisburn. They circumnavigated the small town, where the British Army Headquarters were located, and took the A3 onto the Moira Road. After a mile or so, the trucks started to slow and swung to the right, then stopped. After a few short moments, the trucks were entering HMP Maze Prison, passing a sign saying Tally Lodge. This was the main reception area for all vehicles entering the facility. Turning left and travelling for about 200 metres, the trucks came to a stop. The sound of the tailgates being slung open, alerted the Troops that it was time to get off and, taking their hand luggage, they assembled in three ranks. They were met by the SSM and the OC, who welcomed them to HMP Maze. They were taken into the cookhouse, which was directly opposite what Richard assumed to be the small accommodation huts. They, obediently, followed on, behind the SSM, into the cookhouse and were asked to take seats where they could. There followed a quick introduction to the camp, using a map, which had been set up at the front, for that purpose. The introduction was to last around an hour, after which they assembled again, outside, where the baggage and weapons trucks had arrived. Forming a human chain, they unloaded the trucks, in no time at all. After identifying their own luggage and weapons, they were escorted to their Troop accommodation, by the pre-advance and advanced parties, who were now assembled, to greet them. Martin was one of the members of the Troop, who had flown over early, and he gathered all those from his Troop, and took them into their designated hut. It was divided into small compartments, with two to four men in each. There were a number of rooms allocated for Team Leaders and Team 2ic's. Richard picked a bed space he thought looked comfortable enough, in the cramped space provided. Throwing his Bergen and webbing on the bed, he turned, to see that Ron had chosen the bed next to him.

'Welcome to home for the next four months,' he joked.

'Just like the Ritz, mate. Wonder if we get room service and chamber maids as well?' Was the sarcastic retort from Ron. The pair of them chuckled to themselves, as they began to unpack, putting away their clothing, in the lockers provided. It soon came apparent, that space was going to be at a premium, as the locker was soon filled. Richard stuffed his Bergen under the bed, along with a spare pair of boots and the bag he had carried his hand luggage in. He then draped his webbing over the end of his bed. Martin appeared from around the corner and informed them that the armoury was open, for them to hand in their weapons. The pair finished off their personal admin and headed off to find the SQMS stores and armoury. Once they had handed in their weapons, the rest of the day was spent being issued patrol and riot equipment. This was also to be stored in their Troop accommodation areas, and by the time they were finished, space was indeed limited.

They were told they had time to grab a bite to eat. However, their Troop had drawn the short straw and were the first to provide the manpower for the towers that surrounded the H Blocks. The room was full of the sound of complaining that they always got the shit end of the stick. This was normal, as squaddies just loved to 'whinge' about anything. They made their way to the cookhouse, to be surprised that the quality of the food was of a higher standard than they were used to. This was, probably, due to the fact that the chefs were catering for just one Squadron, albeit a bit larger than normal. An added bonus was that, due to the long hours that they were required to work, a duty chef was on 24 hours a day. They were also allowed to make themselves egg and bacon sarnies on the hot plates provided.

They returned to the room, after filling themselves to the brim, and were met by the Troop Sergeant. He had a list of towers that needed to be manned, over the next 48 hours. It worked out they would be 'stagging' on, for two hours at a time, with a four hour rest period in between. The Sergeant ran through the procedure of changing over sentries. They would be taken round by Land Rover, by one of the Troop NCOs. They would be physically placed in the tower or sangar, and briefed, just as they had practised in Tin City. No one liked this particular task, but they would spend most of the next four months carrying it out. This was not what Richard had expected at all. He thought they would be patrolling the streets most of the time, or be lying in hedges, carrying out surveillance tasks.

The next piece of news felt like a kick to the bollocks. They were also, starting from next week, providing the manpower for the Crumlin Road jail in Belfast. It would be the same sort of duties as in the Maze, with maybe a little more danger attached to it. The Troop were not providing the patrolling capability for Portadown, Craigavon and Lurgan until three weeks' time. They would, however, be responsible for the patrolling and security of the local area, surrounding the prison. The Troop Sergeant pinned up the list of timing for everyone, in the centre of the room. It was up to the posting NCO to ensure he had the right people up, dressed and mounted up, so that they arrived at the towers, in time for the changeover. This meant that, instead of getting the full four hours rest period, by the time they had been dropped off, back at the hut and got their heads down, they would be wakened, at least fifteen minutes prior to their next stag starting. Richard scanned the rota and saw that he was due to start his first two hour stint in twenty minutes time. Gathering his things together, he put on his body armour and webbing and went to the armoury to draw out his weapon. Ron had been drawn on the same rotation and, as they returned from the armoury, they were met by Hesh, who was their posting NCO. They chatted, by the accommodation, waiting for the rest of the sentries to turn up. With everyone accounted for, they dived into the back of the Land Rover and sped off to the first tower, which was only a matter of 200 metres away. The first guy got out and, along with Hesh, entered the bottom of the tower. After a short while, Hesh appeared again, with one of the blokes from the Regiment they were taking over from. As he climbed inside the Land Rover, he had the biggest shit eating grin, anyone could imagine.

'Well, fellas, it's all yours and you're welcome to it. I'll have a beer for you, tomorrow, when I'm thinking about you, freezing your tits off,' he said, in a manner only a squaddie could pull off. It was a standing joke that when Units handed over to one another, a little friendly banter was always present. Richard thought it wouldn't be long before they were doing the same to the blokes that would be taking over from them.

'It can't be that bad,' Ron interjected, not sounding at all convincing.

'No, its worse, mate. I never want to come back here again. Got to have been the longest tour ever.' He said, this time with a serious face, confirming to the new boys this was not going to be fun. They had gone through a lot of training, over the last couple of months, they would be lucky if they used twenty percent of it. It was only day one, but Richard felt depressed already, and his mind wandered back to Germany and Birgit. Another two sentries were replaced, and then it was Richard's turn. The Land Rover stopped outside the second to last tower, and Richard's name was called. He jumped out, following Hesh into the tower. At the bottom of the stairs, was a small loading bay, where he quickly loaded his rifle with a twenty round magazine. Hesh motioned for him to climb the ladder in front of them. Putting the rifle over his shoulder, Richard took hold of the first rung and began to climb towards the opening, fifteen metres above him. As he neared the gap, the grinning face of the sentry he was reliving leaned down and stretched out a hand, to help him up. He muttered his thanks, and turned round, to see Hesh quickly follow him, into the viewing area. The off coming sentry quickly ran through the equipment held in the tower, with Hesh confirming it was all there. He then proceeded to go through the arcs of fire with Richard. On a pillar, hung a folder with the title 'Orders for Tower H' emblazoned on it. Richard was advised that he should make himself fully conversant with every word. It would be his bible, for the whole of the time he was there. Every tower had the same set of orders, with only slight variations, relating to the tower's particular location. With that, Hesh asked if Richard had any questions, then he disappeared back down the ladder, to post his last sentry.

Richard made himself familiar with his surroundings, he then picked up the folder to read through his orders. They were lengthy and detailed, and it took him a good ten minutes to get through them. He, then, picked up the binoculars provided, and scanned the buildings in the centre of the prison. They were divided into separate areas, an area for the admin and seven separate 'H' blocks. These were so named because of their tell-tale shape, and were numbered one through seven. They contained the political prisoners from both the Republican and Loyalist sides of the divide. Everything that went on inside the compound was run by the prison officers. The prison was considered to be one of the most escape-proof prisons in Europe, and held prisoners convicted of taking part in armed paramilitary campaigns during the Troubles On the 25th of September the previous year '*38 Provisional Irish Republican Army (IRA) prisoner escaped from H-Block 7 (H7) of the prison. One prison officer died of a heart attack as a result of the escape and twenty others were injured, including two who were shot with guns that had been smuggled into the prison. The escape was a propaganda coup for the IRA, and a British government minister faced calls to resign. The official inquiry into the escape placed most of the blame onto prison staff, who in turn blamed the escape on political interference in the running of the prison.* (Wikipedia)

The Troops had been told of this before they had deployed and were determined it would not happen on their tour. Richard surveyed the area, which was lit up with floodlights. It reminded him of his time in training, when he had to do the recce of the prison on Dartmoor. However, this prison was a more formidable structure, containing some of the most ingenious inmates found incarcerated in one place. As Richard looked for possible dead spots or areas that could be used as a means of escape, he was startled by the sound of the radio. It was the Ops room, carrying out a communications check. He waited his turn and answered that he could hear them. As the communication check came to an end, Richard noticed an unusual smell. He investigated the tower, searching out the source of strange odour. Sniffing about, he was drawn to the heater, in the corner of the viewing area. It was covered with a metal guard and he could see a substance smoking on it. It took him only moments to recognize what it was.

'The dirty twat!' he exclaimed, not believing what he was looking at. The previous occupant had left him a present. One that would become a bit of a joke, played throughout the tour, among others. The deviant had relieved himself onto the metal guard just before the handover. It hadn't taken long, for his seed to dry from the heat and release its terrible smell. Richard spent the rest of his time trying to prevent himself from gagging, and was pleased to hear the sound of the Land Rover pull up, outside. The posting NCO climbed the stairs, with his relief, and when Richard told him what had happened, he burst into fits of laughter. Richard handed over and followed the NCO down the ladder and after unloading climbed into the waiting Rover. Back at the accommodation area, Richard and a couple of other sentries made their way to the cookhouse. Here, they filled up on toast and egg butties, which would become a bit of a trend, throughout their time in the Maze. Entering the accommodation, after removing his webbing, body armour and placing his rifle by his bed, he fell into a deep sleep.

Over the next 48 hours, Richard's Troop carried out the duties of tower sentries and, by the end of it, were totally shattered. It would take the rest of the week, before their sleep patterns attuned to the constant waking and sleeping rhythms. Thankfully, the week ended and they were preparing to take the trip north to Belfast. They were to relieve First Troop for a week, at the Crumlin road jail, in the heart of the city. The jail itself was situated with the Protestant Shankill Road running parallel to the south, the Catholic Ardoyne to the west and a Catholic School to the north. A hospital was situated on the eastern corner, and, Richard was to find out, would provide an interesting view. They boarded the 4-tonne trucks for the 30 to 40 minute drive to the capital. It felt good to be outside the walls, even for a short time. They would once again be 'prisoners' themselves for a week, on their arrival. The gaol itself was directly opposite Belfast's Court House building.

The Crumlin Road Gaol dates back to 1845 and closed its doors as a working prison in 1996. After extensive renovations the gaol has re-opened as a visitor attraction and conference centre. Today you can take a guided tour of the prison and hear about the history of the site from when women and children were held within its walls through to the political segregation of republican and loyalist prisoners and learn about why the decision was taken to close the prison. http://www.crumlinroadgaol.com/history.html

Driving through the open gate, to the gaol itself, Richard caught a glimpse of the stark, foreboding Victorian building. They were ushered inside, quickly, and were met by First Troop Leader, who took them up the stairs. Climbing the stairs, they passed paintings on the walls, which had been created by Units which had stayed there in the past. Some of them were really quite good, Richard thought and, during the following week, he would add to them. The handover was brief and the Troop began the process of relieving the Troops in the sangars. There were six sangars at the 'Crum' of which, four were permanently manned. One was situated inside the Troops accommodation and looked out over the road, at the Crumlin Road Courthouse. Another two were situated at the corners of the gaol, also on the Crumlin Road. One overlooked an adjacent hospital, while the other was only accessible via a covered, corrugated walkway and was known as sangar ten. The fourth overlooked the visitor's car park on the north side. This was the one that Richard was to occupy, on his first stag. Owing to the few sangars that required to be manned, there was ample time to relax, which was a nice change from the Maze. The posting NCO loaded up each of the lads in turn and, taking them round, placed them in position. Richard was last to be posted and found himself impressed by the heavily armoured, fortified location where he was to spend the next two hours. It was obvious during the handover and receiving his orders why this was. In the past, this rear gate had been part of numerous escape attempts. A truck had tried ramming the gate, as an escape was in progress. To combat this the sangar was equipped with a GPMG, which was loaded with 200 rounds of 'Armoured Piercing' (AP) and tracer 7.62mm ammunition. If this story did not make the occupants of the sangar take note, then nothing else would. Richard spent the entire duration of his spell, looking outwards, transfixed by the vehicles coming and going. He had concentrated so much that, before he knew it, he was being replaced by his relief. On his return to the living area, he plonked himself down, on an old battered sofa, and began to watch the video playing, although it was already halfway through. As he settled down, Ron came into the room, having returned from his two hour stint on sangar ten. This overlooked the Ulster Bank, which was on the junction of Crumlin Road and Agnes Street, which led down to the Shankhill Road. They had been told that, on a previous tour, the sentry posted there had observed two men park outside, in a beat up van. They were both wearing blue overalls and had entered the bank. A few minutes later, they had returned to their vehicle carrying what seemed to be a very heavy weight. The sentry had thought nothing of it, as the van had driven away, at speed. That was, until a message came over the net, to be aware of a robbery, that had taken place at the bank. To say he received a massive bollocking, would be an understatement. This sangar was also famous, for being one that was prone to attack, being, as it was, out on a limb. It was surrounded by Rocket Wire, to prevent attacks from Rocket Propelled Grenades (RPG's). To access the sangar, required a full 100 metres sprint, along the corrugated corridor. This was because, in the past, Republicans had opened up on the structure, after getting wind of sentry change over times.

The time passed slowly over the next week, with nothing of interest to break the monotony. Richard had taken to painting a mural on the wall, outside their sleeping accommodation. He had been a keen artist at school, and on a visit back there, had found one of his pieces of art outside the Headmaster's office. This was ironic, as he was always in trouble at school, where he had summoned, many times, to wait outside that office, to anticipate punishment. His painting hadn't hung there, then, yet on a visit to his school in the early 1980s, there it stood. His mural in Belfast, depicted a soldier in full patrol order, with a Union Flag behind him, complete with a scroll with the Squadron, and tour dates. It brought great praise from his peers and Troop Leader alike. There were other talented men in the Troop, but they were masters of the written word. Richard had taken over a sangar, the day before, from a guy of Polish extraction. He was nicknamed K6, a variation of the name given to a lot of the Polish guys. The K being the initial letter of their last name, and the number 6, denoting he was the sixth K in the Regiment. Relieving him, Richard had started to read through the log book used to write down any unusual occurrences, along with the half hourly radio checks. As he read through, he chuckled to himself as he scanned the poem that K6 had written;

'Paddy oh Paddy make my day

Try oh try to get away

Make for the wall in leaps and bounds

So I may use my baton rounds

If the first wall you do surpass

I'll take you out with CS gas

If CS gas doesn't affect you

I'll put you down with 7.62'

He was well known, throughout the Regiment, for being highly articulate, if not a little eccentric. Richard loved the guy and their paths would cross, later in his career. Another highlight of the week came while manning the sangar overlooking the Hospital. It was around 18:00 and the shifts were handing over, on the wards. Directly opposite the sangar, was the changing area for the nurses, however, the windows were glazed with clear glass, rather than the frosted type. Richard had regularly spent part of his stag massaging his manhood, until he was satisfied. So, although the duties were similar to that of guarding the political prisoners in the Maze, the Crumlin Road had a little diversity and some pleasing distractions.

They had been back at the Maze for three weeks. Richard and the rest of the Troop were starting to get bored, with the whole routine. The boredom had been broken up, by a weekly disco, held in the NAAFI bar. A bus load of eager local, and not so local, young ladies arrived every week for the festivities. They all came from good Protestant, Loyalist backgrounds, having been checked and vetted by the prison staff, prior to their arrival. The squaddies outnumbered them two to one, at least, and were like flies round shit, having not had any female company since leaving home. The previous Saturday, Richard attended, as he was not down for any duties that evening. Although a 'two can rule' was in place, some of the boys pushed the envelope slightly. 'As long as you don't get caught' was the only advice they had been given by their superiors. In the absence of any 'by the book' arseholes, the guys would let their hair down. Richard spent most of the evening at the bar, admiring the view. There were girls draped over blokes, all over the place. A constant ebb and flow of couples walked out of the door and came back after a short while. Having had his fill, Richard decided to return to the room and get his head down. On the way back, he met up with Hesh, who had just returned, from a workout in the gym. As they walked between the blocks, they passed Martin's room window. It was slightly ajar and excited voices, male and female could be heard. Peering in, they saw the pale buttocks of Martin thrusting back and forward. Wrapped around his naked torso, were a pair of tidy legs. A screaming female voice begged to be given it 'harder and faster'. Hesh and Richard fought to stop themselves laughing. Hesh put up his finger to his lips, gesturing for Richard to follow him. They darted across the tarmac, into the cookhouse, which was empty, at that time. Going to the hotplate, Hesh cracked open an egg and placed it on the hot surface, coating it in oil. After frying it for a couple of minutes, he took a spatula and, delicately, removed it from the heat. Exiting the building, they ran across the road, back to the accommodation. As they positioned themselves outside the window, Richard knew what Hesh had in mind. On Hesh's signal, Richard pushed open the window and Hesh launched the sizzling hot, fried egg at Martin's exposed buttocks. As the hot egg collided with his backside, it immediately burst and the yolk ran down the crack of his arse.

'What the fuck?' came the cry of surprise and rage from Martin, as his arse cheeks clenched and he froze, in mid coitus. Hesh and Richard broke into fits of laughter and made off into the darkness, thinking it may have been advisable to let the dust settle, before going into the accommodation. Hesh headed off to the bar, while Richard made his way to the shower block. As he walked into the washroom building, Richard heard the excited screams of another female, as a naked Ron collapsed on top of her. The woman, noticing Richard in the doorway, simply grinned, as Richard turned around and made his way back to the bar.

Next morning, the Troop were in the briefing room, going through their patrol orders, for that day. They had carried out local patrols around the surrounding area, but this time, they were going to be away for a week, working out of a barracks in Portadown. There was an air of excitement in the room. However, Martin was still in a bit of a mood from the previous evening. He still didn't know who had been the phantom egg thrower, and wouldn't find out until after they had returned to Germany.

Two of the teams were going to be situated in the Police Station in Lurgan, and would work together with the Royal Ulster Constabulary (RUC). The briefing finished, everyone made their way to the loading bay. After a quick equipment and communications check, the vehicles made their way towards the M1 motorway, and on to their designated patrol areas. On the way, Richard's two vehicle patrol had been tasked to set up a 'snap' vehicle check point (VCP). As they approached junction twelve on the M1, they exited, taking Dungannon Road, south east towards Portadown. After a couple of miles, Martin, who was the multiple commander, gave the order for them to stop and set up the VCP. The front vehicle came to a halt, positioning itself diagonally across the road. Richard's vehicle did the same, creating a chicane. Soldiers leapt from the vehicle, Ron placed himself in a ditch, with the GPMG facing back up the road. He would act as the cut-off man, if any vehicles attempted to burst through the check point. Richard took up his position, in the centre of the two vehicles, as he was their team's 'chat up' man. Martin's job was to send vehicle details over the air, while Richard talked to the occupants, to extract as much information as he could. Richard grinned to himself, when he saw the registration of the first car to enter the check point. It was German, denoted by the white plates with black lettering. The first few letters indicated to him that it was from a town, not far from where they had been stationed.

'Watch this,' he whispered to Martin, in a surreptitious manner. Martin did not know what he was talking about, at first, but smiled from ear to ear, as the penny dropped. Strolling, casually, over to the driver's side of the vehicle, Richard motioned for the driver to wind down his window.

'Guten Morgen, wie geht es dir' he said, in almost flawless German. The drivers jaw dropped, and he was unable to speak, for a few seconds. Richard thought to himself that this guy never woke up this morning, thinking he would be stopped, in the middle of nowhere, by armed Troops. To top it all, one of those soldiers was speaking to him, in his own mother tongue. Once he had regained his composure, he answered Richard, saying that he was fine. After the routine questions had been asked, and knowing that these were simply tourists, Martin waved them through. They continued to check vehicles, for the next twenty minutes, and were about to leave, when Martin decided to check one last vehicle. Around the bend in the road, appeared a large, high sided van, decorated with the name of a bakery on the side. Richard indicated for him to slow down and pull over. Again, he motioned for the driver to wind his window down. As he peered inside the vehicle, Richard's heart began to race. Under the dashboard, he could see something that looked like the butt of a pistol. Spotting the alarm on Richard's expression, the driver moved towards the inside pocket of his jacket. Richard stepped back, preparing to cock his weapon. In a calm, quiet voice with a deep Scottish lilt, the driver said,

'It's okay, pal, just going for my ID,' and with that, he produced a black leather wallet. Opening it up, he revealed a MOD 90 British Army ID card. Richard did not know what to do or say initially but, within moments, he had assimilated who this character was. He was, obviously, either a member of the 'Det' or Special Forces, working under cover. Richard called over to Martin, who had noticed his reaction and had his weapon trained on the vehicle.

'This one is fine, I'm letting it through' and, hearing this, Martin lowered his weapon.

'No, pal, get me to open up the back and have a rummage about, will you?' the driver whispered to Richard, who nodded his agreement. The occupant obviously wanted to make sure, if anyone was watching, they would not be suspicious. So, for the next five minutes, Richard unloaded a number of trays of pastries and loaves of bread from the back of the truck. After climbing inside and appearing to do a search, he asked the driver to place the trays back in the vehicle. Once complete, the scruffy looking, nondescript individual climbed into his seat, started the engine and drove through the checkpoint.

That had been an interesting morning, Richard thought to himself, as they headed into Portadown. They were to carry out a quick mobile patrol of the town, before heading to the Ulster Defence Regiment barracks, where they would be staying for the week. A couple of hours passed and Richard, glancing at his watch, saw that it was just gone three o'clock. They were on the final part of the patrol and making their way now to camp. The first vehicle was about 50 metres in front of them. Ron and Richard were facing out of the back of the vehicle, so they did not see the large group of youths, at the side of the road. The locals had heard the unmistakeable sound of the lead Land Rover's engine. Bending down, they armed themselves, with anything they could use as a missile. By the time the first Land Rover had passed, their attention was fully focused on the rear one, containing Martin's team. A sudden, dull pain emanated from Richard's cheekbone. His eye socket felt like it was going to explode, as he slowly drifted into darkness. His hand, automatically, went to his left breast pocket where his talisman was kept. Only to find it empty, and the blackness took him.

'Richard, Richard….Richard!' Brigit's voice broke the spell and he looked up from the photograph of the four friends in his garden in Germany, so many years ago, now. Smiling at his wife, knowing that he had answered the question he asked himself all that time ago. Of course, he had found that special bond of friendship. This bond was now with a band of brothers, wearing green, which would last a lifetime.

And there would be more memories to recount in the future.

15181541R00188

Printed in Great Britain
by Amazon.co.uk, Ltd.,
Marston Gate.